"In *The Creator and the Cosmos*, Dr. Hugh Ross conveys the excitement of recent cosmological discoveries. Readers without advanced scientific training will find an accurate presentation of astrophysical research results. Dr. Ross shows how this current research clearly indicates the universe was created with many characteristics fine-tuned for our life. Though many scientists may resist the logical conclusion, the Creator implied by the scientific evidence is exactly consistent with the God revealed in the Bible."

–Kyle M. Cudworth, PhD
Yerkes Observatory

"A compelling summary of scientific evidence that supports belief in God and the Word of God, written on a level even the nontechnically trained layperson can understand."

–Walter L. Bradley, PhD
Professor and head of the department of mechanical engineering
Texas A&M University

"Currently, it is fashionable to believe that the discoveries of science, one and all, are either hostile or simply irrelevant to the propositions of theology. For some time now, Hugh Ross has been one of America's leading thinkers who has steadfastly refuted this claim with hard thinking and up-to-date scientific information. In *The Creator and the Cosmos* we have a treasure chest containing his most recent work, abreast of the latest findings of science, and packaged in an accessible form for a general audience. This book should be in the hands of every serious Christian who thinks about science and the Christian faith, and it should be given to interested inquirers outside the faith."

–J.P. Moreland, PhD
Distinguised Professor of philosophy
Talbot School of Theology, Biola University

"When I originally read the first edition of *The Creator and The Cosmos* in 1995, it had a profound impact on my understanding of how clearly the origin and physical parameters of the universe show the character of the biblical God. With the publication of this new edition the evidence that our universe was designed and created by a transcendent being has grown stronger and more compelling through many new observations and measurements over the last 22 years. Any good scientist knows that one test of a true hypothesis is that the significance of the conclusion should increase as more data is collected and analyzed. Using that criterion, the conclusion that the biblical God created and designed this universe with humans in mind is nearly incontrovertible. This book is required reading for any person who asks if there is sufficient evidence for God obtained through careful observations of nature. The answer is unequivocally, 'yes.'"

–Michael G. Strauss, PhD
David Ross Boyd Professor of Physics
The University of Oklahoma

"Hugh Ross's *The Creator and the Cosmos*, over the past 25 years, has risen to the status of 'a classic' concerning its profound influence upon Christian thought as it relates to modern scientific discovery. Many have come to faith citing their reading of *The Creator and the Cosmos* as one of the key elements that caused them to question their nontheistic positions, ultimately paving the way for their acceptance of the Gospel of Jesus Christ. In this edition, Ross lays down further evidence to the handiwork of God as displayed in the Bible. There are few authors that can take such complex scientific subjects and distill them down for the layperson, while maintaining the highest rigors of citation to substantiate the claims and to direct the reader to the primary scientific research literature. But even with all these scientific exactitudes, the sense of wonder in God's creation is magnificently woven into each chapter in a way that draws the reader to the Creator Himself."

–James Tour, PhD
Professor of Chemistry, Materials Science and NanoEngineering, and Computer Science
Rice University

"Dr. Hugh Ross possesses a unique gift: the ability to convey scientific findings to both the scientific-minded and the layperson. *The Creator and the Cosmos* provides overwhelming support for design in our universe. This latest edition incorporates important twenty-first century scientific discoveries, yet Dr. Ross's style leaves the awe and majesty of the believer's journey intact. The usual tension created by the opposition of faith and science becomes cliché when exposed to Ross's apologetics. In fact, his explanation of science supports faith. This book is a must for doubters, and a delight for those who do not doubt, but yearn to know more of their Creator."

–H. Edwin Young
Senior Pastor
Second Baptist Church (Houston, Texas)

"Few things amaze me like the night sky, and I know that I am far from alone in this. I also know that, like Scripture teaches, these wonders point strongly to God's existence. Who better to guide us through these heavenly treasures than my friend Hugh Ross, as he has shown over and over in his many excellent writings? If I had a night away from my own studies and had the luxury of just reading, this updated volume would most attract my attention. I recommend it highly."

–Gary Habermas
Distinguished Research Professor and Chair, Deptartment of Philosophy
Liberty University

"The Creator and the Cosmos is a tour de force of the beauty, order, and complexity of the universe, emphasizing the finely tuned properties of the universe that allow for life. This book is an interesting read for theists and nontheists, alike."

–Gerald B. Cleaver
Professor and Graduate Program Director, Department of Physics & Division Head-Center
Astrophysics, Space Physics & Engineering Physics
Baylor University

"Dr. Hugh Ross has spent a lifetime integrating his scientific intellect and his passion to represent Jesus Christ fairly in an increasingly cynical world. He speaks the language of the scientific world and he brilliantly navigates this world with Christian grace and deep commitment to both biblical authority and scientific evidence. In this updated version of *The Creator and the Cosmos*, Dr. Ross has acknowledged the growing spate of twenty-first century scientific discoveries that have significant theological implications. The sturdiness of this volume, as a foundational resource, has been given additional strength with its usage of the latest scientific research. Dr. Ross is a gift to Christ's Kingdom, and this updated edition of *The Creator and the Cosmos* only serves to validate his status as a premier Christian apologist."

–Byron D. Klaus
President Emeritus
Assemblies of God Theological Seminary

"It's a thrill to see Hugh Ross update his influential book, *The Creator and the Cosmos*. He chronicles the vast increase of scientific evidence for a designer that has emerged in recent times. And he shows quite convincingly how it uniquely points to the God of the Bible. I highly recommend this book for both Christians and seekers."

–Sean McDowell, PhD
Biola University professor, popular speaker
coauthor of *Evidence that Demands a Verdict*

"Dr. Hugh Ross has once again bridged the secular gap between faith and science. I have had the privilege of reading both the older version and now the updated rendering of *The Creator and the Cosmos*, and I continue to be inspired and informed on the nature of God. It's not about proving God's existence through science, but it is recognizing the order and consistency of the natural laws that unequivocally point to a Mind. From the law of causality and the proof of Einstein's general relativity we know that time had a beginning, and the big bang is a reality through which we know the universe also had a beginning. But what's always amazed me about Dr. Ross is that he alone discovered that the Bible is the only holy book consistent with these scientific facts and many others."

–Lauren Green
Chief religion correspondent, Fox News Channel
Author, *Lighthouse Faith: God as a Living Reality in a World Immersed in Fog*

HUGH ROSS, PhD

The
CREATOR
and the
COSMOS

HOW THE LATEST
SCIENTIFIC DISCOVERIES
REVEAL GOD

Covina, CA

Cover design: 789, Inc.
Interior layout: Christine Talley

Ross, Hugh N., author.
The Creator and the cosmos : how the latest scientific discoveries reveal God / Hugh Ross.
Includes bibliographical references and index. | Covina, CA: RTB Press, 2018.
ISBN 978-1-886653-14-6
LCSH Religion and science. | Astronomy--Religious aspects--Christianity. | Cosmology--Religious aspects--Christianity. | Physics--Religious aspects--Christianity. | BISAC RELIGION/Christian Theology/Apologetics | SCIENCE/Cosmology | SCIENCE/Astronomy
LCC BL253 .R67 2018 | DDC 261.5/5--dc23

Printed in the United States of America

Fourth edition

1 2 3 4 5 6 7 8 9 10 / 22 21 20 19 18

Contents

List of Figures and Tables

Figures

Tables

Preface to the Fourth Edition

I wrote the first edition of *The Creator and the Cosmos* 25 years ago. The first and second editions of *The Creator and the Cosmos* focused attention on twentieth-century discoveries in astronomy and physics that contributed most profoundly to the credibility of faith in the God of the Bible. The third edition, released in 2001, added descriptions of discoveries made at the dawn of the twenty-first century that provided a much stronger scientific case for God's supernatural handiwork in creating and designing the universe for the specific benefit of humanity.

Now, 17 years have transpired since the third edition. Thanks to an amazing array of new telescopes and instruments, both in space and on Earth, cosmology has become a precision science. That precision has yielded exponentially more scientific evidence for God. Thousands of years ago, the Bible promised that the more we learn about the natural realm the more evidence we would uncover for God's handiwork. This fourth edition shows how that biblical claim has been put to the test through discoveries of the past 17 years.

This fourth edition includes more than 90 pages of new content. Some content on the origin of life was dropped since Fazale Rana and I now have a full-length book on the subject. However, I did describe in this edition some recent discoveries on life's origin that are not in our book, *Origins of Life*.

This edition has benefited significantly from the comments and suggestions of people who were compelled by their reading of previous editions to commit their lives to Jesus Christ. Thanks to them and to the many other friends who recommended improvements, readers will, I trust, find much in this fourth edition to further inspire and strengthen their faith in the awesome Creator.

Acknowledgments

My scientist colleagues at Reasons to Believe, Drs. Fazale Rana, Anjeanette Roberts, Dave Rogstad, and Jeff Zweerink deserve a huge thanks. I benefit daily from our discussions. Many of the suggestions and comments incorporated came from members of my Paradoxes Sunday school class and from people who wrote to me after reading of one or more of the first three editions.

Special thanks to astronomers Kyle Cudworth and Jeff Zweerink and to physicists Tim Boyle and Mike Strauss. They caught mistakes, provided additional relevant citations to the scientific literature, and offered valuable recommendations for making the content more understandable.

The readability of this edition was much enhanced by the following members of my editorial team at Reasons to Believe: Linda Kloth, the primary editor, and Sandra Dimas and Jocelyn King. I valued their edits and their efforts to make me a better writer. Thank you, Joe Aguirre, for writing the discussion questions. Thanks also to Colleen Wingenbach for carefully proofreading the text.

Credit for the beautiful cover design goes to Charley Bell and Richard Silva at 789 Inc. The layout and design of the book was done by Christine Talley of Grüv Creative Communications.

Lastly, I want to thank my wife, Kathy, and every member of our staff at Reasons to Believe for granting me the time to do the necessary research and writing, also for their enthusiasm and support of this fourth edition. Without them, I could not have completed this book.

Hugh Ross
2018

Chapter 1

The Awe-Inspiring Night Sky

When I was eight, I started saving money to buy a telescope mirror. It took several years of collecting neighbors' beer and soda pop bottles, but finally I pulled together enough coins to purchase the optics. With my father's help, I designed and built a mount and, at last, peered through the telescope to the heavens above.

I was stunned. I had never seen anything so beautiful, so awesome. The spectacle was too good not to share. I carried my instrument from the backyard to the front so I could invite neighbors to join me. But no invitation was necessary. No sooner had I planted my telescope on the sidewalk than an enthusiastic crowd formed, a crowd that stayed late into the night.

That evening I began to realize many people, maybe all people, are fascinated with the starry hosts. I once thought that the sheer immensity of the heavens was responsible for that fascination. That's part of it, but there's more. There's the mystery of what's really out there, what those specks of light may be, the mystery of how they all got there, and of what lies above and beyond. Gazing at the night sky raises profound questions not only about the universe but also about ourselves.

Universe and You

Cosmology is the study of the universe as a whole—its structure, origin, and development. It's not a subject just for ivory-tower academics. Cosmology is for everyone.

In the words of historian, economist, and former college president Dr. George Roche, "It really does matter, and matter very much, how we think about the cosmos."[1] Roche's point is that our concept of the universe shapes our worldview, our philosophy of life, and thus our daily decisions and actions.

For example, if the universe is not created or is accidental, then it has no objective meaning, and consequently life—including human life—has no meaning. A mechanical chain of events determines everything. Morality and religion may be temporarily useful but are ultimately irrelevant. The Universe (capital U) is ultimate reality.

On the other hand, if the universe is created, then there must be reality beyond the universe. The Creator is that ultimate reality and wields authority over all else. The Creator is the source of life and establishes its meaning and purpose. The Creator's nature defines personality. The Creator's character defines morality.

Thus, to study the origin and development of the universe is, in a sense, to investigate the basis for any meaning and purpose to life. Cosmology has deep theological and philosophical ramifications.

Unfortunately, many researchers refuse to acknowledge this connection. In the name of objectivity, they gather and examine data through a special pair of glasses, the God-is-not-necessary-to-explain-anything glasses. Other researchers see the universe through the God-is-whoever-or-whatever-I-choose glasses. It's rare for them to admit that such lenses represent their theological position, their personal faith.

Though no one is perfectly objective, some researchers are willing to gather and integrate the data to see which theory of origins is most consistent with the facts—whatever that theory may say about the necessity and characteristics of an Originator.

Cosmological Chauvinism

Because cosmology probes such weighty and personal matters, it has evoked possessiveness and competition. Three groups vie for supreme authority on the subject: scientists, theologians, and philosophers.

The chauvinism of physical scientists is exemplified by a pep talk I heard in my undergraduate days at the University of British Columbia. "Not only can a good physicist do physics better than anyone else," said the professor, "he can do anything better than anyone else." He expressed the belief that science training, and physics training in particular, is essential for grappling with the challenges of modern life. In a graduate course on relativity, my professor lamented theologians' past meddling in cosmology. "Today," he boasted, "we have been able to scare most of the ministers out of cosmology with a straightforward application of tensor calculus."[2]

At a meeting of philosophers, I heard a distinguished speaker commiserate with his peers over scientists' bungling intrusion into cosmology. "Even the best physicists," he said, "are lousy philosophers."

At a theology colloquium, I heard from the podium that theologians alone have the right to interpret all science since they are trained in the mother of the sciences, theology. The speaker ended on a dramatic note: "Scientists have only observations. We have revelation!"

Cosmological chauvinism is not simply a manifestation of academic pride. It reflects decades of increasing specialization in education. Universities long ago dropped theology from their science curriculum. Few, if any, seminaries draw students with a background in science. Philosophy students may touch upon theology and science, but usually not in depth. Theology and philosophy students may study the history of their disciplines, but science students rarely do.

The inevitable fruits of such specialization are polarization, conflict, and misunderstanding, not to mention neglect of ordinary people whose tax dollars support much of cosmology research. I realize that specialization is necessary to push forward knowledge frontiers, but imagine how much more efficiently and effectively we could learn about reality if we were to take an interdisciplinary approach, giving adequate attention to historical context.

If specialists will stop intimidating each other and laypeople and instead start dialoguing in understandable terms, anyone who desires can explore and integrate the facts about our universe. Then we all, novices included, can enrich our understanding of the meaning and purpose for the universe, life, and every human being.

 Discussion Questions _____

1. Why is objectivity difficult to maintain, regardless of the field of expertise? Can anyone be truly unbiased?
2. What questions about the beginning of everything do you hope this book addresses?

Chapter 2

My Skeptical Inquiry

My own thinking about the meaning of life began with my wonderment about the cosmos. I was born shortly after World War II in Montreal, Canada. My father was a self-taught engineer, and my mother a nurse. Before and during my early years, my father founded and built up a successful hydraulics engineering business. The company's rapid financial growth proved too great a temptation for Dad's financial partner, who one day withdrew all the funds and vanished. With his last few dollars, my dad brought my mother, my two sisters, and me to Vancouver, British Columbia. The neighborhood in which we settled was poor but culturally diverse. Our neighbors were mostly refugees from eastern Europe and Asia—people who, like my parents, had tasted success but either lost it or left it for survival's sake.

Are Stars Hot?

My parents say they could see in me an intense curiosity about nature from the time I started to talk. I recall one starlit evening when I was seven, walking along the sidewalk with my parents and asking them if the stars are hot. They assured me that they are very hot. When I asked them why, they suggested I go to the library.

My elementary school library was well stocked with books on astronomy. As I read, I was amazed to discover just how hot the stars are and what makes them burn so brightly. I found out that our galaxy contains several hundred billion suns and that our universe holds more than a hundred billion galaxies. I was astonished by the immensity of it all. I was compelled to find out everything I could about it.

At age seven I read every book on physics and astronomy I could find in our school library. That same year I began to do the same in the children's section of the Vancouver Public Library.

By that time I knew I wanted to be an astronomer. Many of my friends also were reading incessantly and choosing career directions. We didn't think of ourselves as precocious. The nonstop rainfall in Vancouver encouraged a lot of indoor activity and provided plenty of time to think.

At age ten I had exhausted the science resources of the children's and youth sections of the Vancouver Public Library and was granted a pass to the adult section. A few years later I was given access to the library of the University of British Columbia. By the time I was sixteen, I was presenting public lectures on astronomy and at seventeen won the Grand Award at the British Columbia Science Fair for my project on variable stars. At sixteen I became the director of observations for the Vancouver branch of the Royal Astronomical Society of Canada (an organization of primarily amateur astronomers). I felt glad to have found so early in life a pursuit I loved.

Who Did All This?

Even as a child I always felt a sense of awe concerning nature. Its beauty, harmony, and staggering complexity left me wondering who or what could be responsible for it all.

By age fifteen, I came to understand that some form of the big bang theory provided the only reasonable explanation for the universe. If the universe arose out of a big bang, it must have had a beginning. If it had a beginning, it must have a Beginner.

From that point on, I never doubted God's existence. But, like the astronomers whose books I read, I presumed that the Beginner was distant and noncommunicative. Surely, I reasoned, a God who built a universe of more than ten-billion-trillion stars would not concern himself with events on an insignificant speck of dust we call Earth.

Ruling Out Holy Books

My high school history studies bothered me because they showed me that the peoples of the world typically take their religions seriously. Knowing that the European philosophers of the Enlightenment largely discounted religion, I first looked for insight from their works. What I discovered, however, were circular arguments, inconsistencies, contradictions, and evasions. I began to appreciate nature all the more, for it never presented me with such twists.

Just to be fair and not to build a case on secondhand resources, I determined to investigate for myself the holy books of the world's major religions. I figured if God was speaking through any of these books (I initially presumed he was not), then the communication would be noticeably distinct from what human beings write. I reasoned that if humans invented a religion, their message would contain errors and inconsistencies, but if the Creator communicated, his message would reflect his supernature. It would be consistent like nature is. I chose history and science as good ways to test the revelations on which various religions are based.

In the first several holy books I examined, my initial hunch was confirmed. I found statements clearly at odds with established history and science (see "The Reincarnation Connection" on p. 106, for an example). I also noted a writing style perhaps best described as esoteric, mysterious, and vague. My great frustration was having to read so much in these books to find something stated specifically enough to be tested. The sophistry and the incongruity with established facts seemed opposite to the Creator's character as suggested to me by nature.

A Word from God?

I was getting a little smug until I picked up a Bible I had received (but not yet read) from the Gideons at my public school. The book's distinctives struck me immediately. It was simple, direct, and specific. I was amazed with the quantity of historical and scientific references and with the detail in them.

It took me a whole evening just to investigate the first chapter. Instead of another bizarre creation myth, here was a journal-like record of Earth's initial conditions—correctly described from the standpoint of astrophysics and geophysics—followed by a summary of the sequence of changes through which Earth came to be inhabited by living things and ultimately by humans. The account was elegant and scientifically accurate. From the stated viewpoint of an observer on Earth's surface, both the order and the description of creation events perfectly matched the established record of nature. I was amazed.

That night I committed myself to spend at least an hour a day going through the Bible to test the accuracy of all its statements on science, geography, and history. I expected this study to take about four weeks. Instead, there was so much to check it took me eighteen months.

At the end of the eighteen months, I had to admit to myself that I had been unsuccessful in finding a single provable error or contradiction. This doesn't mean I understood every passage in the Bible or that I resolved every potential problem. The problems and passages I couldn't yet understand didn't discourage me, however, because I faced the same kinds of issues with the record of nature. But, just as with the record of nature, I was impressed with how much could be understood and resolved.

I was now convinced that the Bible was supernaturally accurate and thus supernaturally inspired. Its perfection could come only from the Creator. I also recognized that the Bible stood alone in revealing God and his dealings with humans from a perspective that demanded more than just the dimensions we mortals can experience (length, width, height, and time). Since humans cannot visualize phenomena in dimensions they cannot experience, finding these ideas in the Bible also argued for a superhuman Author.

As a final exercise, I mathematically determined that the Bible was more reliable by far than some of the laws of physics. For example, I knew from studying physics that there is roughly a one in 10^{80} (that's the number one with eighty zeros following) chance of a sudden reversal in the second law of thermodynamics. But I had calculated (with the help of skeptical friends) the probability of the chance fulfillment of thirteen Bible predictions about specific people and their specific actions. My conservative estimate showed less than one chance in 10^{138} that such predictions could come true without supernatural intervention.[1] That meant the Bible was 10^{58} times more reliable than the second law of thermodynamics on just this one set of predictions. I also derived a similar conclusion based on the many instances in which the Bible accurately forecasted future scientific discoveries.[2]

Acknowledging that my life depended moment by moment on the reliability of the second law of thermodynamics, I saw that my only rational option was to trust in the Bible's Inspirer to at least the same degree as I relied on the laws of physics. I realized, too, what a self-sufficient young man I had been. After a long evening of studying the salvation passages in the New Testament, I humbled myself before God, asking him to forgive me of my self-exaltation and all the offenses resulting from it, and committed myself to follow his directives for my life. At 1:06 in the morning I signed my name on the back page of my Gideon Bible, stating that I had received Christ as my Lord and Savior.[3]

New Evidences
All of the scientific and historical evidences I had collected deeply rooted my confidence in the veracity of the Bible and convinced me that the Creator had indeed communicated through this holy book. I went on to become an astronomer, and my investigations into both the cosmos and the Bible have shown me a more wondrous, personal God behind nature than I could ever have imagined.

Through the years, new evidences have consistently arisen in various fields of science, making the case for Christianity even stronger. By 1986, several breakthrough discoveries uncovered proofs for the God of the Bible so convincingly that, together with others, I formed Reasons to Believe, a ministry committed to communicating these new evidences to as many people as possible.

Several years later, an even more dramatic set of scientific discoveries arose. One of them was called the greatest discovery of the twentieth century. Secular scientists actually reported to the media that these new findings reveal the face of God more clearly than ever. The following chapters explore how and why normally reserved scientists have been moved to speak in such ecstatic terms.

 Discussion Questions _____

1. How would a person go about testing the historical and scientific claims of major religions' holy books? How does the Bible stand up under such testing?
2. Will a preponderance of evidence for the veracity of the Bible convince skeptics, as it did the author? Why or why not? What other factors are involved?

Chapter 3

Big Bang—The Bible Taught It First!

Note: This chapter was composed at the suggestion and with the assistance of Dr. John Rea, professor emeritus of Old Testament at Regent University, Virginia Beach, Virginia.

Most science textbooks on cosmology credit Arno Penzias and Robert Wilson with the discovery that the universe began with a hot big bang creation event. While Penzias and Wilson were the first (1965) to detect the radiation left over from the creation event,[1] they were not the first scientists to recognize that the universe is expanding from an extremely hot and compact beginning. In 1946, George Gamow calculated that only a universe expanding from a near infinitely hot beginning could account for the existing abundance of elements.[2] In 1912, Vesto Slipher observed the shift of spectral lines of galaxies, indicating the velocities of galaxies relative to us.[3] In 1929, observations made by Edwin Hubble established that the velocities of nearly all galaxies result from a general expansion of the universe.[4] Beginning in 1925, astrophysicist and Jesuit priest Abbé Georges Lemaître was the first scientist to promote the idea of a big bang creation event.[5]

The first theoretical scientific evidence for a big bang universe dates back to 1916. That is when Albert Einstein noted that his field equations of general relativity predicted an expanding universe.[6]

Biblical Claims for a Transcendent Cosmic Beginning
All these scientists, however, were upstaged at least 2,500 years earlier by Job, Moses, David, Isaiah, Jeremiah, and other Bible authors. The Bible's prophets and apostles stated explicitly and repeatedly the two most fundamental properties of the big bang, a transcendent cosmic beginning a finite time ago and a universe undergoing a general expansion. In Isaiah 42:5 both properties were

declared: "This is what God the Lord says—the Creator of the heavens, who stretches them out . . . "

The Hebrew verb translated "created" in Isaiah 42:5 (*bara'*) has as its primary definition "bringing into existence something new, something that did not exist before."[7] The proclamation that God created (*bara'*) the entirety of the heavens is stated seven times in the Old Testament (Genesis 1:1; 2:3; 2:4; Psalm 148:5; Isaiah 40:26; 42:5; 45:18). This principle of transcendent creation is made more explicit by passages like Hebrews 11:3, which states that the universe that we humans can measure and detect was made from that which we cannot measure or detect. Also, Isaiah 45:5–22, John 1:3, and Colossians 1:15–17 stipulate that God alone is the agent for the universe's existence. Biblical claims that God predated the universe and was actively involved in causing certain effects before the existence of the universe is found not only in Colossians 1 but also in Proverbs 8:22–31, John 17:24, Ephesians 1:4, 2 Timothy 1:9, Titus 1:2, and 1 Peter 1:20.

Biblical Claims for Cosmic Expansion

The characteristic of the universe stated more frequently than any other in the Bible is its being "stretched out." Five different Bible authors pen such a statement in eleven different verses: Job 9:8, Psalm 104:2, Isaiah 40:22, 42:5, 44:24, 45:12, 48:13, 51:13, Jeremiah 10:12, 51:15, and Zechariah 12:1. Job 37:18 appears to be a twelfth verse to make this statement. However, the word used there for "heavens" or "skies" is *shehaqîm*, which refers to the clouds of fine particles (of water or dust) located in Earth's atmosphere,[8] not the *shamayim*, the heavens of the astronomical universe.[9] Three of the eleven verses—Job 9:8, Isaiah 44:24, and 45:12—make the point that God alone was responsible for the cosmic stretching.

What is particularly interesting about the eleven verses is that different Hebrew verb forms are used to describe the cosmic stretching. Seven verses—Job 9:8, Psalm 104:2, Isaiah 40:22, 42:5, 44:24, 51:13, and Zechariah 12:1—use the Qal active participle form of the verb *natah*. This form of *natah* literally means "the stretcher out of them" (the heavens) and implies continual or ongoing stretching. Four verses—Isaiah 45:12, 48:13, and Jeremiah 10:12, 51:15—use the Qal perfect form. This form of *natah* literally means that the stretching of the heavens was completed or finished some time ago.

That the Bible claims that the stretching out of the heavens is both "finished" and "ongoing" is made even more evident in Isaiah 40:22: "He sits enthroned above the circle of the earth, and its people are like grasshoppers. He stretches out the heavens like a canopy, and spreads them out like a tent to live in." There we find two different verbs used in two different forms. In the first of the final two parallel poetic lines, "stretches out" is the verb *natah* in the Qal active participle form. In the second (final) line the verb "spreads them out" (NASB, NIV, NKJV) is *mathah* (used only this one time in the Old Testament) in the waw consecutive plus Qal imperfect form, so that literally we might translate it "and he has spread them out." The participles in lines one and three of Isaiah 40:22 characterize our sovereign God by his actions in all times, sitting enthroned above the earth and stretching out the heavens, constantly exercising his creative power in his ongoing providential work. This characterization is continued with reference to the past by means of waw consecutive with the imperfect, the conversive form indicating God's completed act of spreading out the heavens. That is, this one verse literally states that God is both continuing to stretch out the heavens and has stretched them out.

This simultaneously finished and ongoing aspect of cosmic stretching is identical to the big bang concept of cosmic expansion. According to this concept, all the physics (specifically, the laws, constants, and equations of physics) are instantly created, designed, and finished at the big bang creation event so as to guarantee an ongoing, continual expansion of the universe at exactly the right rates with respect to time so that physical life will be possible.

This biblical claim for simultaneously finished and ongoing acts of creation, incidentally, is not limited to just the universe's expansion. The same claim is made for God's laying Earth's foundations (Isaiah 51:13, Zechariah 12:1). This is consistent with the geophysical discovery that certain long-lived radiometric elements were placed into the earth's crust a little more than 4 billion years ago in the just-right quantities so as to guarantee the continual building of continents.[10]

Biblical Claims for Cosmic Cooling

Finally, the Bible indirectly argues for a big bang universe by stating that the laws of thermodynamics, gravity, and electromagnetism have universally operated throughout the universe since the cosmic creation event itself. For example, in Jeremiah 33 God uses the fixity of the laws that govern the universe and Earth as an analogy for his immutability (his changelessness).

The laws of thermodynamics state that any expanding system must be cooling simultaneously. Therefore, since the universe has continuously expanded from the cosmic creation event, it must have been much hotter in the past than it is in the present.

In Romans 8:20 we are told that the entire creation has been subjected to "frustration" or "futility." The next verse declares that all of creation was and currently exists in a state of "slavery to decay" or "bondage to corruption." Ecclesiastes 1 and Revelation 21 also support the conclusion that the whole universe suffers from progressive decay. Genesis 2 and 3 teach that work and pain are part of the creation, both before and after Adam's rebellion in Eden. Such ongoing slavery to decay describes well the second law of thermodynamics—the law of physics that states that, as time proceeds, the universe becomes progressively more disordered, decayed, and run down.

In Genesis 1 and in many places throughout Job, Psalms, and Proverbs, we are informed that stars and living organisms have existed since the early times of creation. As explained later in this book (see ch. 17), even the slightest changes in either the laws of gravity, electromagnetism, or thermodynamics would make the stars that are necessary for physical life impossible.

As explained in chapter 5 of this book, stable orbits of planets around stars and of stars around the centers of galaxies are possible only in a universe described by three very large rapidly expanding dimensions of space. Therefore, a big bang, continuously cooling universe should come as no surprise.

Big Bang Fundamentals
Many big bang theories exist. What they all share, however, are three fundamental characteristics: (1) a transcendent cosmic beginning that occurred a finite time ago; (2) a continuous, universal cosmic expansion; and (3) a cosmic cooling from an extremely hot initial state.

All three of the fundamental characteristics of the big bang were explicitly taught in the Bible two to three thousand years before scientists discovered them through their astronomical measurements. Moreover, the Bible alone among all the scriptures of the world's religions expounds these three big bang fundamentals. Scientific proofs for a big bang universe, thus, can do much to establish the existence of the God of the Bible and the accuracy of the words of the Bible.

Beginner's Guide to Modern Big Bang Cosmology
In two camps especially, big bang cosmology remains an explosive topic. Heated reactions—and bitter resistance—arose from opposite directions in the last century but, ironically, for similar reasons. One group of big bang opponents included those who understood the theory's implications, and the other, those who *mis*understood.

People in the first group understood that the big bang denied the notion of an uncreated or self-existent universe. From this perspective, the big bang theory points to a supernatural beginning and a purposeful (hence personal), transcendent (beyond the boundaries of space, time, matter, and energy) Beginner. Those who reject the reality of God or the knowability of God would, of course, find such an idea repugnant, an affront to their religious or philosophical worldview. Similarly, it would offend those who have been trained to view the universe (with a capital U) as ultimate reality and as the totality of all that is real. Again, a religious response.

People in the second group opposed the big bang on the presumption that it argued *for* rather than *against* a godless theory of origins. They associated "big bang" with blind chance. They saw it as a random, chaotic, uncaused explosion when it actually represents exactly the opposite. They continue to reject the date it gives for the beginning of the universe, thinking that to acknowledge about 14 billion years is to discredit the authority of their holy books, whether the Qur'an, the Book of Mormon, or the Bible. Understandably, these people either predicted the theory's ultimate overthrow or chose to live with a contradiction at the core of their belief system.

Despite opposition from outspoken enemies, the fundamentals of the big bang model, which include a cluster of slightly differing models, stand secure. In fact, the model stands more firmly than ever with the aid of its most potent and important allies: the facts of nature and the technological marvels that bring them to light, as well as the men and women who pursue and report those facts. The following chapters offer a summary of the accumulated data supporting the big bang.

A Problematic Term

The big bang is *not* a big "bang" as most laypeople would comprehend the term. This expression conjures up images of bomb blasts or exploding dynamite. Such a "bang" would yield disorder and destruction. In truth, this "bang" represents an immensely powerful yet carefully planned and controlled release of matter, energy, space, and time within the strict confines of carefully fine-tuned physical constants and laws that govern their behavior and interactions. The power and care this explosion reveals exceed human potential for design by multiple orders of magnitude.

Why, then, would astronomers retain the term? The simplest answer is that nicknames, for better or for worse, tend to stick. In this case, the term came not from proponents of the theory but rather, as one might guess, from a hostile opponent. British astronomer Sir Fred Hoyle coined the expression in the 1950s as an attempt to ridicule the big bang, the up-and-coming challenger to his "steady state" hypothesis. He objected to any theory that would place the origin, or Cause, of the universe outside the universe itself, hence, to his thinking, outside the realm of scientific inquiry.[11]

For whatever reason, perhaps because of its simplicity and catchy alliteration, the term stuck. No one found a more memorable, shorthand label for the precisely controlled cosmic expansion from an infinitely or near infinitely compact, hot cosmic 'seed,' brought into existence by a Creator who lives beyond the cosmos. The accurate but unwieldy gave way to the wieldy but misleading.

A Multiplicity of Models

The first attempts to describe the big bang universe, as many as a dozen, proved solid in the broad, simple strokes but weak in the complex details. So, these initial models have been replaced by more refined models. Scientists are used to this process of proposing and refining theoretical models. News reporters—even textbook writers—sometimes misunderstand, though, and inadvertently misrepresent what is happening.

Reports of the overthrow of the "standard big bang model" illustrate the point. That model, developed in the 1960s, identified matter as the one factor determining the rate at which the universe expands from its starting point. It also assumed that all matter in the universe is ordinary matter, the kind that interacts in familiar ways with gravity and radiation. Subsequent discoveries showed that the situation is much more complex. Matter is just one of the determiners of the expansion rate, and an extraordinary kind of matter (called "exotic" matter) not only exists but also more strongly influences the development of the universe than does ordinary matter.

The reported demise of the "standard big bang" model was interpreted by some readers as the end of the big bang. On the contrary, the discoveries that contradicted the standard model gave rise to a more robust model, actually a set of models attempting to answer new questions. More than once, as one of these models has been replaced with a more refined variant, news articles heralded the overthrow of *the* big bang theory when they should have specified *a* big bang model.

Currently, cosmologists (those who study the origin and characteristics of the universe) are investigating at least three or four dozen newer variations on the big bang theme. Scientists expect still more models to arise as technological advances make new data accessible. Such proliferation of slightly variant big bang models speaks of the vitality and viability of the theory.

It makes sense that the first models proposed were simple and sketchy. The observations at that time, while adequate to support the fundamental principles of the big bang, were insufficient to explore and account for the details. As the evidences have become more numerous and more precise, astronomers have discovered additional details and subtleties, features previously beyond their capability to discern.

New details, of course, mean more accurate "reconstructions" of what actually occurred "in the beginning." Each generation of newer, more detailed big bang models permits researchers to make more accurate predictions of what *should be* discovered with the help of new instruments and techniques.

As each wave of predictions proves true, researchers gain more certainty that they are on the right track, and they gain new material with which to construct more accurate and more intricate models. The testing of these models, in turn, gives rise to a new level of certainty and a new generation of predictions and advances. This process has been ongoing for many decades now, and its successes are documented not only in the technical journals but in newspaper headlines worldwide. Let's take a look.

 Discussion Questions _____

1. Is the big bang here to stay? Why or why not?
2. Discuss why the big bang is not a "bang" as most laypeople understand the term. Why is this important from a Creator's perspective?
3. According to the author, two groups of people oppose the big bang. What can you do to help both groups overcome these biases?

Chapter 4

Discovery of the Twentieth Century

On April 24, 1992, newspapers around the world heralded a breakthrough by an American research team. The discovery made the front-page headlines of the *London Times* for five consecutive days. American TV networks gave the story as much as forty minutes of prime-time news coverage.

What was all the fuss about? A team of astrophysicists had reported the latest findings from the Cosmic Background Explorer (COBE) satellite—revealing stunning confirmation of the hot big bang creation event.

Reactions by Scientists

Scientists extolled the event with superlatives. Carlos Frenk, of Britain's Durham University, exclaimed, "[It's] the most exciting thing that's happened in my life as a cosmologist."[1] Theoretical physicist Stephen Hawking, known for understatement, said, "It is the discovery of the century, if not of all time."[2] Michael Turner, astrophysicist with the University of Chicago and Fermilab, termed the discovery "unbelievably important," adding that the "significance of this cannot be overstated. They have found the Holy Grail of cosmology."[3]

Turner's metaphor echoed a familiar theme. George Smoot, University of California at Berkeley astronomer and project leader for the COBE satellite, declared, "What we have found is evidence for the birth of the universe."[4] He added, "It's like looking at God."[5]

Theistic pronouncements abounded. According to science historian Frederic B. Burnham, the community of scientists was prepared to consider the idea that God created the universe "a more respectable hypothesis today than at any time in the last hundred years."[6] Ted Koppel on ABC's *Nightline* began his interview of an astronomer and a physicist by quoting the first two verses of Genesis.[7] The physicist immediately added verse three as also germane to the discovery.[8]

In the wake of this discovery, it was increasingly common for astronomers to draw theistic or deistic conclusions, so much so that the late Geoffrey

Burbidge, of the University of California at San Diego, even complained that his fellow astronomers were rushing off to join "the First Church of Christ of the Big Bang."[9]

Proofs of the Big Bang

All this excitement arose because findings from the COBE satellite helped solve a haunting mystery of the big bang model. The hot big bang model says that the entire physical universe—all the matter and energy, and even the four dimensions of space and time—burst forth from a state of infinite, or near infinite, density, temperature, and pressure. The observable universe expanded from a volume infinitesimally smaller than the period at the end of this sentence, and it continues to expand.

Before April 1992, astrophysicists knew a great deal about how the universe began. Only one small but important component was missing. It was as if they knew how the machine was assembled and how it worked except for one part.

Actually, the entire machine itself and many of its basic components were predicted by physicists working in the early part of the twentieth century. Richard Tolman recognized in 1922 that since the universe is expanding, it must be cooling off from an exceptionally high initial temperature.[10] The laws of thermodynamics say that any expanding system must be cooling simultaneously. George Gamow discovered in 1946 that only a rapid cooling of the cosmos from near infinitely high temperatures could account for how protons and neutrons fused together, forming a universe that today is about 74% hydrogen, 24% helium, and 2% heavier elements.[11]

As for the one missing part, they knew what it should look like, and they knew approximately where to look for it: the COBE satellite. This satellite (see fig. 4.1) was designed specifically to find this missing part—namely, the explanation for how galaxies form out of a big bang.

The Cosmic Oven

Astronomers knew, based on Tolman and Gamow's deductions, that the universe's beginning and subsequent development resembled a hot kitchen oven. When the oven door is opened, heat trapped inside escapes. Dissipation of the oven's heat takes place as the heat expands outward from the oven. Radiant energy confined to a few cubic feet now spreads throughout the kitchen's several hundred cubic feet. As it does, the oven cavity eventually cools down to the temperature of the room, which is now just a little warmer than it was before.

If one knows the peak temperature of the oven cavity, the volume of that

Figure 4.1: Cosmic Background Explorer (COBE) Satellite
—Courtesy of Jet Propulsion Laboratory, NASA

cavity, and the volume of the room throughout which the oven's heat is dissipated, then the amount by which the room will warm up can be determined.

If one were using the opening of the oven door to dry out some wet towels, it would be important to control the temperature of the oven as well as the rate at which the oven disperses heat to the room. If the oven were too hot, or the dispersion too slow, the towels would scorch. But, if the oven were too cool, or the heat dissipation too rapid (say the room was too large or the towels too far away), the towels would remain damp.

Similarly, if the universe were to expand too slowly, during the first few minutes of the universe's history, it would spend too much time in the temperature range where the nuclear fusion of elements occurs. Too many of the nucleons (protons and neutrons) would fuse together to form heavier elements. This would result in too many of the heavier elements and too few of the lighter elements essential for life chemistry. On the other hand, if the expansion were too rapid, the universe would spend too little time in the nuclear fusion temperature range. Too few of the nucleons would fuse into lighter elements. Future stars would produce an inadequate quantity of the heavier elements essential for life chemistry.

Following this oven analogy, Gamow's research team in 1948 calculated what temperature conditions would be necessary to yield the currently observed abundances of elements. They concluded that a faint glow measuring only about 5° centigrade above absolute zero (absolute zero = -273° centigrade or -460° Fahrenheit) should be found everywhere throughout the universe.[12]

At the time, such a low temperature was hopelessly beyond the capabilities of telescopes and detectors to measure. But by 1964 Arno Penzias and Robert Wilson put together an instrument that successfully measured, at radio wavelengths, the cosmic microwave background radiation (i.e., heat) at a temperature about 3° centigrade above absolute zero.[13] Since that initial discovery, the cosmic microwave background radiation was measured to much greater accuracy and at many more wavelengths.[14] But at most of the wavelengths, the cosmic microwave background radiation remained blocked out by the earth's atmosphere and, therefore, was beyond detection. Only a telescope operating in outer space could see well enough to detect what scientists were after.

First COBE Discovery

The first COBE results, reported in January 1990,[15] showed that the universe was like a perfect radiator, dissipating virtually all its available energy (see fig. 4.2). The data showed the background radiation temperature to be very low and smooth. No irregularities in the temperature larger than one part in 10,000 were detected.

This extraordinarily low and smooth temperature in the cosmic microwave background radiation convinced astronomers that the universe must have had an extremely hot beginning about 15 billion years ago. The finding essentially ruled out many alternative models for the universe, such as the steady state model (no beginning, see ch. 8) and the oscillating universe model (multiple beginnings, see ch. 9). How were scientists able to conclude from these COBE findings that the universe had a hot beginning only several billion years ago? For some clues, let's return to our analogy of the kitchen oven.

Suppose the oven were surrounded by thousands of thermometers, each placed at the same distance from the oven. Suppose also that sometime after the oven had been heated, turned off, and its door opened, each thermometer indicated the same temperature. The only possible conclusion would be that heat flow from the oven cavity to the room totally dominated the room's normal temperature-disturbing air flows. Such dominance would imply that the original temperature of the oven cavity must have been much greater than the room's temperature. In addition, if those thousands of thermometers indicated

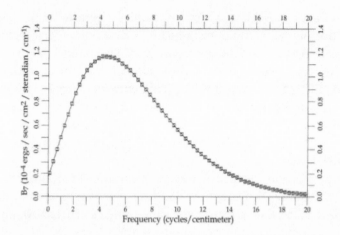

Figure 4.2: COBE's First Measurements of the Cosmic Background Radiation Spectrum at the North Galactic Pole

The measured temperature for the background radiation was 2.735° centigrade above absolute zero. Deviations between COBE's results and the spectrum for a perfect radiator (curve) measured less than 1% over the entire range of observed frequencies.

—*Courtesy of John Mather, Goddard, NASA*

a very low temperature, we would conclude that considerable time had passed since the opening of the oven door.

Fantastic Explosion

Temperature measurements from COBE provided convincing evidence of a hot origin for the cosmos. The cool and uniform temperature of the cosmic microwave background radiation and its close fit to the spectrum of a perfect radiator established that the universe suffered an enormous degradation of energy. Energy degradation is measured by a quantity called entropy. Entropy describes the degree to which energy in a closed system disperses, or radiates (as heat), and thus ceases to be available to perform work. *Specific entropy* is the measure of the amount of entropy per proton for a particular system.

A burning candle serves as a good example of a highly entropic system, one that efficiently radiates energy away. It has a specific entropy of about two. Only very hot explosions have much higher specific entropies. The specific entropy of the universe—about one billion—is enormous beyond all comparison. Even supernova explosions, the most entropic (and radiant) of events now occurring in the universe, have specific entropies a hundred times less.

Only a hot big bang could account for such a huge specific entropy. For those bothered to learn that the universe is such an "inefficient" machine, note that only a universe with a huge specific entropy can produce the elements necessary for life.[16] Moreover, if the specific entropy were any greater or any less, stars and planets would never have existed at any time in the universe's history.[17]

Second COBE Discovery

The smoothness of the cosmic microwave background radiation confirmed a hot big bang beginning for the universe. But it posed a potential problem for a development stage that astronomers determined occurred roughly a half-billion years after the creation event. Astronomers knew that the background radiation could not be *perfectly* smooth. At least some level of nonuniformity, however minute in comparison with the overall smoothness, in the cosmic background radiation would be necessary to explain the formation of star clusters, galaxies, and clusters of galaxies.

The whole range of reasonable theories for how galaxies form required temperature fluctuations roughly ten times smaller than what COBE had the capability to detect in 1990. Fortunately, an extra two years of observations by COBE yielded results, announced on April 24, 1992, that were between ten and a hundred times more precise than the measurements from 1990.

These newly refined COBE measurements showed irregularities in the background radiation as large as about one part in 100,000,[18] just what astrophysicists thought they would find.[19] What's more, the measurements solved an intriguing mystery. They narrowed the galaxy formation theories to those that include both ordinary dark matter and an amazing component called exotic dark matter. (Astronomers in the twenty-first century typically use the term "dark matter" to refer to the sum of ordinary and exotic dark matter.) More on this in chapters 5 and 6.

Confirmations

The COBE results (see fig. 4.3) did draw some initial challenges from a few astronomers, including the late Geoffrey Burbidge.[20] To most astronomers their skepticism seemed unwarranted since the temperature irregularities showed up at three different wavelengths of observation.

Within a few months, corroborative evidence began to accumulate. A balloon-borne experiment, making measurements at four different wavelengths

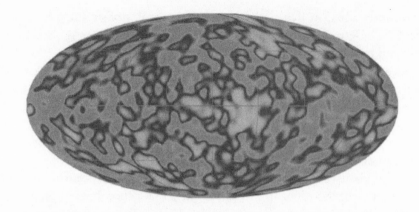

Figure 4.3: Microwave Map of the Whole Sky Made from One Year of Data Taken by COBE's Differential Microwave Radiometers (DMR)

The Milky Way Galaxy lies horizontally across the middle of the map. Astronomers used data from all three DMR wavelengths to model and remove emissions from our galaxy. This map revealed, for the first time, temperature fluctuations in the cosmic background radiation. Amplitudes of the fluctuations explain the birth and growth of galaxies and galaxy clusters.

—Photo courtesy of Jet Propulsion Laboratory, NASA

shorter than the three measured by COBE, showed temperature fluctuations lining up perfectly with those in the COBE maps. Edward Cheng, leader of the experiment, concluded, "With two totally different systems, it's very unlikely that random noise would give rise to the same lumps at the same places in the sky."[21]

Twelve months later, two radiometers operating in Tenerife, Spain, detected actual structure in the cosmic microwave background radiation. Whereas the COBE and balloon measurements were sensitive enough to establish that fluctuations in the cosmic microwave background radiation did indeed exist, they could not accurately delineate the location and size of individual features. This delineation was achieved through fully independent radiometers operating at three different wavelengths longer than the wavelengths observed by COBE and the balloon-borne instruments. Fluctuation structures as large as 10 degrees across were found, and the amplitude of these structures proved completely consistent with the earlier statistical detections by COBE and the balloon-borne experiment.[22]

A few weeks after the release of the Tenerife results, cosmic microwave background radiation fluctuations on angular scales of about 1 degree were detected. These measurements also proved consistent with the detections by COBE and the balloon-borne experiment.[23]

Since then, over a dozen different sets of new observations have confirmed the cosmic microwave background radiation fluctuations.[24] In fact, the latest observations are of such high quality that they are shedding light on other creation parameters, such as the values of the cosmic mass density, the cosmological constant, and the quantities of various forms of dark matter (see the following two chapters).

Independent confirmation comes from a variety of recent detections of dark matter (see ch. 5). The important point is that galaxy formation no longer casts doubt on big bang creation models.

Third COBE Discovery

Deviations between the 1990 COBE results and the spectrum for a perfect radiator measured less than 1% over the entire range of observed frequencies (see fig. 4.2). Data released from the COBE research team (see fig. 4.4) at an American Astronomical Society meeting in January 1993 reduced the deviation to less than 0.03%. The new data also yielded the most precise measure to date of the temperature of the cosmic background radiation, 2.726 kelvin (K; that is 2.726° centigrade above absolute zero), a measure that is accurate to within 0.01 K[25] and completely consistent with newer independent measurements.[26]

These new results did more than just prove the universe began with a hot big bang. They told us which kind of hot big bang. The 1990 results left room for the possibility that the big bang could have been a tightly spaced succession of "little" bangs. The 1993 results ruled out that possibility. The universe must have erupted from a single explosive event that by itself accounts for at least 99.97% of the radiant energy in the universe.

With a single explosive creation event accounting for so much of the universe's radiation, astronomers concluded that the temperature fluctuations in the cosmic background radiation, not disturbances arising from subsequent small cosmic bang events, must have transformed the smooth primordial cosmos into today's universe of clumped clusters of galaxies.

Watching the Universe Cool Down

Astronomers can now witness the universe getting colder and colder as it gets older and older. Through direct observations they can show that the universe was hotter in the past than it is today. By comparing actual past temperatures

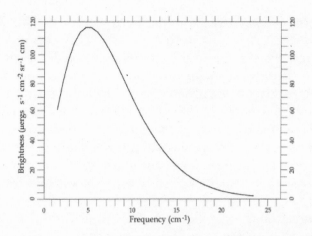

Figure 4.4: 1993 COBE Satellite Results of the Spectrum of the Cosmic Background Radiation

Deviations between COBE's measurements and the spectrum for a perfect radiator (curve) are less than 0.03% over the entire range of observed frequencies. This is strong direct evidence for a hot big bang creation event.

—*Courtesy of John Mather, Goddard, NASA*

of the universe with temperatures predicted by a hot big bang creation event, astronomers can offer a simple, dramatic proof for cosmic creation.

To clarify, the temperature 2.726 K for the cosmic background radiation is for the present era. Because radiation from great distances takes much longer to reach us, temperatures at such distances reveal the cosmic heat at earlier times. If the hot big bang model is correct, observations at great distances should yield higher temperatures for the cosmic background radiation. For this reason, astronomers long desired to measure the cosmic background radiation at great distances.

In September 1994 that desire was fulfilled. The newly opened Keck Telescope enabled astronomers to measure spectral lines of carbon in two gas clouds so distant that their radiation represents an epoch when the universe was about one-fourth its present age. Astronomers selected lines that would provide a sensitive measure of the temperature of the cosmic background radiation. According to the hot big bang model, the background radiation for the universe at this early epoch should be 7.58 K. The Keck Telescope observations indicated 7.4 ± 0.8 K.[27] In the words of David Meyer, Northwestern University astrophysicist, these measurements are "strikingly consistent with the Big Bang theory."[28]

In December 1996, the same team of astronomers made a second measurement using the identical technique on a more distant gas cloud.[29] The measured temperature was just slightly above 8 K. The hot big bang model at this epoch predicts a temperature of 8.105 K. In 2000, a different team measured a gas cloud whose distance shows us the universe at about one-sixth its present age. The detected background radiation temperature of just under 10 K matched that predicted by the hot big bang model at that epoch.[30] Once again, all the measurements are strikingly consistent with a big bang creation event.

Big Bang Picture Album

The simplest-to-grasp evidence for the big bang comes from pictures. With the help of various imaging devices, one can enjoy a kind of time-lapse of the big bang. The images show the universe at various ages, similar to how a series of photos can show a person from infancy onward.

Such photos of the universe are made possible by light (or radiation) travel time. Observing a distant galaxy whose light took 5 billion years to enter an Earth-based telescope allows us to see how that galaxy looked 5 billion years ago when the light began its journey through space. In one sense, astronomers can only capture glimpses of the past, not of the present, as they peer out into space.

Thanks to the Keck and Hubble Space Telescopes, astronomers now have a photo history of the universe that covers the past 13 billion years. It begins when the universe was only about half a billion years old when clumps of stars and gas were merging to form the first galaxies and follows it to "middle age," where it yet remains. The images in figure 4.5 present highlights from the past 12 billion years of this cosmic photo album. They show how both elliptical and spiral galaxies grow in size and develop in structure as the universe matures from two billion years old to five billion years old to nine billion years old to its present age.

Figure 4.3 deserves special attention. It captures that moment in cosmic history when atomic nuclei first capture electrons to make atoms, before any stars or galaxies existed. It shows us the universe at just 380,000 years of age, only 0.003% of its current age.

These images testify that the universe is anything but static. It expanded from a tiny volume and changed according to a predictable pattern as it grew— a big bang pattern.[31] A picture is still worth a thousand words, perhaps more.

Figure 4.5: A Photo Album History of the Universe

These Hubble Space Telescope images show elliptical and spiral galaxies at stages roughly equivalent to infancy, childhood, youth, and middle age (its current developmental stage).

—*Courtesy of R. STScI/NASA*

Stability of Stars and Orbits Proves Big Bang

Perhaps the most concrete big bang evidence is that stable orbits and stable stars are possible *only* in a big bang universe. Physical life would be impossible unless planets orbit with stability, stars burn with stability, and stars orbit galaxy cores with stability.[32]

Such stability demands not just any force of gravity, but gravity operating according to the inverse square law. Gravity operating at that level demands three large rapidly expanding dimensions of space (length, width, height)—the big bang universe.

In two dimensions of space, gravity would obey a different law. Specifically, objects with mass would attract one another in proportion to the inverse of the distance separating them. In four space dimensions, gravity would obey a different law. Specifically, massive bodies would attract one another in proportion to the inverse of the cube of the distance separating them. Such distinct laws guarantee, for example, that planets would either be ejected away from their stars or gobbled up by them.

Stability under the influence of gravity, in turn, demands that the three dynamic space dimensions be large (significantly unwound from their original tight curl).[33] Otherwise galaxies would be so close together as to wreak havoc on stellar orbits, and stars would be so close together as to wreak havoc on planets' orbits. When galaxies are too close together, galaxy collisions and close encounters catastrophically disturb stars' orbits. Likewise, when stars are too close together, their mutual gravitational tugs catastrophically disturb the orbits of their planets.

The three dimensions of space must be expanding at a particular rate, as well. A universe that expands too slowly will produce only neutron stars and black holes. A universe that expands too rapidly will produce no stars at all and thus no planets and no stable orbits.

The simple fact is this: galaxies, stars, and planets exist, and they exist with adequate stability to allow humans to exist and observe them. This fact alone argues for the big bang. What's more, it argues for a specific subset of big bang models.

Mounting Evidences

These twentieth-century evidences for a big bang creation event are impressive enough by themselves. The twenty-first century brings even more spectacular evidences to an already overwhelming vindication of the Bible's doctrine of cosmic creation. Such evidences are presented in the next chapter.

 Discussion Questions _____

1. If the COBE satellite findings and subsequent confirmations were really "the discovery of the century, if not of all time," then why is the big bang still debated?
2. What is meant by a "photo album history of the universe"? How can this illustration help laypeople understand that history and, in turn, evidence for the big bang creation event?
3. How often do we think of conditions other than those in the universe, where "physical life would be impossible unless planets orbit with stability, stars burn with stability, and stars orbit galaxy cores with stability"? Does it give us pause?

Chapter 5

Twenty-First Century Discoveries, Part I

The journal *Science* gave "the discovery of the cosmological constant" the "breakthrough of the year" award for 1998.[1] That the cosmological constant qualifies as the breakthrough of the year, if not the decade or the century, arises from its implication that the big bang is the most exquisitely designed entity known to man. In the words of physicist Lawrence Krauss, a self-described atheist, the cosmological constant "would involve the most extreme fine-tuning problem known in physics."[2]

Since that breakthrough discovery, technological advances have expanded the possibilities of additional discoveries beyond what was ever possible before the turn of the century. Other dramatic discoveries have been unveiled, revealing, for example, the geometry of the universe, the cosmic inflation event, and accurate measures of cosmic expansion rates throughout the history of the universe. Together with the cosmological constant, these discoveries provide a treasure trove of evidence worth sifting through.

What Is the Cosmological Constant?
When Albert Einstein first proposed his theory of general relativity, he immediately noted it predicted the universe was expanding from a beginning, from an infinitesimal volume. This flatly contradicted the reigning cosmological model of his day. That model proposed an infinitely old universe held in a static state throughout infinite time.

There were several philosophical biases expressed in this infinitely old, static universe. One gave the mechanisms of evolution the ideal chemistry for infinite time so that God need not be invoked to explain the origin of life.[3]

To save the static universe model, Einstein introduced ad hoc into his general relativity equations a cosmological constant to perfectly cancel the effects of gravity everywhere in the universe.[4] When astronomers proved that the universe indeed was and is expanding from a cosmic beginning, Einstein re-jected his proposed cosmological constant calling it "the greatest blunder" of his scientific career.[5]

Now, more than 80 years later, astronomers have resurrected Einstein's constant (more generally known as "dark energy") from oblivion. However, the value they are attaching to it is very different, and their rationale for it is likewise very different.

What exactly is this cosmological constant? It refers to a single constant of physics that presumes to explain the behavior of what is now recognized to be the dominant component of the universe—dark energy. Other models for dark energy appeal to two or more physical constants or to more complex constructs to explain its behavior.

What Is Dark Energy?

Dark energy refers to the self-stretching property of the space-time fabric, or surface, of the universe. Space (because of dark energy, and independent of matter and of any heat or light) stretches itself. Moreover, the larger the space-time envelope of the universe grows, the more stretching energy it gains. This gaining of stretching energy causes some science writers to refer to dark energy as an anti-gravity factor. The effect of dark energy on the space-time envelope of the universe is to make two massive bodies appear to repel one another. Moreover, the farther apart two bodies are from one another the more strongly they will appear to repel one another.

In contrast, gravity acts as a brake on cosmic expansion. According to the law of gravity, two massive bodies attract one another, and the closer two mas-sive bodies are to one another the more strongly they will attract. Since the uni-verse contains a lot of mass, gravity works to pull the massive bodies together and thereby slows down cosmic expansion.

How does science resolve the two opposing forces in this model of the uni-verse? The model stipulates that, when the universe is young (and, therefore, more compact), gravity's effect on cosmic dynamics would be powerful while dark energy's would be weak. However, when the universe is older (and, there-fore, more spread out), dark energy's effect would become progressively stron-ger while gravity's would become weaker. Thus, if scientists measure cosmic expansion rates through time, they will know whether gravity operates alone or if dark energy also proves to be present. If gravity alone influences cosmic dynamics, astronomers will observe that the expansion of the universe slows down throughout cosmic history. The slowing down effect will be seen to get progressively weaker as the universe ages. However, if both gravity and dark energy are operable, astronomers will see cosmic expansion transition from slowing down to speeding up.

What method could astronomers use to observe the expansion rates of the universe throughout most of its hstory?

The Discovery

The yardstick of choice for measuring cosmic expansion throughout the universe's history are type Ia supernovae (see "Type Ia Supernovae" in this chapter). Because type Ia supernovae are very bright, they can be seen at great distances that correspond to when the universe was billions of years younger than it is now.

Type Ia supernovae also have identical or near identical brightness. So, astronomers can determine how far away each type Ia supernova is from us by comparing the light from different type Ia supernovae. The spectral lines astronomers measure in the light from a particular supernova tell them how fast that supernova is moving away from us (see "Redshift Velocities" in this chapter). Thus, with measurements on dozens of type Ia supernovae covering a wide variety of distances, astronomers can determine the universe's expansion rate at various ages.

Using their observations of 50 type Ia supernovae, a team of 20 astronomers led by Adam Riess[6] prompted the 1998 breakthrough-of-the-year award. However, their analysis made no attempt to account for the clumpy character of the universe (the observation that matter in the universe is clumped into galaxies, stars, and dark matter of various forms). As noted by cosmologists in 1932, any departure from a perfectly uniform universe (smooth matter distribution) will result in a slightly faster expansion rate.[7] Therefore, before one can claim the discovery of dark energy, one must separate the faster expansion due to cosmic clumping from that due to a cosmological constant.

A second team of 31 astronomers, the initial members of the Supernova Cosmology Project, published results in the *Astrophysical Journal* on June 1, 1999.[8] With 42 additional type Ia supernovae in their data bank, they could consider the effect of small-scale clumping of matter. They demonstrated that, for all realistic models of cosmic clumping, dark energy must exist. Also, the uncertainties in their measurements were much less than that of the previous attempt. The type Ia supernova observations demonstrated that the universe's rate of expansion was slowing down for the first approximately 7 billion years of its history and speeding up for the last approximatey 7 billion years.

TYPE Ia SUPERNOVAE

A supernova is the catastrophic explosion that occurs at the end of stellar burning for massive stars. At the brightest part of its explosion, a supernova will outshine a galaxy of a hundred billion stars.

Typically, more massive stars produce brighter explosions. A star will not become a supernova unless its mass at the end of its burning cycle exceeds 1.4 solar masses.

A type Ia supernova occurs when a burnt-out star (called a white dwarf, whose mass lies just below the 1.4 solar mass limit) gains mass by accretion from a companion star (its gravity is strong enough to tear mass away from its companion). When the white dwarf reaches 1.4 solar masses, it explodes as a supernova. Because all type Ia supernovae have the same mass, they all manifest the same, or nearly identical, peak brightness. Therefore, they are good indicators of distance.

The database of type Ia supernovae now numbers 740. In a paper published in October 2016, three physicists claimed that their analysis of this larger database showed only "marginal" evidence for cosmic acceleration and, thus, the evidence for dark energy might be in doubt.[9] Their analysis revealed only a 99.73% certainty that the cosmic expansion rate is accelerating. In astronomy and physics the standard for certainty is 99.99994% (5 sigma or 5 standard deviations).

The three physicists' analysis of the supernova database, however, was different from that employed by astronomers who specialize in supernova studies. The teams who do specialize in supernova studies noted long ago that supernovae at great distances, and hence much earlier formation times, possess different elemental abundances, which give rise to slightly different light curve properties. When these selection effects are fully considered, the certainty that the cosmic expansion rate is accelerating, based on supernova data alone, rises to better than 99.996%.[10]

The 5 sigma bar for certainty, again from supernova data alone, may be attained soon. Supernova surveys currently underway are projected to yield several thousand type Ia supernovae suitable for cosmological analysis within the next few years.[11]

REDSHIFT VELOCITIES

The lines that astronomers see in a star's spectrum indicate the wavelengths at which certain elements and compounds in the star are either emitting or absorbing light. If the star is moving toward us, the wave crests become bunched together and thus appear to us at shorter wavelengths. If the star is moving away from us, the wave crests become stretched out and thus appear to us at longer wavelengths. By measuring the amount by which a star's spectral lines are shifted toward longer (that is, redder) wavelengths, astronomers can determine the velocity at which that star is moving away from us. For stars at sufficiently large distances, the motion away from us is caused almost entirely by the expansion of space, not by the galaxy moving through space.

Discovery Confirmations

The two teams who discovered the acceleration of the cosmic expansion rate were awarded the Nobel Prize in Physics in 2011. Per their practice, the Nobel committee waited until the discovery was confirmed by independent lines of research.

In addition to type Ia supernova, the dynamics of galaxy clusters, pairs of galaxies, gravitational lenses, effect, baryon acoustic oscillations, gamma-ray burst events, and the redshift dependence of what astronomers term the Alcock-Paczynski all yield measurements of cosmic expansion rates over wide ranges of dates throughout cosmic history. These independent measurements, apart from type Ia supernovae, unequivocally show that the cosmic expansion rate is accelerating throughout the last half of the universe's history and that dark energy is the dominant component of the universe.[12]

With several major supernova survey efforts now underway, the type Ia supernova database is about to get much larger and deeper—and may soon provide further confirmations of cosmic acceleration. Already, astronomers who are part of the Panoramic Survey Telescope and Rapid Response System (Pan-STARRS) Medium Deep Survey team have discovered over 5,000 likely supernovae.[13] They estimate that at least 1,000 of these supernovae are type Ia supernovae. The Dark Energy Survey is a 5-year program (2013–2018) to observe over 300 million galaxies for supernova events. The expected haul of supernova discoveries is more than 5,000. At least 1,000 are anticipated to be type Ia supernovae. While there is overlap between the Pan-STARRS and Dark Energy Surveys, the total haul of new type Ia supernova discoveries is estimated to exceed 1,500.

Two other supernova survey teams are using the Hubble Space Telescope to detect very distant supernovae at various ages of the universe, as close as just 2.5 billion years after the cosmic creation event. These two surveys, Cluster Lensing And Supernova Survey with Hubble (CLASH) and Cosmic Assembly Near-infrared Deep Extragalactic Legacy Survey (CANDELS), will so sufficiently add to the type Ia supernova database that astronomers will be able to accurately determine cosmic expansion rates throughout the past 11.3 billion years.

Again, the presence of dark energy supports a big bang universe model, complete with the theological implications attached. How certain are scientists about cosmic expansion rates and related characteristics of the universe? Additional twenty-first century discoveries provide a clearer picture.

Flat-Out Confirmed

The supernova database is not the only evidence astronomers possess for an accelerating cosmic expansion rate. The strongest evidence comes from: (1) detailed maps of the cosmic microwave background radiation (i.e., radiation leftover from the cosmic creation event); and (2) measurements of baryon acoustic oscillations (regular, periodic fluctuations in the density of ordinary matter at length scales as great or greater than clusters of galaxies).

These maps and measurements reveal the geometry of the universe, which in turn reveals the total cosmic density. Measurements of the total cosmic density combined with measurements of the individual contributions to the total cosmic density provides the most detailed cosmic creation model to date. Furthermore, these measurements yield one of the most rigorous and compelling evidences for the big bang creation model.

For a flat geometry universe, the cosmic spatial curvature parameter, Ω_k, exactly equals zero, and the general relativistic total cosmic density parameter, Ω_{total}, exactly equals 1.0. For a curved geometry universe, Ω_{total} must equal 1.0 minus the measured value for Ω_k.

Only four factors can possibly contribute to the total cosmic density: mass density (ordinary visible matter plus ordinary dark matter plus exotic dark matter), Ω_m; relativistic particle density (photons and neutrinos), Ω_{rel}; gravity wave energy density, Ω_{gw}; and dark energy density, Ω_Λ. Therefore, if astronomers can accurately measure Ω_k, Ω_m, Ω_{rel}, and Ω_{gw}, then they get the value of Ω_Λ

$(\Omega_\Lambda = 1.0 - \Omega_k - \Omega_m - \Omega_{rel} - \Omega_{gw})$. If the value of Ω_Λ proves to be indisputably greater than zero, then dark energy is a major component of the universe and the cosmic expansion rate at late dates in cosmic history is accelerating.

Both the Wilkinson Microwave Anisotropy Probe (WMAP) and Planck maps of the cosmic microwave background radiation established that the geometry of the universe is flat or very nearly flat. WMAP determined that the cosmic spatial curvature parameter, Ω_k, $= -0.0027 \pm 0.0039$.[14] From Planck, the cosmic spatial curvature parameter $= 0.0008 \pm 0.0039$.[15] Analysis of the cosmic baryon acoustic oscillations from the Sloan Digital Sky Survey-III Baryon Oscillation Spectroscopic Survey established that $\Omega_k = -0.0007 \pm 0.0030$.[16] An average of these values yields $\Omega_k = -0.0009 \pm 0.0014$. This value affirms that the universe is either spatially flat or very close to being spatially flat.

Cosmic Density Components

To prove that dark energy is real and that the cosmic expansion rate is accelerating, astronomers must determine accurate measures of Ω_m, Ω_{rel}, and Ω_{gw}. In its first observing run, the Advanced LIGO gravity wave telescope placed a highly constrained upper limit on the value of Ω_{gw}. With 95% confidence, the LIGO Scientific Collaboration determined $\Omega_{gw} < 1.7 \times 10^{-7}$.[17]

The very tiny maximum possible value for Ω_{gw} means that the gravity wave energy density has no meaningful impact on the total cosmic density or the dynamics of the universe. That is, it plays no significant role either in the early history of the universe or in its future.

By analyzing detailed maps of the cosmic microwave background radiation, astronomers can produce a value for Ω_{rel}. Their calculations based on WMAP data yielded $\Omega_{rel} = 8.52 \times 10^{-5}$.[18]

For the past three decades, the holy grail of cosmology has been astronomers' quest to determine an accurate value for Ω_m. Only since 2015 have accurate measurements been forthcoming. Twelve different research teams now have published precise measurements based on observational databases ranging from the cosmic microwave background radiation, to galaxy clusters, to galaxies, to voids between galaxies and galaxy clusters, to supernovae, to nonlinear mass clustering. An arithmetic mean of these twelve recent measurements of mass density yields Ω_m equal to 0.2934 ± 0.0107.[19] See table 5.1 for a summary of values for the cosmic density components.

Like It or Not, Dark Energy Is Real!

The most accurate and reliable evidence for dark energy comes from the simple

Table 5.1: Values of Cosmic Density Components

density component	symbol	measured value
mass density	Ω_m	0.2934 ± 0.0107
relativistic particle density	Ω_{rel}	8.52×10^{-5}
gravity wave energy density	Ω_{gw}	$< 1.7 \times 10^{-7}$
dark energy density	Ω_Λ	0.707 ± 0.012
cosmic spatial curvature parameter	Ω_k	-0.0009 ± 0.0014 (average)
total cosmic density	Ω_{total}	1.000 ± 0.001

subtraction, $\Omega_\Lambda = 1.0 - \Omega_k - \Omega_m - \Omega_{rel} - \Omega_{gw}$. Inputting the values for Ω_k, Ω_m, Ω_{rel}, and Ω_{gw} yields a dark energy density value of 0.707 ± 0.012. This value of Ω_Λ establishes that dark energy is the major component of the universe, and that the cosmic expansion rate has been accelerating for the last half of the universe's history.

These numbers presume that general relativity reliably describes the movements of massive bodies in the universe. This presumption is now beyond doubt, since observations show that general relativity reliably predicts movements of massive bodies to better than a ten trillionth of a percent precision (see ch. 10).

For more than two decades many atheists and virtually all young-earth creationists have adamantly denied the existence of dark energy. From an atheistic perspective, dark energy implies a relatively recent cosmic beginning. This beginning is so recent it defies naturalistic explanations for the origin of life and a history of life that makes possible the origin and existence of human beings who attain a global high-technology civilization.

Dark energy finds disfavor with atheists because of the extreme fine-tuning design it implies. This disfavor was evident in an interview physicist Philip Ball, then a senior editor for the British journal *Nature*, conducted with theoretical physicists Lisa Dyson, Matthew Kleban, and Leonard Susskind concerning a paper they had written. In a summary of the interview published in *Nature*, Ball quotes Dyson, Kleban, and Susskind, "Arranging the cosmos as we think it is arranged . . . would have required a miracle."[20] In the same article, Ball states that Dyson, Kleban, and Susskind said the existence of dark energy would imply that an "unknown agent intervened in the evolution [of the Universe] for reasons of its own."[21] The trio concluded their research paper with these words, "Perhaps the only reasonable conclusion is that we do not live in a world with a true cosmological constant."[22] Cosmological constant is another term for dark energy, and thus what they mean is that if atheism is presumed true, then dark energy must not be real.

Dark energy is also problematic from a young-earth perspective, but for an opposite reason. If dark energy is real, then the universe is too old for a young-earth interpretation of the Genesis 1 creation days and the Genesis 5 and 11 genealogies.

Like it or not, dark energy is real. With a measure as accurate as $\Omega = 0.708 \pm 0.012$ there no longer is any rational basis for doubting its existence. In fact, it makes up more than two-thirds of the "stuff" of the universe. Those who believe in the God of the Bible should appreciate dark energy. It implies that the universe has a beginning in finite time just like the Bible repeatedly declares (see ch. 3). Furthermore, the fine-tuning design it implies means that a known Agent who can operate from beyond space and time has miraculously intervened in the history of the universe for reasons of his own.

Most Spectacular Measureable Fine-Tuning Design

The fine-tuning referred to by Dyson, Kleban, and Susskind really does pose a problem for the atheistic and agnostic worldviews. In a paper published in the *Astrophysical Journal*, astronomer and critic of creationism Lawrence Krauss wrote that the existence of dark energy "would involve the most extreme fine-tuning problem known in physics."[23] Physicists Florian Bauer, Joan Solà, and Hrvoje Štefančić wrote in *Physics Letters B*, "The cosmological constant (CC) problem is the biggest enigma of theoretical physics ever."[24]

The fine-tuning resides in the need for the universe to expand at just-right rates throughout the entirety of cosmic history for life—especially advanced life—to possibly exist. This life requires just-right galaxies, stars, and planets to exist with the just-right spatial density at just-right times in the history of the universe.

To get any kind of galaxies, stars, and planets to appear at all demands exquisite fine-tuning of the cosmic expansion rate. In a universe that expands too rapidly from the cosmic creation event, gravity will be unable to pull the primordial gas into clumps to form galaxies, stars, planets, asteroids, or comets. In a universe that expands too slowly, gravity will suck all the primordial gas into black holes and neutron stars.

To get the kinds of stars, planets, asteroids, and comets needed to make advanced life possible requires extreme fine-tuning of the cosmic creation rates throughout the entire history of the universe. It also takes exquisite fine-tuning of both the cosmic mass density and the space energy density (aka dark energy).

The cosmic mass density not only factors into the rates at which the universe expands, it determines what kinds of elements will exist in the universe. It also determines how much of the universe's primordial hydrogen is converted into helium through nuclear fusion during the first few minutes of the universe's history. If too little helium is produced, then future stars will fail to make sufficient quantities of elements heavier than helium. If too much helium is manufactured, then future stars will quickly convert much of their hydrogen and helium into elements as heavy or heavier than iron. In both scenarios, the quantities of carbon, nitrogen, oxygen, phosphorus, and potassium that physical life requires would be insufficient.

The cosmic mass density must be exquisitely fine-tuned to get the just-right ratio of hydrogen to helium arising from the first few minutes of cosmic history. Without that exquisite fine-tuning, future stars would not produce all the elements life requires in the just-right abundance ratios that life needs. However, this fine-tuned value for the cosmic mass density means that mass, by itself, will not generate the needed cosmic expansion rates to guarantee that the galaxies, stars, planets, asteroids, and comets required for advanced life to appear at the just-right times and locations. Dark energy must come to the rescue to make up the difference.

For dark energy to come to the rescue, however, fine-tuning at orders of magnitude more than what is required for the cosmic mass density is required. We know there must be a source or sources for dark energy. The original source or sources of dark energy are at least 122 orders of magnitude larger than the amount detected today. This implies that somehow such source(s) canceled one another out, leaving just the small amount of dark energy, only one part in 10^{122}, detected by astronomers today.

The fine-tuning in dark energy and the cosmic mass density is real. Exactly where the fine-tuning comes from and currently resides is still under investigation. I discuss the current status of this investigation in appendix B of my book, *Why the Universe Is the Way It Is.*[25]

A fine-tuning measure of one part in 10^{122} ranks as the most spectacular fine-tuning measurement so far achieved by scientists. This fine-tuning is 10^{43} times more exquisite than someone blindfolded, with just one try, randomly picking out a single marked proton from all the protons existing within the entire extent of the observable universe! Or, if one were to compare the fine-tuning design of dark energy to make advanced life possible with the best example of fine-tuning design achieved by humans,[26] the design of dark energy would rank about 10^{99} times superior, that is, superior by a factor of one thousand trillion trillion trillion trillion trillion trillion trillion trillion times.

What does this superior fine-tuning design say about the One who created the universe? It implies that at a minimum this One is 10^{99} times more intelligent and more knowledgable than the most brilliant scientists and engineers. Or, it implies that this One is 10^{99} times better funded and more technologically equipped—that is, more powerful—than our best-endowed scientists and engineers. The bottom line is that since intellect and power are attributes that only a personal being can possess and use (e.g., the fine-tuning design that astronomers have determined in dark energy, not to mention the fine-tuning design in many dozens of other parameters of the universe and the laws of physics; see ch. 14), then the cosmic Creator must be a personal being.

Facing a Challenge

Quintessence is a hypothesized phenomenon that some physicists claim would reduce the necessity of extreme design inherent in the cosmic density terms. Nontheistic astronomers' disdain for the implications of those measurements became evident in abstracts of their research papers. Astronomers Idit Zehavi and Avishai Dekel wrote, "This type of universe . . . requires a degree of fine tuning in the initial conditions that is in apparent conflict with 'common wisdom.'"[27] Physicist Norbert Straumann called the "cosmic coincidence problem" disturbing.[28]

Quintessence offers an escape for the nontheist—or does it? If quintessence represents a variation over time in the term describing the pressure of the universe divided by the term describing its density, *and* if one carefully chooses the initial value of this pressure-to-density ratio, *and* if one sets its rate of variation to a specific value, *then* perhaps a significant amount of the apparent design in the cosmic density terms could be removed.

To date no evidence for quintessence exists. However, we know the universe contains dark matter. If the right kind of dark matter particles exist, and if they exist in the just-right abundance with the just-right distribution, then the desired quintessence would become possible.

At this point, most readers will have figured out that this appeal to quintessence is simply a design trade-off. Design eliminated from the cosmic density terms would be replaced, at least in part, by new design in the pressure-to-density ratio, or in the kind, amount, and distribution of dark matter particles. As physicist Varun Sahni explained, "Time varying models of dark energy [Λ]

can, to a certain extent, ameliorate the fine-tuning problem (faced by Λ), but do not resolve the puzzle of cosmic coincidence."[29] As a team of 32 astronomers pointed out, the discovery of quintessence could confront nontheists with as much or more evidence for design than it would eliminate.[30]

Human limitations will always hinder our assessment of cosmic design. Researchers will either underestimate or overestimate the true level of design in any given characteristic. Sometimes they will see it where it is not manifest; sometimes they will overlook it where it is. However, the more we learn about the universe, the more indications of design we discover (see chs. 14 and 16). The more we learn about the universe, the more accurate our estimates of the level of design in its characteristics. The strength of the case for God can be judged by the direction of the trend line. Through the years, as we learn more and more about the universe, the fine-tuning appears more exquisite *and* the list of features that reflect fine-tuning grows longer—not shorter.

Precise Moment in Time

In an *Astrophysical Journal* article, Lawrence Krauss and Glenn Starkman together lament the future of astronomy.[31] Why the despair? The measure of dark energy tells us that from now on the universe will expand faster and faster. This accelerating expansion implies that more and more objects in the universe will eventually disappear from our view. Distant objects currently observable are moving away from us at velocities exceeding the velocity of light. Thus, they will be beyond the theoretical limits of any existing *or possible* telescopes. Astronomers will have less and less of the universe to look at and enjoy.

Contemplation of this fact gives Christians a sense of wonder, not despair. It shows that God created humanity at the precise moment in history (and enabled us to develop the necessary standard of living and technology) when we would have the optimal view of his vast and wondrous creation. If we had arrived much earlier in cosmic history, we would have seen less since the age of the universe limits both the distance out to which we can see and the number and kinds of objects that would have formed in the universe. If we had arrived later, we would have seen less because of the accelerating expansion of the universe.

Now is the best possible time to be an astronomer. *Now* the heavens declare (more loudly than ever) the glory and righteousness of God.[32] We also are at the best possible location for prime viewing.[33] We have hope, not despair. God, the Creator, has written that as soon as he completes the conquest of evil, he will replace this awesome universe with one even more glorious, possessing radically different physics, dimensions, splendors, and rewards far beyond our capacity to think or imagine.[34]

 Discussion Questions _____

1. Scientific evidence for the cosmological constant (dark energy) appears to be unassailable and yet two groups resist it due to its implications. Discuss who the two groups are, the objections, and responses.
2. How does the cosmic mass density factor into the universe's fine-tuning?
3. What is "quintessence"? Does it present a realistic challenge to design evidence?
4. If "now is the best possible time to be an astronomer" according to the author, is it also the best time for *anyone* to observe the heavens? What can we learn?

Chapter 6

Twenty-First Century Discoveries, Part II

As amazing as the breakthrough cosmological discoveries at the beginning of the twenty-first century were for advancing our understanding of the universe's origin and history, astronomers were not done. The breakthrough discoveries made during the opening years of the twenty-first century paved the way for equally stunning new discoveries. Just like the discoveries described in the previous chapter provided more evidence for the handiwork and glory of God, so, too, do the discoveries described in this chapter. The discoveries of the cosmological constant (dark energy) and a flat, or very nearly flat, geometry for the universe, as shown in the previous chapter, easily rank as the most dramatic cosmic discoveries of the early twenty-first century. They are by no means, however, the only potent new evidences for a big bang creation event.

While chapter 4 established that scientists found concrete evidence for the hot big bang model by the end of the twentieth century, it by no means ended further research and studies. Scientists are continually measuring additional characteristics of the universe, seeking to refine and add understanding to the origin and history of the universe. In addition to the discoveries described in the previous chapter, twenty-first century discoveries in areas such as elemental abundances, galaxy types, distributions, and movements, the velocity of cosmic expansion, cosmic cooling, star types, and primordial magnetic fields provide greater understanding of the universe and further confirmation of the big bang creation model. The element helium provides a good example.

Helium Abundance Matches Big Bang Prediction
The big bang theory says that most of the helium in the universe formed very soon after the creation event. According to the big bang theory, the universe was infinitely or nearly infinitely hot at the creation moment. As the cosmos expanded, it cooled, much like the combustion chamber in a piston engine.

By the time the universe was one millisecond old, it had settled down into a sea of protons, neutrons, and electrons. The only element in existence at that time was simple hydrogen, described by a single proton. For about twenty seconds, when the universe was a little less than four minutes old, it reached the right temperature for nuclear fusion to occur. During that time, protons and neutrons fused together to form elements heavier than simple hydrogen.

According to the theory, nearly one-fourth of the universe's original hydrogen, by mass, was converted into helium during that twenty-second period. Except for tiny amounts of lithium, beryllium, boron, and deuterium (which is hydrogen with both a proton and a neutron in its nucleus), all other elements that exist in the universe were produced much later, along with a little extra helium, in the nuclear furnaces at the cores of stars.

According to the big bang theory, the exact amount of the universe's original hydrogen that was fused into helium during the first four minutes of the universe's history was determined by the cosmic density of baryons (the sum of protons and neutrons). Detailed maps of the cosmic microwave background radiation yield accurate measures of the cosmic baryon density. The cosmic baryon density measure from the Planck map of the cosmic background radiation provides a predicted primordial helium abundance (helium abundance before the universe's first stars form) of 0.24668 ± 0.00013 of the universe's original mass of hydrogen.[1]

This predicted value, based on the big bang theory, can be tested by observations of the helium abundance in gaseous nebulae (giant clouds of gas and dust where new stars are forming) that have experienced very little star formation. Stars pollute gaseous nebulae with the products of their nuclear burning. These products consist of additional helium, plus elements heavier than helium that astronomers simply refer to as "metals." By measuring the amounts of helium and metals in the most metal-poor gaseous nebulae in many distant galaxies, astronomers can accurately extrapolate, from the differing metal contents they measure in a large sample of gaseous nebulae, the amount of helium all gaseous nebulae possessed before any star burning began.

Two different teams of astronomers have published their determination of the primordial helium abundance from measurements made on distant metal-poor gaseous nebulae. A Mexican-Spanish team obtained a value for the primordial helium abundance of 0.2446 ± 0.0029[2] while an American team produced a value of 0.2449 ± 0.0040.[3] This remarkable agreement between prediction and observations today ranks as one of the most spectacular verifications of the big bang creation model, and the standard big bang nucleosynthesis theory in particular.

Deuterium Abundance Matches Big Bang Too

According to big bang theory, whatever quantity of deuterium (heavy hydrogen) and lithium that exists today was produced during the first four minutes of creation. Not all that deuterium and lithium remains, however, for stellar burning gobbles up those elements, rather than producing more.

In seeking to measure the abundance of deuterium and lithium and to compare that amount with the amount predicted by the big bang model, astronomers focused again on distant metal-poor systems. As with helium, the cosmic baryon density measure from the Planck map of the cosmic background radiation provides a predicted primordial deuterium abundance of $2.606 \pm 0.053 \times 10^{-5}$ of the universe's original mass of hydrogen.[4] Based on an analysis of the measured deuterium abundance in the most metal-poor damped Lyman alpha systems (large concentrations of hydrogen gas detected in the spectra of quasars) currently known, a team of American and British astronomers determined that the primordial deuterium abundance is $2.547 \pm 0.033 \times 10^{-5}$.[5] As the Planck Collaboration team wrote, this agreement between the big bang prediction and observation is "a remarkable success for the standard theory of BBN [big bang nucleosynthesis]."[6] In a review paper, physicist Brian Fields wrote, "This concordance represents a great success for the hot big bang cosmology."[7]

Lithium Abundance Problem?

Comparing the primordial lithium abundance predicted by the big bang model with the observed primordial lithium abundance is much more challenging than comparisons between theory and observations for helium and deuterium. The predicted lithium abundance derived from the Planck cosmic microwave background radiation map under the presumption of big bang cosmology is about a factor of a hundred thousand times less than for primordial deuterium and a factor of a billion times less than for primordial helium. The predicted primordial lithium abundance is $4.95 \pm 0.39 \times 10^{-10}$ of the universe's original mass of hydrogen.[8]

This extremely low abundance of lithium is affirmed by astronomical observations. Lithium spectral lines in astronomical sources are so weak that astronomers are unable to obtain a useful detection in any star outside our galaxy. They are limited to observing lithium in metal-poor stars in our galaxy.

Observations published in 2005 of a sample of metal-poor stars in the halo of our galaxy yielded a ratio of lithium to hydrogen equal to $1.66 \pm 0.35 \times 10^{-10}$.[9]

Subsequent observations published in 2012 by two different teams of astronomers produced lithium-to-hydrogen ratios of 1.91–2.88 x 10^{-10} and 3.80 ± 0.77 x 10^{-10}, respectively.[10] Two sets of observations of stars in metal-poor Milky Way Galaxy globular clusters produced lithium-to-hydrogen ratios of 3.72 ± 0.96 x 10^{-10} and 1.95–2.24 x 10^{-10}, respectively.[11]

All the observational values lie below the predicted value. While one could argue that the two larger values are in statistical agreement with the predicted value, the other measurements depart from the predicted value by a factor of 1.72–2.98 times. This discord is known as the lithium problem.

The announced detection of the lithium-6 isotope in three galactic halo stars[12] makes the lithium problem much worse. However, a follow-up study revealed that "none of the three analyzed stars have a significant detection of ^{6}Li."[13]

Astronomers have proposed several reasonable solutions to what remains of the lithium problem. The most obvious is to point out that all observations to date measure the present lithium abundance, not the lithium abundance at epochs close to the cosmic creation event. As astronomers Corinne Charbonnel and Francesca Primas deduced, "We are then left with the conclusion that the Li abundance along the plateau is not the pristine one, but that halo stars have undergone surface depletion during their evolution."[14] Astronomers Elisabeth Vangioni and Alain Coc add that since it is well known that stellar burning consumes lithium, it may be a mistake to presume "that lithium has not been depleted at the surfaces of these stars" and that "the presently observed abundances can be assumed to be equal to the initial one."[15] Astronomer Brian Fields demonstrated that if at any time during a star's youth its near surface layers experienced temperatures exceeding 2.5 x 10^6 kelvin, that exposure would cause substantial destruction of lithium.[16]

That stellar destruction of lithium likely explains the lithium abundance problem finds strong support from the recent observation of interstellar lithium in the Small Magellanic Cloud (SMC). The SMC is a dwarf galaxy located 197,000 light-years away. Compared to the Milky Way Galaxy, the interstellar gas in the SMC is metal-poor. High-resolution spectra of the interstellar medium seen as absorption lines in the light of the bright SMC star, Sk 143, revealed a lithium-to-hydrogen ratio of 4.79 ± 1.48 x 10^{-10}.[17] This value is fully consistent with the predicted primordial lithium abundance, although clearly higher precision measurements would be desirable.

There is hope that the next generation of super-telescopes will have the power to accurately measure lithium abundances in nearby metal-poor galaxies and even in sources billions of light-years away and hence billions of years ago. It will take observations of stars billions of light-years away to determine exactly how much lithium is destroyed by stellar burning. However, given how feeble the lithium spectral lines will be, it is a faint hope that such determinations soon will be forthcoming.

If needed, there may be a nuclear physics solution to the lithium problem. If beryllium-7 destruction in nucleosynthesis is greater than what current models predict, that destruction by itself could solve the lithium problem. Presently, the relevant nucleosynthesis resonances (a nucleosynthesis resonance is where one isotope possesses almost exactly the same energy level as one or two other isotopes) that determine rates of beryllium-7 destruction are poorly measured.[18] There is also the possibility of an unknown resonance.

Possible cosmological solutions to the lithium problem include long-term exposure of stellar surfaces to cosmic rays,[19] the decay of relatively long-lived negatively charged exotic dark matter particles (the most likely candidate being the second-lightest supersymmetric particle),[20] photon cooling,[21] and a weak primordial magnetic field.[22] Long-term exposure to cosmic rays definitely occurs. The degree to which this exposure destroys lithium has yet to be determined. The observational upper limits on a primordial magnetic field (primordial magnetic fields are addressed later in this chapter), 1 nanogauss on size scales of several million light-years,[23] is close to the value required, by itself, to solve the lithium problem.

A team of Japanese and American astronomers pointed out that three of the above-mentioned possible solutions (higher past stellar surface temperatures, cosmic rays, primordial magnetic field) are known to have at least some impact on lowering the lithium abundance on stellar surfaces from the primordial value.[24] Thus, they propose that the most reasonable solution to the lithium problem is a combination of these three factors plus possibly small contributions from photon cooling and the decay of exotic particles.

Spreading Apart of Galaxies

If the universe really is expanding from a space-time beginning, then as astronomers observe farther and farther away, and hence further and further back in time, they should observe that far away galaxies and galaxy clusters will be jammed more tightly together than those nearby. Thanks to several images of galaxies and galaxy clusters at varying distances taken by large telescopes, this important prediction of big bang cosmology can be put to a stringent test.

Images of galaxies whose light has taken more than 10 billion years to reach

**12 billion light
years away**

2 billion light years away

Figure 6.1: Galaxy Separations at Two Different Distances
Image credits: NASA, ESA, ACS Science Team, N. Benitez and H. Ford (JHU), T. Broadhurst (Racah Institute of Physics/Hebrew University), M. Clampin and G. Hartig (STScI), G. Illingworth (UCO/ Lick Observatory)

us show that typically the galaxies are so tightly packed together that their mutual gravity results in them ripping spiral arms and other galactic structures away from one another. For example, the left image in figure 6.1 shows galaxies when the universe was just 2–3 billion years old. The right image in figure 6.1 shows a different set of galaxies when the universe was about 12 billion years old. The spatial scale is the same for both images. Galaxies in the right image are dramatically farther apart from one another than the galaxies in the left image.

An examination of the hundreds of images astronomers have taken of galaxy groups and galaxy clusters shows a smooth progression of increasing separation between galaxy clusters and galaxies as the universe gets older and older. Extrapolating this spreading apart as the universe gets older, back to the time of the universe's beginning, establishes that the universe began infinitesimally small.

Cosmic Expansion Velocity Matches Big Bang Prediction
An obvious way to test the big bang creation model is to affirm that the universe is indeed expanding from an infinitesimal volume and to measure the rate of its expansion from the beginning up to the present moment. While this task may seem simple in principle, in practice it is not. Measurements of adequate precision are enormously difficult to make. Only in the last few years

have measurements as accurate (or nearly so) as the other big bang proofs become possible.

Four precision methods for measuring the cosmic expansion rate recently have been developed and applied (see table 5.1). The average of the four, plus a compilation by astronomers Yun Chen, Suresh Kumar, and Bharat Ratra of more than 600 measurements, yields a rate of 68.65 ± 1.21 kilometers per second per megaparsec (a megaparsec = the distance light travels in 3.26 million years). A mean of all nine values in table 6.1 yields a cosmic expansion rate of 68.64 ± 1.83.

The reciprocal of the cosmic expansion rate (with slight adjustments arising from the values of the cosmic mass density, dark energy density, and geometry of the universe) straightforwardly yields the age of the universe. The age of the universe so deduced is 13.78 ± 0.26 billion years.[25] This expansion-rate derived age of the universe compares remarkably well with the following cosmic ages determined from the measured sizes of the hot and cold spots in maps of the cosmic background radiation:

inferred age of the universe (WMAP)[26]   13.772 ± 0.059 Gy
inferred age of the universe (Planck)[27]   13.813 ± 0.047 Gy
(gigayear = 1 billion years)

The expansion-rate age for the universe also is consistent with cosmic ages derived from the abundances of long-lived radiometric isotopes like uranium-238 and thorium-232, and with the measured ages of the oldest stars (see "Oldest Stars Tell Their Story" on p. 74).

The cosmic expansion time turns out to be critical for the existence of physical life. The possibility of stable orbits for stars and planets, a necessity for life's survival, depends on both the cosmic expansion rate and the duration of cosmic expansion (see "Stability of Stars and Orbits Proves Big Bang" on p. 43).

Cosmic Cooling

Biblical declarations (see ch. 3) of the universe expanding from a space-time beginning under unchanging physical laws, where one of those laws is a pervasive law of decay, implies that the universe must continually cool as it ages. This conclusion is the heart of the hot big bang creation model.

The law of decay (see Romans 8:19–22), aka the second law of thermodynamics, states that any system that expands must become colder in direct proportion to the amount of expansion the system has experienced. An

Table 6.1: Latest Precision Measurements of the Cosmic Expansion Rate

measuring method	cosmic expansion rate (kilometers/second/megaparsec)
masers in NGC 6264 (direct distance method)[28]	68 ± 9.0
masers in NGC 5765b (direct distance method)[29]	66.0 ± 6.0
masers in UGC 3789 (direct distance method)[30]	68.9 ± 7.1
masers in NGC 4258 (direct distance method)[31]	72.0 ± 3.0
cosmic background radiation temperature fluctuations (WMAP)[32]	69.32 ± 0.80
cosmic background radiation temperature fluctuations (Planck)[33]	67.3 ± 1.2
baryon acoustic oscillation[34]	67.3 ± 1.1
cepheids/type Ia supernovae (corrected for star formation bias)[35]	70.6 ± 2.6
Chen, Kumar, Ratra compilation[36]	68.3 ± 2.7
mean value	**68.64 ± 1.83**

everyday example is the piston engine in diesel automobiles and trucks. When the piston chamber expands, the temperature inside the chamber drops below the ignition point of the diesel fuel, and so the fuel in the chamber does not ignite. When the piston chamber is compressed, the gas temperature in the chamber rises to the fuel's ignition point. The fuel in the chamber ignites and explodes. Because of the degree to which the piston chamber is compressed, there is no need for spark plugs.

If one knows how long the universe has been expanding since the beginning of space and time (the age of the universe) and the rates at which the universe has been expanding since the beginning of space and time, then based on what the Bible says about the attributes of the universe (space-time beginning, expanding universe, unchanging physical laws, pervasive law of decay), one can determine a predicted cooling curve for temperature of the radiation left over from the cosmic creation event, aka the cosmic microwave background radiation. Astronomers can test this predicted cooling curve by making measurements of the cosmic background radiation's temperature at various cosmological epochs.

There are two methods for determining these past cosmic temperatures:

1. Astronomers can measure the fine structure spectral lines from the interstellar gas present in quasar spectra whose transition energies are excited by the photon bath from the cosmic background radiation.

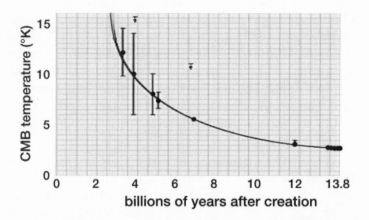

Figure 6.2: Evidence of Cooling from the Big Bang Creation Event

The curve is the predicted cooling of the universe according to the biblically described features of the origin and history of the universe with a cosmic age of 13.79 billion years and an average cosmic expansion rate at 68.65 kilometers/second/megaparsec. The dots and error bars are actual temperature measurements of the cosmic microwave background radiation (i.e., radiation remaining from the cosmic creation event) made at different distances or lookback times.

Credit: Reasons to Believe

2. Astronomers can measure what is known as the Sunyaev-Zeldovich anisotropies that arise from the inverse Compton scattering of photons by free electrons in the potential wells of galaxy clusters.

To date, astronomers have used these methods to determine the temperature of the cosmic microwave background radiation at 13 different cosmological epochs, ranging from the present to 12 billion years ago.[37] Figure 6.2 shows a plot of these measurements relative to the predicted cooling curve. The measurement in the middle of the curve corresponding to 8 billion years ago is the most recent and most accurate measurement.[38] The error bars on this measurement are less than the thickness of the line showing the predicted cooling curve, and this measurement sits right on the predicted cooling curve. In the words of seven astronomers who published a detailed study of the cooling of the cosmic microwave background (CMB) radiation temperature, "No significant deviations from the redshift dependence of the CMB temperature predicted in the standard model have been found."[39] And, "independently of theoretical expectations, measurements of the temperature-redshift relation of the CMB black-body temperature provide a strong consistency check of the current Big Bang paradigm."[40]

Cosmic Inflation

For physical life to be possible the universe must be continually expanding and cooling. As noted, the universe must expand at exquisitely fine-tuned rates throughout its history. For life to be possible in the universe, the stars must not be too young nor too old. The universe must be homogeneous and uniform on large scales, but not small scales. Distances between stars and galaxies must not be too great nor too little. It also is important that the universe be thermally connected on all size scales.

The latter requirement is affirmed by maps of the cosmic microwave background radiation. The other requirements can be met only if the universe experiences an extremely short period of hyper-fast expansion, or inflation, when it is very young.

In the big bang creation model the universe begins with such an extremely hot temperature and such an extremely small volume that all four forces of physics—electromagnetism, weak nuclear force, strong nuclear force, and gravity—had equal strength and blended together to operate as a single force. In the first fraction of a second after the cosmic creation event, the single force first separates into two forces (gravity and the strong-electroweak force), then into three forces (gravity, the strong nuclear force, and the electroweak force), and finally into the four forces of physics that operate in the universe today.

At each of the force separation events, symmetry breaking occurs. (Symmetry breaking is the process by which a physical system in a symmetrical state, in this case the universe, ends up in an asymmetrical state.) Specifically, as the forces of physics decoupled from one another as a result of cosmic cooling, they lost their symmetry and the universe became more disordered.

In 1981, MIT physicist Alan Guth explained how cosmic inflation is an expected outcome of the symmetry breaking that occurs when (due to cosmic cooling) the strong-electroweak force separates into the strong nuclear force and the electroweak force.[41] In Guth's model the inflation event lasted *from* sometime between 10^{-36} and 10^{-35} seconds *to* sometime between 10^{-33} and 10^{-32} seconds after the cosmic creation event. (In other words, the hyper-rapid expansion of the universe started between 10^{-36} and 10^{-35} seconds after the cosmic creation event and ended between 10^{-33} and 10^{-32} seconds after the cosmic creation event.)

If a cosmic inflation event did occur very early in the universe's history, it would leave an unmistakable signature in measurements of the polarization modes of the cosmic microwave background radiation. In particular, an accurate measure of the E-mode (transverse magnetic mode) signal in maps of the cosmic microwave background reveals what astronomers call the scalar spectral index, n_s.

For a universe with no inflation event, n_s equals 1.0 or greater. For a universe that had a simple inflation event, n_s equals exactly 0.95. For a universe that has had a complex inflation event, n_s equals 0.96–0.97.

Three instruments have produced determinations of n_s with sufficient precision to test whether the universe had a past inflation event. These instruments are the WMAP and Planck satellites and the South Pole Telescope (SPT). The nine-year data set from the Wilkinson Microwave Anisotropy Probe satellite determined that the cosmic scalar spectral index, $n_s = 0.9608 \pm 0.0080$.[42] The fifteen-month data set from the Planck satellite map of the cosmic microwave background radiation established that the cosmic scalar spectral index, $n_s = 0.9603 \pm 0.0073$.[43] The SPT research team's measurements, in combination with the latest results from the WMAP and Planck satellites, yielded the most accurate determination to date. The value they published was $n_s = 0.9593 \pm 0.0067$.[44] The error estimate, ± 0.0067, implies that there is less than 1 chance in 900,000,000 that the universe did *not* experience an inflation event very early in its history. Thus, no reasonable doubt remains that a cosmic inflation event indeed occurred.

Primordial Magnetic Fields

One of the holy grails of modern cosmology is the quest to find the universe's primordial magnetic fields. These fields, whose strengths typically are measured in units of gauss or tesla (one gauss = 0.0001 tesla, which approximately equals the Earth's magnetic field strength), are thought to arise from the symmetry-breaking events (see explanations under the previous subhead, Cosmic Inflation) that occurred during the first split second after the hot big bang cosmic creation event.

At one or more of the three cosmic symmetry-breaking events, plus a later one at 10^{-6} seconds after the cosmic creation event when the universe has cooled sufficiently that quarks can bind together to make protons and neutrons, a small fraction of the free energy released during the phase transitions could be converted into what later becomes large-scale (size scale exceeding 3 million light-years) magnetic fields. Currently, astronomers possess no other explanation for the possible existence of such large-scale magnetic fields other than their origination in one or more of these very early transition events. Hence, they refer to such fields as "primordial magnetic fields."

Detecting large-scale magnetic fields in the universe and accurately measuring their properties, therefore, could give us a much more detailed picture of the early history of the universe. That more detailed picture, in turn, could yield additional insights into how the physics and properties of the universe expanding according to the big bang creation model were designed to make physical life, and advanced life in particular, possible.

There is more. If large-scale magnetic fields exist in the universe and if these magnetic fields are as strong as about 0.1 nanogauss (1 nanogauss = one billionth of a gauss), then they could explain the suggestion or hint of non-gaussianity in the Planck satellite map of the universe's cosmic microwave background radiation (the radiation left over from the cosmic creation event). They also could explain the microgauss magnetic fields that astronomers have observed in large spiral galaxies. Additionally, they could help explain the lithium abundances astronomers observe in stars.

Such strong large-scale magnetic fields would predict an earlier first formation date for dwarf galaxies, an earlier time for the reionization of the universe, an earlier time for the formation of structure in the universe, and an earlier and more abundant formation of molecular hydrogen. Earlier and more abundant molecular hydrogen in the universe would mean that Population III stars, the universe's firstborn stars (addressed later in this chapter), would be more abundant and manifest a greater range of masses. Exactly how much earlier or how different the predicted properties would be depends on the strength of these possible large-scale magnetic fields.

Small- and Medium-Scale Magnetic Field Measurements

Earth's magnetic field is approximately 1 gauss, as is the Sun's general magnetic field. Jupiter has the strongest general magnetic field of any solar system body at about 10 gauss. The Milky Way Galaxy's general magnetic field is about one microgauss (0.000001 gauss). Nearby spiral galaxies possess magnetic fields ranging from 1–50 microgauss on size scales of 10,000–30,000 light-years. In clusters of galaxies on size scales of 20,000–40,000 light-years, astronomers have detected magnetic fields of a few microgauss.

Astronomers have found indisputable evidence for magnetic fields on all the size scales they have searched except for the very largest. What they have observed, however, is that the larger the size scale, the weaker the magnetic field.

Attempted Large-Scale Magnetic Field Measurements

In 2010 two astronomers, based on the assumption that halos around the gamma-ray images of quasars and blazars (extremely bright quasars) are caused by intergalactic magnetic fields, determined that the intergalactic magnetic field on size scales of several million light-years is about 1 femtogauss (10^{-15} gauss).[45] In the same year two other astronomers, based on their nondetection of billion-electron-volt gamma-ray emission from a cascade initiated by trillion-electron-volt gamma rays that they did observe in blazars, established that the strength of intergalactic magnetic fields must be at least 3×10^{-16} gauss.[46]

Before 2017, the best assumption-free measurement of large-scale intergalactic magnetic fields came from analysis of maps of the cosmic background radiation. The Planck Collaboration used anisotropies in the Planck satellite map of the cosmic background radiation to show that large-scale intergalactic magnetic fields could be no stronger than 0.9–5.6 nanogauss.[47] (One nanogauss = 0.000000001 gauss or one-billionth of a gauss.) The range of upper limits they determined depended on which hot big bang creation model they chose and what features of primordial magnetic fields they presumed. The POLARBEAR Collaboration based on the POLARBEAR map of the cosmic background radiation established an upper limit of 3.9 nanogauss.[48]

A New Large-Scale Magnetic Field Measurement
In the September 10, 2017 issue of the *Astrophysical Journal*, three astronomers established a much superior limit on the strength of potential primordial magnetic fields.[49] They combined data from the four best maps of the cosmic microwave background radiation, namely from Planck, BICEP2/Keck Array, POLARBEAR, and SPTpol. Their analysis showed that intergalactic magnetic fields on size scales larger than 3 million light-years could not be any stronger than 0.91 gauss.[50]

Near Future Large-Scale Magnetic Field Measurements
This new upper limit for primordial magnetic fields is tantalizingly close to the values (~0.1 nanogauss) where the cosmological creation model implications get very interesting. Thus, the three astronomers project what we can expect from cosmic background radiation mapping efforts that are already underway and another one that is due to begin shortly.

Those observational efforts already underway that possess the sensitivity to measure primordial magnetic field strengths weaker than 0.1 nanogauss include the South Pole Telescope (SPT)–3G and the Simons Array. The three astronomers demonstrate that by the end of the current decade the combination of the SPT–3G and Simons Array experiments will be able to detect primordial magnetic fields as weak as 0.05 nanogauss.[51]

Starting in 2020, another experiment, the CMB-S4, will begin collecting data. The three astronomers show that sometime during the 2020s the CMB-S4 will be able to detect primordial magnetic fields as weak as 0.01 nanogauss.[52] Detectability at the 0.01 nanogauss level is guaranteed to deliver a much more detailed big bang creation model and much better and more detailed understanding of both the early and later development stages of the universe.

Star Populations Fit Big Bang

From elements like helium providing stronger proofs for the big bang to expansion rates yielding a confirmed age of the universe, astronomical twenty-first century discoveries abound. The age and makeup of stars also shed light on big bang predictions about characteristics of the universe. The big bang creation model predicts a hierarchy in star formation. Since the big bang creation event results in the universe's ordinary matter being composed of 76% hydrogen, 24% helium, and a trace amount of lithium, the firstborn stars, at least initially, will be composed of these three elements. (The percentages stated here are by mass. About 92% of the universe's original number of atoms are hydrogen and about 8% are helium.)

A challenge to big bang creation models arose when astronomers were not able to detect a star that was completely without elements heavier than lithium. Astronomers responded to this challenge by explaining that the big bang model predicts that firstborn stars would be undetectable with presently existing telescopes. In big bang models, the first stars would have formed more than 13.4 billion years ago, when the universe was less than 0.4 billion years old. This means that to observe them in their initial state, we must measure the spectra of individual stars at distances corresponding to when the universe was less than 0.4 billion years old. No telescope presently exists with the power to measure the spectra of individual stars at that great distance.

Astronomers recognize three different generations of stars, each with unique element properties. All stars larger than several times the Sun's mass explode at the end of their nuclear burning and, therefore, salt the interstellar medium with their ashes. The more massive the star, the faster it burns up its nuclear fuel and the sooner it explodes. Thus, the largest of the first-generation stars relatively quickly pollute the interstellar medium. The second generation of stars incorporates these ashes when they form. These second-generation stars comprise most of the stars in the universe. From 0.001 to 1% of their composition is made up of elements heavier than hydrogen, helium, and lithium. Third-generation stars incorporate the ashes of exploded second-generation stars. About 1–4% of the composition of third-generation stars is comprised of elements heavier than hydrogen, helium, and lithium.

Astronomers refer to third-generation stars as Population I (Pop I) stars, second-generation stars as Population II (Pop II) stars, and first-generation stars as Population III (Pop III) stars. The Sun is a Pop I star. In big bang cosmology, life is only possible on a planet orbiting a Pop I star.

Some big bang creation models predicted that all Pop III stars would be supergiant stars and would accordingly go through their entire burning phase in just a few million years or less. In those models all the still-shining Pop III stars existed more than 13.4 billion years ago. For astronomers to observe Pop III stars, they must look more than 13.4 billion light-years away from Earth. Current telescope technology is unable to access individual stars at these great distances.

Many other big bang creation models, however, predicted that at least a few Pop III stars would not be supergiants. These stars with much lower masses could burn for billions of years. Therefore, some of them may be close enough that astronomers could detect them and measure their spectra.

Such old Pop III stars, though, would not be in their initial pristine state. Over their several-billion-year burning history their stellar atmospheres would have accreted a small quantity of heavy elements from the interstellar medium. This medium would be polluted by the ashes of exploded supergiant Pop III and supergiant Pop II stars. Yet, for low mass Pop III stars residing in regions of space where the density of stars is sparse, the pollution level would be extremely low. Consequently, there would be no doubt when astronomers are observing an old Pop III star, aka a Pop III survivor, rather than any kind of Pop II star.

After a long and diligent search, astronomers discovered three of these Pop III survivors. The one most deficient in heavy elements is SMSS J031300.36-670839.3 (SM0313 for short).[53] Roughly 75% the Sun's mass, SM0313 is 13.6 billion years old, making it the oldest known star with an accurate age determination. Compared to the Sun, it has less than one 30 millionth the density of iron.[54] While iron was undetectable in the spectrum of SM0313, astronomers were able to detect calcium. Compared to the Sun, SM0313 possesses 18.2 million times less calcium per unit mass. The other two Pop III survivors, HE 1327-2326 and HR 0107-5240, respectively, possess 500,000 and 250,000 times less iron per unit mass than the Sun.[55]

A team of Japanese astronomers placed these iron and calcium abundance measures into a cosmological context by developing a detailed theoretical model.[56] They investigated the change of iron abundance on the surfaces of Pop III survivors through accretion from the interstellar medium in the framework of hierarchal star formation. Their calculations showed that Pop III survivors can accumulate up to a 100,000th (0.00001%) as much iron per unit mass as the Sun. It would be impossible for any Pop II star to possess so little iron. On this basis, they concluded that any star possessing less than 100,000 times iron per unit mass than the Sun must be a Pop III survivor.

The observational measurements and theoretical calculations described here establish that Pop III stars really do exist. When the James Webb Space Telescope and ground-based telescopes with mirror diameters exceeding 100 feet become operational, astronomers will likely detect many more Pop III survivors, as well as newborn Pop III stars in their initial pristine state.

Oldest Stars Tell Their Story

Pop III survivor stars and the most heavy element deficient (metal-poor) Pop II stars present another way to test the big bang creation model by measuring their ages. Adding the known ages of these stars, plus the time from the beginning of the universe to the big bang model's predicted time of their initial formation, should match the age of the universe determined from other methods predicated on the big bang model.

The spectral characteristics of the Pop III survivor stars described above establish that they were polluted by the ashes expelled from Pop III stars with masses ranging from 10 to 70 times the Sun's mass.[57] Stars this massive burn their nuclear fuel and explode as supernovae in time scales less than a few million years. The ashes these stars expel into the gas clouds that produce the next generation of stars (Pop II stars) will contain the long-lived radioisotopes uranium-238 (half-life = 4.468 billion years) and thorium-232 (half-life = 14.05 billion years).

By measuring the abundance of uranium-238 and/or thorium-232 in low-mass, metal-poor (and therefore long-lived) Pop II stars, astronomers can determine the ages of the oldest visible stars. They can add to these ages the fastest time the big bang model would permit such stars to form after the cosmic creation event to obtain an age measure for the universe.

Astronomers have detected uranium and thorium in a large number of Pop II stars. However, in only three low-mass, metal-poor Pop II stars have they successfully measured the uranium abundance. Their best measurement came from the star HE 1523-0901, in which they were able to compare the abundance of uranium and thorium to the non-radioactive elements europium, osmium, and iridium.[58] The weighted radiometric age for HE 1523-0901 is 13.2 ± 1.5 billion years.[59] For the star CS 31082-001 one team of astronomers obtained a radiometric age of 12.5 ± 3.0 billion years,[60] while a second team measured an age equaling 14.0 ± 2.4 billion years.[61] Adding a 0.5-billion-year formation time to HE 1523-0901's age and the average of the two age measurements for CS 31082-001 yields an estimate for the universe's age ~13.7 billion years, an estimate consistent with all other age determinations for the universe.

The cooling of white dwarfs gives astronomers a second stellar age-dating method for ascertaining the age of the universe. White dwarfs are stars that have burned all their nuclear fuel and are in the process of cooling down, much like the burned-out embers of a wood fire. Astronomers can determine the ages of globular star clusters by measuring the bottom of the white dwarf cooling sequence for white dwarfs residing in the clusters. Measurements of the bottom of the white dwarf cooling sequence for the globular cluster M4 shows an age of 11.8 ± 0.6 billion years[62] and for the globular cluster NGC 6397 an age of 12.8 ± 0.6 billion years.[63] Adding the formation times for these two clusters (relative to the cosmic creation event) delivers an age for the universe of about 14 billion years.

Theological Reaction to Big Bang Cosmology

Though the case for the big bang, that is, a transcendent cosmic creation event, rests on compelling (some might say *overwhelming*) evidence, the theory still has its critics. Some skepticism may be attributable to the communication gap between scientists and the rest of the world. Some evidences are so new that most people have yet to hear of them. Some evidences, including the older ones, are so technical that few people understand their significance. The need for better education and clearer communication remains. In fact, it motivates the publication of this book.

Communication and education gaps explain only some of the skepticism, however. Spiritual issues also weigh in. The few astronomers who still oppose the big bang openly object not on scientific grounds but on personal, theological grounds.

In my first book, *The Fingerprint of God*, I tell the story of astronomers' early reaction to findings that affirmed a cosmic beginning, and hence Beginner.[64] Some openly stated their views of the big bang as "repugnant"[65] or "crackpot."[66] For decades they invented one cosmic hypothesis after another in a futile attempt to get around the glaring facts. When all their hypotheses failed the tests of observational checks, many of those astronomers conceded, perhaps reluctantly, the cosmic origin prize to the big bang.

Today, only a handful of astronomers still hold out against the big bang and its philosophical implications. Their resistance, however, is based not on what observations and experiments can test, but rather on what observations and experiments can never test. Though their articles appear in science journals, they engage in metaphysics rather than in physics, in theology (more accurately, antitheology) rather than science. These metaphysical gymnastics disguised as science are the subject of chapters 7, 8, 9, 12, and 13. In chapters 10 and 11, I describe powerful new evidences that the Cause of the universe transcends matter, energy, and the ten space-time dimensions associated with matter and energy. In chapters 14–18, I look at how new scientific discoveries identify many of the personal attributes of the universe's Cause. We will see how new science reveals not only that a god exists but exactly what kind of God created the universe.

 Discussion Questions _____

1. Scientific evidence for the cosmological constant (dark energy) appears to be unassailable and yet two groups resist it due to its implications. Discuss who the two groups are, the objections, and responses.
2. Does the "lithium abundance problem" present a challenge to the big bang model?
3. According to the author, a pervasive law of decay implies that the universe must continually become cooler as it ages and this conclusion is "the heart of the hot big bang creation model." Does this notion find biblical support? Explain.
4. Discuss the differences between Population I, II, and III stars and why they matter in a big bang creation model.
5. Despite overwhelming evidence, some astronomers oppose the big bang not on scientific, but on personal, theological grounds. How can we avoid doing the same thing in matters of truth in other areas?

Chapter 7

Einstein's Challenge

Until Albert Einstein's theory of general relativity came along in the early part of the twentieth century, scientists saw no reason to question the notion that the universe is infinite and everywhere the same. After all, the philosophical and scientific underpinnings of this view had been hammered into place by one of the most influential thinkers of all time, Immanuel Kant (1724–1804).

An Infinite Perspective

Kant reasoned that an Infinite Being could be reflected in nothing less than an infinite universe.[1] How the universe came to be is immaterial and therefore unknowable, according to Kant. He concerned himself with how the universe works. His studies convinced him that everything in the universe could be accounted for by the laws of mechanics described by Sir Isaac Newton (1643–1727). On that assumption, he built the first in a series of mechanistic models for the universe.

Kant extended his reasoning beyond physical science into the realm of biology. He saw that a static (with life-favorable conditions persisting indefinitely), infinitely old, and infinitely large universe would allow the possibility of an infinite number of random chances. With an infinite number of building blocks (atoms and molecules) and an infinite number of chances to assemble them in random ways (given appropriate physical and chemical conditions existing for infinite time), any kind of final product would be possible—even something as highly complex as a German philosopher.[2] His attempt to construct a model for life's origin was abandoned only when he realized that a scientific understanding of the internal workings of organisms was missing.

Perhaps the major credit for Darwinism and the multitude of *isms* that sprang from it belongs to Immanuel Kant.[3]

THE PARADOX OF THE DARK NIGHT SKY

Why does it get dark when the Sun sets? This question is not so trite as it sounds. In the context of an approximately static, infinitely old, and infinitely large universe, the light from all the stars would add up to an infinite brightness.

The brightness of a light source is diminished by four for every doubling of its distance. For example, a light bulb at the center of a one-foot diameter globe will illuminate the globe's surface four times brighter than the same bulb at the center of a two-foot diameter. This is because the two-foot diameter globe has a surface area four times larger than the one-foot diameter globe. So, since Jupiter, for example, is five times more distant from the Sun than Earth, the sunlight it receives is twenty-five times dimmer.

Consequently, if stars are evenly spaced from one another, the light received from them on Earth doubles for each doubling of the diameter of space. This is because with each doubling of the distance from Earth, the volume of space, and thus the number of stars within that volume, increases eight times, while the light received from the stars, on average twice as distant, decreases by only four times. Hence, if the distance from Earth is doubled indefinitely, to an infinite distance, the accumulated light from all the stars must reach infinite brightness. So the night sky should be infinitely luminous.

This conclusion, nevertheless, did not stop proponents of an infinite universe. They claimed clouds of dust between the stars would absorb starlight sufficiently to allow the night sky to be dark even in an infinite universe. They overlooked (until 1960), however, a basic principle of thermodynamics: given sufficient time, a body will radiate away as much energy as it receives. Therefore, even that interstellar dust eventually would become as hot as the stars and radiate just as much energy. Thus, the universe in some respect must be finite. (See "Hubble Time and Young-Universe Creationism" on p. 86.)

As Far as the Eye Can See

As evidence that what we think about the cosmos matters, no century prior to the nineteenth had seen such dramatic change in people's concepts about life and reality. The view of an infinite cosmos, in which these changes were rooted, received greater and greater theoretical and observational support. As stronger optics carried astronomers deeper into the heavens, all they could see

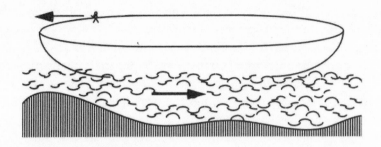

Figure 7.1: Principle of Invariance

If a ship's captain were jogging along his vessel at 10 mph while the ship sailed at 10 mph, the captain would be moving at 20 mph (relative to the shore) when jogging in the direction of the ship's motion, and 0 mph when jogging in the opposite direction. This law we have known since the days of Galileo. However, in velocity of light experiments, the motion of the observer proves entirely irrelevant. The velocity of light does not vary with the motion of the observer.

Credit: Reasons to Beileve

was more of the same kinds of stars and nebulae (gas clouds) they had already seen up close.

Thousands of stars and a few dozen nebulae became billions of stars and millions of nebulae. It seemed endless. Astronomers and laypeople alike were boggled by the immensity of it all.

Further support for Kant's universe model came from the amazing triumph of Newton's laws of motion. As astronomers documented the motions of planets, of satellites orbiting the planets, of comets and asteroids, of binary stars, and of stars in star clusters, everything matched what those laws predicted. Kant's claim that everything about and in the universe could be accounted for by the laws of mechanics was substantially bolstered.

The combination of astronomers' observations and an apparent answer to the paradox of the dark night sky (see "The Paradox of the Dark Night Sky" on p. 78) resulted in the elevation of Kant's cosmological model from a hypothesis to a theory. By the end of the nineteenth century it was cast in concrete.

Einstein Discovers Relativity

The concrete began to crack, however, almost before it dried. As physicists made their first accurate measurements of the velocity of light, they were taken by surprise (see fig. 7.1). A revolution was beginning. It would be deduced that:

(1) no absolute reference system exists from which motions in space can be measured, and (2) the velocity of light with respect to all observers never varies. The velocities of the observers are irrelevant.

In 1905, German-born Swiss engineer Albert Einstein (1879–1955), who studied physics in his spare time, published several papers of enormous significance. Two of them spelled out these conclusions about the constancy of the velocity of light.[4] He called the findings the principle of invariance, but others referred to them as relativity, and that name stuck.

Once this initial theory of relativity (later dubbed "special" since it focused only on velocity) was solidly established,[5] Einstein went to work on the extension of the theory, an effort that demanded every ounce of his genius. The results, published in 1915 and 1916,[6] were the equations of general relativity, equations that carry profound implications about the nature and origin of the universe.

Einstein Discovers the Beginner
For one, these equations show that the universe is not static. They show that the universe either is contracting or expanding. The velocities of galaxies reveal that it is the latter. The universe simultaneously is expanding. What phenomenon behaves this way? There is one: an explosion.

For example, when a grenade is detonated, the pieces of the grenade expand outward from the pin assembly. As they expand, they collide with material (air molecules, buildings, furniture, etc.) that slows them down (deceleration). If the universe is the aftermath of an explosion, then there must have been a beginning to the explosion—a moment at which the pin was pulled. By the simple law of cause and effect, it must have had a Beginner—someone to pull the pin.

Einstein's own worldview initially kept him from adopting such a conclusion. Rather, in 1917, he hypothesized a self-stretching property of space that would perfectly cancel out the deceleration and expansion factors[7] (see "Einstein's Repulsive 'Force'" in this chapter).

In 1929, astronomer Edwin Hubble (1889–1953) proved from his measurements on forty different galaxies that the galaxies indeed are expanding away from one another. Moreover, he demonstrated that the expansion matched the same manner predicted by Einstein's original formulation of general relativity[8] (see fig. 7.2). In the face of this proof, Einstein grudgingly abandoned his hypothesized self-stretching space property and acknowledged "the necessity for a beginning"[9] and "the presence of a superior reasoning power."[10]

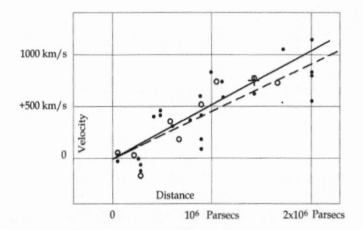

Figure 7.2: Hubble's Original Velocity-Distance Relation[11]

Velocities (kilometers per second) at which several galaxies are moving away from us are plotted against estimated distances. One parsec equals 3.26 light-years, where one light-year equals 5.9 trillion miles. The cross represents the mean of measurements made on twenty-two other galaxies. All measurements shown here were made before 1929.

As Hubble's plot demonstrates, the more distant the galaxy, the faster it moves away from us. Such a relationship between velocity and distance implies that the entire universe must be experiencing a general expansion.

—*From the Proceedings of the National Academy of Sciences*

As noted under "The Discovery" in chapter 5, however, an international team of astronomers has discovered that Einstein was right about the existence of a self-stretching property of space, but wrong about the value of the constant that governs the self-stretching property. The discovery establishes that the universe always has been expanding and from now on will continue to expand at an ever-accelerating rate.

Einstein's God

Einstein's acknowledgment of a "superior reasoning power," however, was not to be mistaken as acknowledging the God of the Bible. For instance, when rabbis and priests came to congratulate Einstein on his discovery of God, he confessed that, while he was convinced God brought the universe into existence and was intelligent and creative, he denied that God was personal.

Of course, those clergy had a stock response to Einstein's denial: How can

EINSTEIN'S REPULSIVE "FORCE"

Einstein's equations of general relativity predicted an exploding universe and, hence, the need for a beginning. To avoid the conclusion of a beginning (and thus a Beginner), Einstein suggested, through an added term to his equations, that there might exist the equivalent of an undiscovered "force" of physics operating everywhere in the universe.

Einstein's added term is really a hypothesized self-stretching property of the space dimensions or space fabric of the universe. The larger the universe grows, that is, the more stretched out the space fabric of the universe becomes, the more energy that fabric gains to continue the stretching.

The net effect of Einstein's added term (neglecting the fundamental forces) is that all bodies would appear to repel one another. Moreover, the strength of the apparent repulsion would increase the more apart bodies are from one another. Einstein proposed a value for the constant (he labeled it the "cosmological constant") governing the self-stretching property of space so that everywhere and at every time in the universe the self-stretching property would perfectly cancel out the effects of gravity (which attracts massive bodies close to each other with ever-increasing strength the closer the bodies get to one another). Thereby, the universe would forever remain dynamically static.

Einstein's cosmological constant was a convenient loophole for another reason. Though no astronomer had ever detected the constant's effect, Einstein and others could claim that the limited distance of our probing out into the cosmos prevented verification. Today that excuse is gone. Astronomers not only are seeing out to the farthest reaches of the cosmos, they are able to make cosmic expansion measures of unprecedented accuracy.

A large team of astronomers discovered (see "The Discovery," on p. 47) that Einstein was right about the existence of a cosmological constant but wrong about its value. Their discovery establishes that the universe always has been expanding and from now on will continue to expand at an ever-accelerating rate.

a Being who is intelligent and creative not also be personal? Einstein brushed past their objection, a valid one, by raising the paradox of God's omnipotence and man's responsibility for his choices:

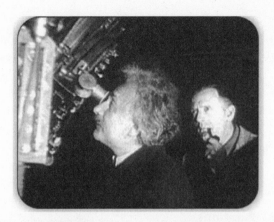

Figure 7.3: Einstein and Hubble

Photo shows (from left) Albert Einstein and Edwin Hubble at the Mount Wilson 100-inch telescope near Pasadena, California, where Hubble made his observations that demonstrated the galaxies are expanding away from one another.

—*Photo courtesy of the Huntington Library*

> If this Being is omnipotent, then every occurrence, including every human action, every human thought, and every human feeling and aspiration is also His work; how is it possible to think of holding men responsible for their deeds and thoughts before such an almighty Being? In giving out punishment and rewards He would to a certain extent be passing judgment on Himself. How can this be combined with the goodness and righteousness ascribed to Him?[12]

None of the clergy Einstein encountered ever gave him a satisfactory answer to his objection. Typically, they responded by saying that God has not yet revealed the answer. They encouraged him to endure patiently and blindly trust the All-Knowing One.

Regrettably, Einstein lacked the persistence to pursue an answer further. He took for granted the biblical knowledge of these religious professionals and assumed that the Bible failed to adequately address this crucially important issue.

Lacking a solution to the paradox of God's predestination and human beings' free choice, Einstein, like many other powerful intellects through the centuries, ruled out the existence of a personal God. Nevertheless, and to his credit, Einstein held unswervingly, against enormous peer pressure, to belief in a Creator.

I am grieved that no one ever offered Einstein the clear, biblical resolution to the paradox he posed. (Based on the scientifically established transdimensional capabilities of the Creator [see chs. 10, 11, and 18], I offer such a resolution in my book *Beyond the Cosmos*.[13]) I am also sad that Einstein did not live long enough to see the accumulation of scientific evidence for a personal, caring Creator (see chs. 15 and 17). These might have sparked in him a willingness to reconsider his conclusion.

 Discussion Questions _____

1. What role did Immanuel Kant serve in how scientists viewed the universe? What finally changed the reigning paradigm?
2. Einstein evidently did not believe in the personal God of the Bible. If he were alive today, would the evidence convince him otherwise? Why or why not?

Chapter 8

Closing Loopholes: Round One

E instein fought the idea of a beginning, but other researchers fought harder. Why? Consider how much was at stake, how many ideas, theories, and isms had already been built on the foundation of an infinitely old universe. If that foundation was removed and replaced by one with completely different specifications, much or most of what had been built on top of it would come tumbling down, or at least require major reconstruction.

Foundational changes of major proportion have occurred in history, but only through time and struggle. The revolution launched by Copernicus (1473–1543), shifting people's concept of reality from an Earth-centered to a Sun-centered astronomical system, took well over a century. Some still resist it today. Ironically, resistance to both Copernicus's and Einstein's work was fueled by fear of what their new view said about God and the Bible. Sixteenth-century scholars feared a loss of respect for both. Twentieth- and twenty-first century scholars often fear an increase of respect for both.

The desire to keep God out of the picture was no hidden agenda but a clearly expressed one. British cosmologist Sir Arthur Eddington (1882–1944) expressed his feelings clearly: "Philosophically, the notion of a beginning of the present order of Nature is repugnant. . . . I should like to find a genuine loophole."[1] And, "We [must] allow evolution an infinite time to get started."[2]

The battle was on to protect certain belief systems, especially evolutionism (the belief that inorganic material evolves into simple cells and later into advanced life without any input from a divine Being), and to defeat the notion of a beginning, with its obvious implications.

The Hubble Time
A challenge for big bang opponents came when Edwin Hubble's research not only confirmed that the universe is expanding but also measured the rate of

HUBBLE TIME AND YOUNG-UNIVERSE CREATIONISM

Ironically, one of the attempted end runs around the Hubble time has been made by a vocal segment of the Christian community. Rather than seeing the Hubble time as a proof for a recent creation event and thus a strike against materialist philosophies, they see it as proof for an ancient cosmos with enough time for strictly natural evolutionary processes to work. Perhaps like many people of the nineteenth century, billions of years appears to them as a time frame essentially equivalent to infinite time.

This group of creationists insists that a literal reading of the Bible demands a creation date for the cosmos of only some six to ten thousand years ago. They interpret the creation days of Genesis 1 as six consecutive twenty-four-hour periods.

Not all Bible-believing Christians accept this interpretation, however. As many Hebrew scholars point out, a literal reading of Genesis can just as well support six geologic epochs for the creation days. Both a literal and consistent reading of the Bible, an interpretation that integrates all relevant Bible passages, lends ample support for the creation days being long time periods. From this view, astronomy and the Bible are not in conflict over the creation date; they agree. Readers interested in more detail about this creation-date controversy from both a biblical and scientific perspective will find it in my book *A Matter of Days*, 2nd edition.

its expansion. With that measurement (adjusted a little for the slowing down caused by gravity) and a rough estimate of the distance to the farthest-out galaxies, it was no complicated matter to produce a ballpark figure for when the universe began—the Hubble time. It was somewhere in the range of a few billion to several billion years.

Whatever illusions certain paleontologists and origin-of-life theorists may have embraced, many astronomers recognized that billions of years was hopelessly too brief for atoms to assemble into living things free of any input from a divine Designer (see ch. 16).[3] Therefore, many of them invested enormous energy and creativity in attempts to escape the limits imposed by the Hubble time. Two of these models became especially popular.

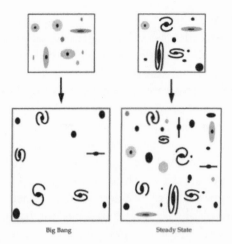

Figure 8.1: Big Bang Growth versus Steady State Growth

In a big bang universe, the density of matter thins out and the mean age for the galaxies advances. All big bang models predict a finite age for the universe. In a steady state universe, new matter is spontaneously and continuously created. The density of matter remains the same, and the mean age for the galaxies is constant. On a large scale, nothing changes with time. All steady state models assume the universe is infinite in age and extent. Since the light of very distant galaxies takes considerable time to reach us, astronomers can look into the past to see which growth pattern the universe follows.

Credit: Reasons to Believe

Steady State Universe

In 1948, three British astrophysicists, Herman Bondi, Thomas Gold, and Fred Hoyle, circumvented the beginning via "continual creation."[4] Their models suggested that creation of matter is an act of nature, even a law of nature, not a one-time miracle from outside of nature. Skipping past any attempt to explain the expansion of the universe, they proposed that the voids resulting from expansion are filled by the continual, spontaneous self-creation of new matter (see fig. 8.1).

The champions of this steady state hypothesis made their theological position clear from the start. Bondi and Hoyle declared their opposition to the notion that anything could transcend the realm of nature.[5] Hoyle made no bones about his opposition to Christianity. To his thinking, "the Universe is everything" and to suggest otherwise is "crackpot."[6]

Testing the Steady State

During the past several decades, astronomers developed a series of observational and theoretical tests to prove or disprove the steady state model.[7] Amazingly, the simplest test, devised by Sir James Jeans in the 1920s, was applied last of all. Jeans pointed out that a universe that has no beginning and no end should manifest a "steady" population. That is, the number of stars and galaxies in various stages of development should be proportional to the time required to pass through these stages. There should be balanced numbers of newly formed, young, middle-aged, elderly, and extinct stars and galaxies.[8]

What do we find? A host of "youthful" stars, with ages ranging from a few days to about 13.5 billion years (see "Oldest Stars Tell Their Story" on p. 74). If 13.5 billion years seems old, let me assure you, it is not, compared to most stars' life expectancy. Most stars in the universe can burn for more than 80 billion years.[9] For the minority (about 20%) of stars that have burned out, none of them have been cooling long enough to transition from white dwarfs to black dwarfs. That transition would take about 100 billion years or more.

In the population of galaxies, the steady state model met with yet more trouble. All, or nearly all, are approximately the same age. For distances closer than a half billion light-years (corresponding to light travel times, or lookback times, of less than a half billion years we see virtually no newly formed galaxies. The very few that are reported, most astronomers agree, are the aftermaths of collisions between mature galaxies. Galaxies in the universe are so tightly packed that such collisions are expected to occur from time to time.

As noted in chapter 6 under "Spreading Apart of Galaxies," the spatial separation between galaxy clusters and galaxies is not the same at all lookback times as predicted by the steady state model. The farther away astronomers observe, and hence the farther back in time, the more tightly packed together are the galaxy clusters and galaxies (see fig. 6.1).

As for older galaxies (meaning more than 14 billion years old), we see none. Neither are there any extinct varieties. The death knell rang for steady state models when American astronomer Donald Hamilton determined that all the galaxies were formed at approximately the same time,[10] as the big bang predicts.

The death knell rang again with the discovery that the cosmic microwave background radiation spectrum perfectly fit that of a black-body radiator (see discussion and figures under "First COBE Discovery" and "Third COBE Discovery" in ch. 4). Such a fit establishes that the universe was very much hotter in the past than it is now. The measured cooling curve (see fig. 6.2) of the

EVOLUTION AS EVIDENCE FOR CREATION

The word evolution evokes strong meaning and emotion for many people. In the life sciences, it is seen to oppose divine creation. In the physical sciences, evolution simply refers to change taking place with respect to time. So defined, it is theologically neutral. No claim is made as to whether the observed changes are naturally driven or supernaturally driven.

This neutral definition applies in astronomy. Interestingly, in the clash between the steady state and big bang models, we witness the apparent irony that new evidences for the evolution of the universe actually establish that the universe was *created* in the relatively recent past. In this respect the Bible's teachings on creation include "evolution" since it frames the entire creation account into a chronology of change through time—ten major creation events sequenced over six creation days.

The theological thrust of the steady state models was that no personal involvement from God was necessary to explain our existence. Steady state principles say the universe has not evolved and that it has existed for infinite time. Thus, the dice of chance could have been thrown an infinite number of times under favorable natural conditions to explain the assembling of atoms into organisms.

But, observational proofs now affirm that the universe has evolved, very significantly, from a beginning about 13.8 billion years ago.[11] Thus, our existence cannot be attributed to the natural realm's lucky throw of the dice (see ch. 16). Moreover, the big bang determines that the cause of the universe is functionally equivalent to the God of the Bible, a Being beyond the matter, energy, space, and time of the cosmos (see chs. 10 and 11).

temperature of the cosmic microwave background radiation with respect to lookback time establishes that the universe was near infinitely hot at its beginning about 13.8 billion years ago and has cooled as a result of continual cosmic expansion.

Under the weight of these and several other independent refutations,[12] plus evidence that the darkness of intergalactic space must result from the finite ages of all the galaxies[13] (see "The Paradox of the Dark Night Sky" in ch. 7), the steady state models eventually staggered and fell.

Quasi-Steady-State Universe (First Modification)

As noted in books by both Christian[14] and non-Christian astronomers,[15] and even by steady state model proponents themselves,[16] steady state models have been decisively proven wrong by observational advances. In addition to the failures noted in this chapter, the established character of the cosmic microwave background radiation, the abundance of the elements, the dispersal of galaxies with respect to time, the cosmic entropy measure, and the accelerating expansion of the universe clearly refute the possibility that we live in a steady state universe.

Rather than concede a cosmic Beginner, however, proponents of the steady state theory first modified their models into what they term a quasi-steady-state universe. The three most vocal proponents, astronomers Fred Hoyle, Geoffrey Burbidge, and Jayant Narlikar, published their modified steady state model in the 357-page book *A Different Approach to Cosmology: From a Static Universe through the Big Bang towards Reality*. Instead of new matter continuously coming into existence from everywhere in the universe, in the quasi-steady-state model new matter is sporadically created in the nuclei of large active galaxies (galaxies with explosive events occurring in their cores).[17]

In contrast with the big bang interpretation, quasi-steady-state proponents would replace a single primordial fireball arising from a transcendent creation event about 13.8 billion years ago with a great many time-separated "primordial" fireballs, which would result from the creation and ejection of matter from the centers of large galaxies. Rather than attributing the activity in the nuclei of large galaxies to supergiant black holes sucking in matter, they claim that these nuclei are spewing out matter as a result of some hidden creation mechanism. Quasars would not be very distant super-energetic galaxies but rather relatively nearby hot spots ejected from regular galaxies. In the quasi-steady-state model, even though the universe continually expands, it maintains roughly the same density through newly created matter filling in the voids of space generated by cosmic expansion. Like the steady state model, the universe would have an infinite past.

Quasars and Helium Challenge Quasi-Steady-State Cosmology (First Modification)

Many quasar images indeed do appear adjacent to galaxy images. However, such appearances are also expected in a big bang universe. With the universe only 13.8 billion years old, foreground galaxies still so crowd the field of view that it is inevitable for background quasars to appear adjacent to them. Also, it

 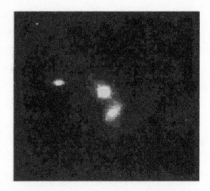

Figure 8.2: Images from the Hubble Space Telescope of New-Born Quasars

In the image on the left, a large galaxy (center) is colliding with a supergiant galaxy (bottom) at about a million miles per hour. The image on the right shows another such collision.
Credit: NASA

is no longer true that quasars appear only as very bright points of light. With the advent of several 10-meter diameter optical telescopes, astronomers have been able to detect faint wisps of galaxy parts enveloping the quasars. Thus, quasars are not isolated point sources. They are the nuclei of enormous galaxies in their early, formative stages.

Big bang astronomers deduce that quasars are supergiant black holes, with masses millions to billions of times greater than the Sun's, residing at the centers of supergiant galaxies and fueled by huge amounts of gas being sucked inside. The amount of gas in a supergiant galaxy reaches a peak somewhere between the galaxy's infancy and early adulthood. A problem, however, is that some quasars are so powerful that not even the maximum gas in a supergiant galaxy would provide it with enough fuel. To get the power output up to the observed levels, a young, supergiant galaxy would need to steal a lot of gas from nearby galaxies.

According to Hubble Space Telescope images, this latter scenario accurately describes reality. In figure 8.2, we see one large galaxy colliding with a supergiant galaxy at about a million miles per hour. This collision provides all the gas needed to sustain the quasar in the nucleus of the supergiant.[18]

In a big bang universe, we expect galaxies at large lookback distances (times) to be packed together more tightly than they are today. Hubble Space Telescope images provide support for this tighter packing.[19] Therefore, we would expect quasars to be most abundant when the universe is a few billion years old.

Specifically, we would expect no quasars to exist in real time today, that is, at distances corresponding to short light-travel times. Too much gas had already been consumed. Consequently, at distances corresponding up to about three-quarters the big bang age of the universe, quasars should be rare. Meanwhile, at distances equivalent to about a fifth to a quarter the age of the universe, they should be abundant. Finally, at distances equivalent to about a twentieth the age of the universe they should, again, be rare. This near absence is expected because at one-twentieth of big bang cosmic history, insufficient condensed gas clouds would have formed to sustain more than a few quasars.

Reliable space density surveys of quasars began to be published in 1994–1996. These surveys confirmed the big bang predictions while contradicting the quasi-steady-state predictions.[20] Since then, newer observations have substantially added to the weight of evidence for the big bang and against the quasi-steady-state.[21]

Quasi-steady-state proponents are forced to deny that giant black holes exist in the central cores of giant active galaxies. While for two decades astronomers' observations have established that supermassive, supercondensed bodies must exist in the cores of giant galaxies, they could not definitely prove that they were black holes. This changed when researchers found a way to measure the spin velocities in the inner regions surrounding such supercondensed bodies. These velocities measured close to one-third the velocity of light, a result that can only be explained if the supercondensed bodies are black holes exceeding a million solar masses.[22]

Quasi-steady-state proponents go to extreme lengths arguing that the shifting of the spectral lines of quasars toward longer or redder wavelengths does not imply that the quasars are at great distances. (Remember that in the big bang model, the redshift of an object is an indicator of distance, so that the greater its redshift, the greater its distance.) They claimed the high velocities indicated by the redshifts resulted from the quasars being ejected from galactic nuclei, not from a big bang cosmic expansion. While very few astronomers have ever accepted this proposition and noted that the proposition implies that some quasars would be ejected in our direction and thus generate blue-shifted spectral lines, a direct refutation seemed impossible given the extreme distances of quasars implied by the big bang theory. The problem is that the big bang distances are out of reach for all distance-measuring methods except for those based on the shifting of spectral lines.

Astronomers broke this impasse on direct-distance measuring methods, however, during the early part of the twenty-first century. At radio wavelengths, it is possible to link widely separated telescopes together to build an interferometer with the equivalent resolving power of a 5,000–6,000-mile-diameter telescope. Exploiting such an instrument, a team of American astronomers achieved a direct distance measurement based on the trigonometric method familiar to land surveyors for the quasar 3C 279.[23] They determined that 3C 279 must be at least 5.9 billion light-years away. This establishes that the big bang interpretation of quasars is correct and the quasi-steady-state interpretation is wrong.

In the quasi-steady-state model, all the helium in the universe comes from nuclear burning that takes place inside stars. To account for all the helium we observe in the universe, such burning must proceed for at least 100 billion years. Astronomers fail to see any stars or galaxies anywhere in the universe older than 14 billion years (see "Oldest Stars Tell Their Story"on p. 74). Moreover, while stars are efficient in distributing elements heavier than helium to the interstellar medium (through explosions), most of the helium produced by stars remains trapped inside dead stars that haven't exploded as supernovae. The ratio of heavy elements to helium in both the interstellar medium and intergalactic medium is consistent with the big bang. That same ratio contradicts the quasi-steady-state model.

Many other refutations of the quasi-steady-state model abound. The most significant that remain are the density of baryons (protons plus neutrons) in the universe,[24] the density of exotic matter,[25] and the characteristics of the cosmic microwave background radiation.[26]

New Quasi-Steady-State Cosmology (Second Modification)
In an attempt to respond to the devastating challenges from the cosmic microwave background radiation maps to their original quasi-steady-state cosmological (QSSC) model, Burbidge, Narlikar, and others developed a new version of their model.[27] In this new model, they proposed a creation field that produces a *negative* energy density. They further proposed that this negative energy density, while inconsequential at low redshifts, becomes dominant at high redshifts.

The result is that in their QSSC model the universe oscillates between two finite scale sizes. That is, they claim the universe oscillates between episodes of expansion and episodes of contraction. However, the scale sizes increase with time. In the new QSSC model "the universe has a steady long term expansion in addition to the oscillations."[28] Furthermore, in the new QSSC model, new matter is created not only in the nuclei of galaxies but also "at the start of each oscillation."[29]

The goal of the new QSSC model is to match as closely as possible the standard ΛCDM hot big bang creation model—a model wherein dark energy, Λ ("Lambda"), is the dominant component of the universe, followed by the second most dominant component, cold dark matter (CDM)—without invoking a finite beginning of matter, energy, space, and time. In the new QSSC model, the last time the universe transitioned from contraction to expansion is "almost" the same as the time since the cosmic beginning in the standard ΛCDM hot big bang creation model. It is only "almost" because the starting volume for the expansion period is larger than the infinitesimally small volume for the ΛCDM hot big bang model.

In this new QSSC model, astronomers should be able to see beyond the expansion starting point and observe sources in the universe's past contraction episode. Sources seen in the contraction episode of the universe's history, according to the new QSSC model, will exhibit their spectra being blueshifted instead of redshifted. This prediction has not borne out. All the most distant sources astronomers observe are redshifted, and the greater their distance the greater the redshifting.

The new QSSC model tries to solve the problem of the cosmic microwave background radiation by appealing to carbon and iron "whiskers" in the intergalactic medium to convert starlight into cosmic background radiation photons. Such dust also is expected in the ΛCDM hot big bang model, but not nearly at the abundance levels required for the new QSSC model.

Dust in the universe, in addition to contributing to the cosmic microwave background radiation, also generates a cosmic infrared background radiation. Precision maps of the cosmic infrared background radiation reveal exactly how much dust exists in interstellar and intergalactic space. Data from detectors onboard the Planck, Herschel, and COBE satellites and from the James Clerk Maxwell Telescope on Mauna Kea in Hawaii show that the amount of dust needed by all versions of the QSSC model is ruled out.[30]

In particular, the amount of intergalactic dust required by the QSSC models adds up to a mass density greater than 0.0001 (expressed as $\Omega_{dust} > 10^{-4}$).[31] The amount of intergalactic dust allowed by observations is between .000001 and .000008 ($\Omega_{dust} = 1 \sim 8 \times 10^{-6}$), about one hundredth of the minimum amount QSSC requires.[32]

In the QSSC model there is no dark energy and the amount of matter in the universe is several times greater than for the ΛCDM hot big bang model. The quantity of matter needed for the QSSC models conflicts with multiple independent observational measures of the cosmic mass density (see ch. 5).

Philosophical End Run

The defeat of the steady state models and their offspring, the quasi-steady-state models, led nontheistic astronomers to express a momentary lament and then a newfound hope. The prestigious British journal *Nature* published this statement from physicist John Gribbin:

> The biggest problem with the Big Bang theory of the origin of the Universe is philosophical—perhaps even theological— what was there before the bang? This problem alone was sufficient to give a great initial impetus to the Steady State theory; but with that theory now sadly in conflict with the observations, the best way round this initial difficulty is provided by a model in which the universe expands from a singularity [that is, a beginning], collapses back again, and repeats the cycle indefinitely.[33]

Gribbin signaled the change in direction for those committed to finding some way around a single transcendent cosmic creation event just some 14 billion years ago.

 Discussion Questions _____

1. Fred Hoyle proposed a steady state hypothesis and opposed Christianity, remarking that "the Universe is everything" and to suggest otherwise is "crackpot." Why did he make such an assertion?
2. What observational difficulties did the first version of the quasi-steady state model face? How did the second version fare?
3. At this point in the book it appears that some scientists have done everything possible to avoid a model with implications that point to a transcendent cause. Can we appreciate, from an atheistic perspective, their concern? How would we have proceeded?

Chapter 9

Closing Loopholes: Round Two

Research that crushed the steady state and quasi-steady-state universe models simultaneously built up the big bang, with its implications of a beginning and a Beginner. Cosmologists who yet resisted this turn of research resurrected a model for the universe proposed thousands of years ago by Hindu teachers and later by Roman philosophers—the reincarnating or oscillating universe. The appeal of this model is that it seems to allow for the relatively recent beginning (as in the Hubble time) while retaining the possibility of infinite or nearly infinite time.

Bouncing Universe

The familiar law of gravity says that massive bodies tend to attract each other. We also know that the mutual attraction of massive bodies in the universe acts as a brake on the expansion of the universe. As you may recall from the earlier discussion of critical mass, the expansion of the universe could be brought to a halt by gravity if the universe contained enough mass. But that's not all gravity could do. It could throw the expansion into reverse and shrink the universe back to a tiny volume.

Here's where the oscillating universe model shows imagination. It suggests that rather than crunching back into a "singularity" (an infinitely shrunken space representing the boundary at which space ceases to exist or at which space comes into existence), the imploding universe somehow bounces back and begins a new cycle of expansion. Some unknown bounce mechanism is invoked to make this happen (see fig. 9.1).

According to Princeton physicist Robert Dicke (1916–1997), an infinite number of these cycles of expansion and contraction of the universe would "relieve us of the necessity of understanding the origin of matter at any finite time in the past."[1] The creation event becomes irrelevant, and our existence

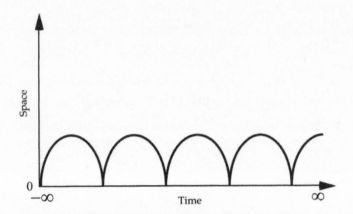

Figure 9.1: The Infinitely Oscillating Universe Model

In the oscillating universe model suggested by physicists like Robert Dicke and John Gribbin, the universe alternates for infinite time between phases of expansion and contraction. Gravity halts the expansion and generates a succeeding phase of contraction. An unknown physical mechanism is proposed to somehow bounce the universe from a period of contraction into a period of expansion, and the characteristics of the contraction and expansion phases are presumed not to vary significantly with time.

Credit: Reasons to Believe

could be attributed to one lucky bounce. After all, given an infinite number of cosmic bounces, it is argued that surely one would produce all the conditions necessary to convert particles and atoms into human beings through strictly natural processes.

In 1965, when the oscillating universe model first emerged as a serious theory,[2] many astronomers launched an all-out effort to find sufficient mass to halt and reverse the expansion of the universe. As noted in chapter 5 ("Flat Out Confirmed" and "Cosmic Density Components"), however, all the evidence—both observational and theoretical—points in the opposite direction. Even with the consideration of exotic matter, the total mass falls considerably short of what would be needed to force an eventual collapse of the universe. The latest measurements establish a cosmic mass density that is roughly 29% (0.2934 ± 0.0107) of what is needed to reverse cosmic expansion.[3]

Rebound Problem
But missing mass is not the only difficulty. Even if the universe did contain enough mass to reverse its expansion, and even if a bounce mechanism were

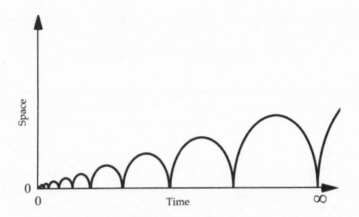

Figure 9.2: Thermodynamic Dissipation within an Oscillating Universe

Even if the universe conceivably could oscillate, it could not have been oscillating for infinite time. The laws of thermodynamics compel the maximum diameter of the universe to increase from cycle to cycle. Therefore, such a universe could look forward to an infinitely long future, but only a finite past. The ultimate moment of creation, at most, could be pushed back to only about a trillion years ago.

   Notice that as time goes on the humps grow larger and larger. Looking backward in time, they grow smaller and smaller to a starting point in the not-too-distant past. From the perspective of physics, the universe could not bounce more than about a dozen times—a number far short of infinity.

Credit: Reasons to Believe

discovered or devised theoretically, the number of bounces or oscillations would be limited because of entropy (energy degradation).

The second law of thermodynamics tells us that the entropy of the universe increases with time. This entropy increase means a decrease in the energy available to perform mechanical work, such as bouncing. So less and less mechanical energy would be available with each bounce to make the bounce happen.

The decrease in mechanical energy from bounce to bounce has two ramifications. First, it means that with each bounce, the universe expands farther out before it begins collapsing. Picture the action of a ball attached by a rubber band to a wooden paddle. When the rubber band is new, its elasticity is greatest, and it yanks the ball back powerfully. But as it gets warmed up and stretched several times, it loses some of its pull on the ball, and the ball goes out farther from the paddle more easily. A similar effect for the cosmos is diagramed in figure 9.2.

WILL THE UNIVERSE EVER COLLAPSE?

Discussion of the merits of an oscillating universe model becomes academic if the universe lacks the mass to halt its expansion and force a subsequent collapse. The latest measurements now establish beyond any reasonable doubt that there is insufficient mass to halt cosmic expansion.[4]

As further proof against an eventual collapse, the discoveries that the universe's space fabric has an ongoing self-stretching property (dark energy) and that it has a spatially flat geometry establish that the universe will continue to expand forever. Moreover, the universe will expand at a progressively faster and faster rate. For more details, see chapter 5.

The second ramification of entropy lies in its effect on the bounce energy. Not only is mechanical energy for contraction lost with each bounce, but so is energy for rebounding. If a rubber ball is dropped from a height of three feet above a hardwood floor, it will rebound, but it will not come up three feet. Some of the energy in the ball was radiated away through friction into heat when the ball hit the floor. In fact, each time the ball hits the floor more mechanical energy is converted into heat, and eventually the ball stops bouncing.

A ball with a high mechanical efficiency, for example a volleyball inflated to a high air pressure, may bounce a dozen times before it comes to a stop on the floor. A ball with a low mechanical efficiency, for example a somewhat deflated foam-rubber ball, may bounce only twice before it stops.

But the universe has far less mechanical efficiency than a foam-rubber ball. In 1983 and 1984, American astrophysicists Marc Sher, Alan Guth, and Sidney Bludman demonstrated that even if the universe contained enough mass to halt its current expansion, any ultimate collapse would end in a thud, not a bounce.[5] In terms of mechanical energy, the universe more closely resembles a wet lump of clay than an inflated volleyball (see table 9.1). Sher and Guth confidently entitled their paper "The Impossibility of a Bouncing Universe."

Quantum Gravity Speculations
Sher, Guth, and Bludman weren't alone in demonstrating the impossibility of

Table 9.1: Mechanical Efficiencies of Some Common Systems

If the universe oscillates, then that means it behaves like an engine or a system designed to perform work. The ability of a system or engine to perform work or to oscillate depends on its mechanical efficiency. The universe literally ranks as the worst
engine in all existence. Its mechanical efficiency is so low that oscillation is impossible.

System or Engine	Mechanical Efficiency
diesel engine	40%
gasoline engine	30%
steam engine	13%
human body engine	1%
universe	0.00000001%

a cosmic bounce. Two Russian physicists, Igor Novikov and Yakov Zeldovich,
developed their own proof based on the geometry of collapsing structures.[6]
But none of the five researchers dealt with the theoretical possibilities for oscillation that arise from the quantum gravity era, presumably because so little
is yet known about that era. But it did seem to offer an infinitesimal straw for
diehards to grasp.

Arnold Sikkema and Werner Israel grasped it, hypothesizing bizarre effects
of merging black holes in that split second when all the matter and energy of
the universe would still have been contained in a very tiny volume.[7] These men
honestly admitted that no consistent theory of quantum gravity yet exists. It
must be noted, too, that the oscillation theory they proposed yields at most
only a sharply limited number of bounces. It offers no escape from the notion
of a beginning in the not-so-distant past.

That slender straw grasped by Sikkema and Israel was crushed by Russian physicist Andrei Linde. At a symposium on the large-scale structure of
the universe, Linde demonstrated that the universe, with the characteristics we
observe, cannot have arisen from a bounce in the quantum gravity era. Why?

There are two considerations:

1. During the collapse phase toward a hypothetical bounce, at least one
    region or volume (technically called a "domain") in the universe would
    utterly resist being crushed to the tiny volume necessary for the exotic

effects of quantum gravity to take over.[8]
2.   The bounce, if it could take place, would not produce sufficient matter.[9]

Let me explain. The universe, before the hypothetical bounce, begins with a huge amount of space curvature and little or no matter. But, as the universe expands, space is stretched, reducing the curvature. This loss of curvature is transformed into matter and, in the process, a huge amount of entropy is generated. Because of the enormous entropy produced, the process is not reversible. Matter cannot be converted back into the needed space curvature. Thus, the universe we live in cannot be the product of oscillation even if the bounces are hypothesized to occur in the quantum gravity era.

Physicist Roger Penrose, co-author with Stephen Hawking on the first of the space-time theorems, affirmed this conclusion when answering the question, "Do you think that quantum gravity removes singularities?"[10] His reply, "I don't think it can be quite like that. If it were like that, the big bang would have resulted from a previously collapsing phase. We must ask how that previous phase could have had such a low entropy. This picture would sacrifice the best chance we have of explaining the second law. Moreover, the singularities of collapsing and expanding universes would have to be somehow joined together, but they seem to have very different geometries."[11]

Probing the Quantum Gravity Era

Physicists are designing theories to cope with conditions before the universe was even 10^{-43} seconds old (less than a quadrillionth-quadrillionth-trillionth second). At 10^{-43} seconds, the force of gravity within the universe becomes comparable to the strong nuclear force. (The strong nuclear force holds protons and neutrons together in the nucleus of the atom.) Before this epoch in the history of the universe, gravity may possibly be modified by quantum mechanical effects. Hence this early stage of the universe is called the quantum gravity era.

The energy densities that exist during the quantum gravity era lie far beyond the capabilities of even the most powerful particle accelerators (a particle accelerator longer than 50 times the distance to the most distant galaxy in the universe is needed). Many theoreticians have presumed, therefore, that they are free to speculate any physical conditions or, for that matter, any physical laws they desire. However, since such physics are obviously beyond the possibility of observational verification, it would by definition fall outside the realm of science and into the realm of metaphysics.

Nevertheless, even though the energies during the quantum gravity era are far beyond current experimental physics, a powerful indirect observational check does exist—the present universe in which we live. If a quantum gravity theory cannot explain how the present universe developed from the initial quantum state, it must be incorrect. By this means, a number of quantum gravity theories can be ruled out.

Astronomers can rule out many more quantum gravity theories through observations of distant quasars and gamma-ray sources. In quantum gravity models, the foaminess of space-time is a theoretical consequence of the energy uncertainty principle. While such individual space-time fluctuations (foam) would be infinitesimally small, depending on the particular quantum gravity model, the fluctuations would accumulate (become frothier) over long path lengths. This accumulation would blur the images of the most distantly observed sources, such as quasars. The blurring effect would be most pronounced at short wavelengths, particularly in gamma rays emitted by quasars, blazars (the brightest known quasars), and gamma-ray burst objects (gamma-ray emissions from the collapses of the most massive stars or from the merging of neutron stars[12]).

In some quantum gravity models, the blurring effect would make such detection of distant quasars and gamma-ray sources impossible.[13] Therefore, these models are clearly eliminated by astronomers' successful observations of these sources. Constraints on the blurring of the images of distant quasars, blazars, and gamma-burst objects rule out random walk (randomly varying quantum foam) quantum gravity models,[14] as well as holographic quantum gravity models.[15] (Holographic cosmic models are an outcome of string theories that suggest the entire universe may be seen as two-dimensional information on a cosmological horizon beyond our field of view.) As four European astrophysicists concluded, "All the main QG [quantum gravity] scenarios are excluded."[16]

Of course, nontheistic quantum gravity theorists are busy developing other scenarios. However, because of the lack of blurred images of distant quasars, blazars, and gamma-burst objects, their speculations now are much more constrained. Future observations of quasar, blazar, and gamma-burst objects may constrain their speculations even further. The lack of blurred images, and hence of very frothy space-time foam, demonstrates the biblical principle that the more we learn about nature the more evidence we will uncover for the supernatural handiwork of God.

Another result from the lack of blurred images at great distances is that the universe's space-time fabric is smooth to a high degree, out to great distances and deep into the quantum gravity realm. This smoothness implies the likely ubiquitous application of both the theories of special relativity and general relativity. This ubiquitous application means that the space-time theorems (see ch. 10) establishing that a causal Agent beyond space and time created the universe are unlikely to be overturned by some exotic physics operating during the quantum gravity era. It also yields by far the strongest constraint on possible variations in the velocity of light. It establishes that the velocity of light in a vacuum cannot vary by more than a few parts in 100 million trillion trillion (10^{32}).[17]

The lack of observed image blurring has implications beyond the validity of the space-time theorems. Many physicists, in their attempts to avoid the theological implications of big bang cosmology, speculate that the laws of physics break down before the universe is a trillionth of a quadrillionth of a quadrillionth of a second old, that is, previous to 10^{-43} seconds after the cosmic creation event. The observed lack of blurred images of very distant sources means that if such a breakdown does occur, the physical laws do not break down by very much.

Another possible observational probe of quantum gravity physics would be the discovery of a pulsar-black hole binary (a pulsar closely orbiting a black hole) and subsequent measurements of the orbital characteristics and orbital changes of that pulsar-black hole binary. Pulsars (highly magnetized and rapidly rotating neutron stars and white dwarfs) rank as the most accurate natural clocks in the universe. Timing the repetitive signals from a pulsar beam, as a pulsar orbits just outside the event horizon of a black hole (where gravity begins to become so powerful that not even light can escape), will allow astronomers to determine the degree and the manner in which information escapes from a black hole.[18]

In particular, quantum fluctuations in the space-time geometry just outside a black hole's event horizon will cause an increase in the measured root mean square deviation of the arrival times of pulsar's pulses traveling from near the event horizon. Depending on the quantum gravity model and the black hole's mass, the root mean square deviation can range from less than a microsecond to several minutes. Thus, such a determination will provide a powerful means for testing competing models of quantum gravity.[19]

While astronomers have not yet detected a pulsar-black hole binary, the currently operating gravity wave telescope LIGO (Laser Interferometer Gravitational-Wave Observatory), the planned and designed gravity wave telescope

LISA (Laser Interferometer Space Antenna), and the radio telescope SKA (Square Kilometre Array, with a scheduled 2018 construction start date) will likely soon discover at least a few pulsar-black hole binaries.

Alternate Field, Force, Brane, and Geometry Speculations

Many theoretical attempts to escape a singular cosmic beginning by invoking a bounce from a previous period of cosmic contraction have shown up in twenty-first century scientific literature.[20] They are all variations on a theme in that they all propose the introduction of some unknown, undiscovered physics to alter the physics we do know, can measure, and understand.

In some of these cosmic scenarios, theoreticians speculate that some kind of unknown scalar field (see "What Is a Scalar Field?" on p. 107) acts as a third factor, in addition to gravity and the self-stretching property of the universe's space fabric. This third factor, they presume, is sufficiently dominant at critical epochs in the universe's history to transform the cosmos from a system manifesting a single transcendent beginning to one that has multiple nonsingular (that is, nontranscendent) beginnings.

In other cosmic scenarios, theoreticians speculate far beyond typical quantum gravity models by invoking radically different laws of gravity and quantum mechanics. One of the more popular of these speculations is a scenario known as loop quantum cosmology (LQC). In LQC, a hypothesized quantum geometry generates a repulsive force that is totally negligible when the universe is older than 10^{-43} seconds, but is totally dominant when the universe is younger than 10^{-43} seconds. The net effect of the hypothesized quantum geometry is to create a quantum bridge between a contracting and expanding phase of the universe. This radical, untestable hypothesis lives in the realm of imaginative metaphysics, apart from testable science.

In yet other cosmic scenarios, theoreticians suggest that other large spatial dimensions (called branes) accompany length, width, and height, or that the universe's spatial geometry or shape radically changes beyond the limits of our observations. In brane cosmology, the three-dimensional universe that we observe is encased in higher dimensional space, often referred to as hyperspace. Many of the cosmic brane models merely tweak the standard big bang creation model to explain in more detail why the force of gravity appears to be so weak[21] and the value of the cosmological constant so small.[22] Others, however, attempt to modify the big bang model into a universe that oscillates between periods of contraction and expansion.

What all these scenarios share, with one minor exception,[23] is that they are immune from possible experimental or observational falsification. No physical technology existing or possible will permit astronomers to observe phenomena earlier than 10^{-35} seconds after the creation event in big bang cosmology. No physically possible technology will allow physicists to duplicate the energy density conditions that existed when the universe was younger than 10^{-35} seconds after the creation event in big bang cosmology. Thus, many scientists prefer to classify these scenarios as metaphysics (see ch. 16, "Responding to Nonempirical, Nontheistic Cosmic Models").

How might a minority of scientists persist in these singularity-defying theories? A less satisfactory test of these speculations is that for any one of these scenarios to possibly be true it must be able to generate the features of the universe that astronomers observe. This test is less satisfactory in that it provides no positive evidence for the scenario. It merely shows that the scenario's explanation for the universe is not an absolute impossibility. This test, however, can be made more robust in showing at least a pathway toward falsification. One pathway would be if theoretical difficulties become progressively more challenging as physicists attempt to develop the scenario or that the theoretical parameter space under which the scenario can operate becomes progressively more restrictive. So far, the trend for all these alternate scenarios has been toward a progressively shrinking theoretical parameter space.[24]

The Reincarnation Connection

Most ancient and modern Eastern religions (including Hinduism, Buddhism, and most new age philosophies, among others) are rooted in the doctrine of cosmic reincarnation, the oscillating universe. The popularity of these teachings soared in the West with the popularity of the oscillating universe model.

I watched this trend rise during my graduate student days at the University of Toronto. When several of my peers embraced some of the Hindu or Buddhist sects in vogue, I asked them why. They quoted passages from their scriptures concerning the never-ending cycles of birth, growth, collapse, death, and rebirth of the cosmos, and of ourselves as one with it—the "reality" described by the oscillating universe model.

What clinched their commitment, they said, was the amazing accuracy of Hindu scriptures in predicting the period of oscillation, the time between successive rebirths. These writings said 4.32 billion years.[25] Astrophysicists of the day (the 1970s) said about 20 billion years—if the oscillating universe model were to prove correct.

My friends reasoned that for the ancient Hindus to get that close to the

WHAT IS A SCALAR FIELD?

In cosmology, a scalar field is either a force or an energy term in the equations of general relativity that affects the dynamics of the universe. It can be constant or a function of either spatial position or time. Gravity as formulated by Newton's laws of motion and by Einstein's theory of general relativity are scalar fields. However, when cosmologists talk or write about a scalar field or fields, they are almost always referring to fields that either augment or subtract from the dynamical effects that would arise from gravity alone. Such adjustments to gravity can be either simple or complex functions of space and time.

There is growing consensus among astronomers that a scalar field (or fields) is responsible for dark energy. What lacks a consensus is whether there are other scalar fields, besides the Higgs field, that impact the dynamical history of the universe.

right answer, Hinduism must be more than a humanly crafted religion. It must come from some superhuman source. This bit of rational support, combined with the enchantment of anything non-Western and nontraditional, plus an aversion to the moral values of Christianity, was enough to draw them into one of the branch faiths of Hinduism.

But that rational rug has been pulled out. Reality is not described by infinite cycles of cosmic reincarnation. The worldview underlying Hinduism and its many derivatives has proven incorrect.

 Discussion Questions _____

1. What are some basic features of the oscillating universe model and how has it withstood scientific testing?
2. Do quantum gravity theories appear to offer a way around the hot big bang model? Explain.
3. Why do you suppose people cling to worldviews that rely on reincarnation, which has been ruled out scientifically?

Chapter 10

Science Discovers the Creation of Time

With the collapse of the oscillating universe model, attempts to get around the Hubble time (no more than about 14 billion years since the universe began) turned in a new direction. Holdouts for an infinitely old universe hypothesize that the fundamental laws of nature as we know them are either incorrect or break down under special conditions.

Escape from Reality

From this battlefront came the work of amateur plasma physicist Eric Lerner, author of *The Big Bang Never Happened*. Lerner notes that the laws of nature cannot explain the amazing advance in life's complexity on Earth over the past 4 billion years.[1] He acknowledges that this advance violates the second law of thermodynamics, which says that systems tend to degrade from higher to lower levels of order, complexity, and information.

Since Lerner rejects the existence of a Creator, he is forced to conclude that the second law of thermodynamics broke down.[2] And if the second law of thermodynamics broke down for organisms on Earth, then it could have broken down for the entire physical cosmos, he suggests.[3] Since the second law ties in with one of the ways we measure time (the rate at which entropy, or energy degradation, increases), Lerner concludes that our observations of the age of the universe are incorrect, that they cannot be used to argue for a beginning of the cosmos just some billions of years ago. There was no big bang, he says, thus no Creator.

The circularity of Lerner's reasoning seems obvious. Starting with the supposition that God does not exist, Lerner reinterprets the laws of nature. Then he uses this reinterpretation to support the conclusion that God does not exist.

An observational refutation of Lerner's hypothesis arises from stellar physics. The kinds of stars that are necessary to make physical life possible in the universe are extremely sensitive to even slight changes in the major laws or constants of physics—stars couldn't lead stable lives without them. Yet we clearly observe the existence of stable burning stars of all different masses at all different distances from us (see chs. 6 and 15 for details), which establishes the constancy of physics throughout the history of the universe. Thus, measuring the physical condition of stars at varying distances affirms that Lerner's end run around a transcendent creation event fails.

The constancy of physics case leads to another swing-and-miss. In the era before stars existed, namely, the first half billion years or so of cosmic history, the measured physical conditions of the cosmic background radiation also affirm no changes have occurred in the physical laws and constants.

The measured abundances of light elements in the universe provides an equally emphatic refutation of Lerner's cosmic model. In Lerner's model, stars make all the helium. However, for every kilogram of helium produced by stellar burning, about 0.3 kilograms of elements heavier than helium are produced. The measured quantity of heavier-than-helium elements compared to helium in the most metal-rich stars is about 12:1, not 3:1 as proposed by Lerner's model. In the metal-poor stars that dominate the universe's stellar population the ratio ranges from 240:1 to 1,600,000:1.

No God of the Gaps

Even working within the laws of physics, researchers with an anti-God bias often make blind leaps of faith to escape any evidence of God's involvement in the universe. For centuries Christians were criticized for their God-of-the-gaps arguments. Sometimes that criticism was deserved. Christians tended to use gaps in understanding or data to build a case for God's miraculous intervention. Then, when scientific discoveries uncovered a natural explanation for the "divine phenomenon," ridicule was heaped not only on those proposing the divine explanation but also on belief in God's existence.

In the twenty-first century we see the reverse of the God-of-the-gaps arguments. Nontheists, confronted with problems when ample research leads to no natural explanations and instead points to the supernatural, utterly reject the possibility of the supernatural and insist on a natural explanation even if it means resorting to absurdity.

For example, steady state models were supported by an imagined force of physics for which there was not one shred of observational or experimental evidence. The oscillating universe model depended on an imagined bounce mechanism for which there was likewise not one shred of observational or experimental evidence. Similar appeals to imagined forces and phenomena have been the basis for all the cosmological models proposed to avoid the big bang implications about God (see chs. 8 and 9). The disproof of these models and the ongoing appeal by nontheists to more and more bizarre unknowns and unknowables seem to reflect the growing strength of the case for theism (see chs. 8, 9, 13, and 16).

Testing the Gaps

Is it the God-of-the-gaps or the no-God-of-the-gaps? One way to find out is to eliminate the gaps through advancing scientific research. Increased knowledge about a system may reveal a natural explanation for the supposed supernatural phenomenon. Conversely, progressing knowledge may demonstrate that the natural explanations increasingly fail (predictions of future scientific discoveries that prove incorrect and explanations that prove less comprehensive) while the supernatural explanations increasingly succeed (yield more detailed and more comprehensive explanations and greater predictive success).

What matters are not isolated examples of theistic or atheistic researchers being proven wrong in their hypothesized explanations. Christian theists, for example, believe that natural explanations in the record of nature are the norm and divine supernatural explanations are the exception. Thus, the demonstration that one of their supernatural explorations proves to be a natural one poses no threat to their belief in the God of the Bible.

What counts is the overall trend. As we learn more and more about the universe, Earth, and life, does the evidence for God's existence and design of the natural realm get stronger or weaker? If the atheist is right and the theist is wrong, then the more we discover about the cosmos, Earth, and life, the weaker the evidence for divine transcendence and design will become. On the other hand, if the theist is right and the atheist is wrong, then the more we learn about the cosmos, Earth, and life, the stronger the evidence for divine transcendence and design will become.

Time and Its Beginning

Even before the death of the oscillating universe model, the failure of those cosmological models that rejected the finite age of the universe was uncovered. In a series of papers published from 1966 to 1970, three astrophysicists, Stephen Hawking, George Ellis, and Roger Penrose, extended the solution of the equations of general relativity to include space and time.[4] The result was called the space-time theorem of general relativity.[5] Four assumptions undergirded the theorem:

1. Time always progresses forward, never backward.
2. Gravity always is attractive.
3. The universe contains enough mass to generate at least one black hole.
4. General relativity reliably describes the dynamics of the universe (the movements of massive bodies in the universe).

The conclusion of the space-time theorem guarantees a past singular boundary for the universe. This singular boundary means that not only are matter and energy traceable back to a beginning but space and time are as well. In Hawking's words, "time itself must have a beginning."[6]

A beginning of space and time implies a causal Agent beyond space and time who brought matter, energy, space, and time into existence. As Hawking wrote in his best-selling book, *A Brief History of Time*, "Many people do not like the idea that time has a beginning, probably because it smacks of divine intervention."[7]

Efforts to escape the theological consequences of the theorem led to the discovery that its conclusions are valid over even broader conditions. In particular, theoretical physicists Arvind Borde and Alexander Vilenkin devoted a decade to determining whether an escape from a cosmic beginning and its implied cosmic Beginner was possible.[8] However, all the escape models they developed would not permit the existence of physical life in the universe. They found this result to be true not only for the non-inflationary big bang cosmological models that Hawking, Ellis, and Penrose had considered but also for the entire family of cosmic inflation models (see "Cosmic Inflation" on p. 68).[9]

Borde and Vilenkin demonstrated that regardless of the universe's homogeneity, uniformity, isotropy, or lack thereof, and regardless of the universe's energy conditions or what kind of inflation event the universe experienced, the universe must have had a beginning.[10] Together with physicist Alan Guth, they concluded that any universe that expands on average throughout its history (a requirement for physical life to exist) must be traced back in finite time to an actual beginning that includes the creation of space and time.[11] The theorem developed by Borde, Guth, and Vilenkin, based on the validity of general relativity, even applies to a universe that cycles between expansion and contraction, as long as, on average, more expansion occurs than contraction. As Vilenkin wrote in a subsequent book,

> With the proof now in place, cosmologists can no longer hide
> behind the possibility of a past eternal universe. There is no
> escape, they have to face the problem of a cosmic beginning.[12]

The problem is that a cosmic beginning implies a cosmic Beginner, a cosmic Beginner who creates from beyond space and time.

The Borde-Guth-Vilenkin theorem proves that cosmic inflation must have had a beginning. In big bang cosmology, the cosmic inflation event starts when the universe is less than 10^{-35} seconds from the big bang. This epoch is close enough to the beginning for most people, and for all practical purposes to be the beginning.

As noted in the previous chapter, however, some atheist theoretical physicists appeal to the quantum gravity era, when the universe was less than 10^{-43} seconds old. Quantum gravity, they say, allows them to speculate. Their speculations lead them to conclude that, despite all the physical evidence for a cosmic beginning, the universe really is eternal. The best known of those speculations is the quantum eternity theorem developed by Sean Carroll.[13]

To date, nontheistic physicists have dominated the scientific literature on quantum gravity models. Naturally, these models expunge a cosmic beginning. Thus, one can be misled into concluding that all quantum gravity models posit an eternal universe. However, quantum gravity models exist that fully sustain a cosmic beginning a finite time ago.[14]

These models not only make possible a cosmic beginning, but also prove a cosmic beginning in finite time on the condition that the quantum gravity era environment is "semi-classical." In a semi-classical environment the quantum space-time fluctuations are not large. As described in the previous chapter under "Probing the Quantum Gravity Era," observations of the images of distant quasars and blazars indeed appear to establish that quantum space-time fluctuations in the quantum gravity era cannot be large.

Proof of the beginning of time probably ranks as the most theologically significant theorem. This great significance arises from the theorem establishing that the universe must be caused by some Entity capable of creating the universe entirely independent of space and time. Such an entity matches the attributes of the God of the Bible but is contradicted by the gods of the eastern (and indeed all other) religions who create within space and time.

As noted at the start of this section, the space-time theorems depend upon four assumptions. The first three assumptions are beyond dispute. The fourth, that general relativity reliably describes the movements of massive bodies throughout the universe, took astronomers a century to fully establish.

Thumbs Up for General Relativity

What was needed to solidify the proof for the beginning of time was evidence that general relativity truly does tell the story about the universe's dynamics. Fully aware of the importance of observational confirmation, Einstein proposed three tests at the time of his theory's publication.[15] Within two years, in 1918, a team led by British astronomer Arthur Eddington met the conditions for the first test when they proved that the Sun's gravity bends starlight by the amount general relativity predicted.[16] This finding generated considerable excitement, but with a probable error of about 10% in the measurement, scientists were not satisfied.

In the years following, progress in reducing the probable errors was frustratingly slow. By 1970 five more tests had been added to Einstein's three. Accuracy of confirmation had improved from 10% to 1%,[17] but still not enough to convince all skeptics. Some theoreticians began to speculate that the universe, though dominated by general relativity, might also be influenced to a tiny degree by an unknown force field.[18] This speculation and imprecision cast just enough doubt on the space-time theorems to dampen enthusiasm for them, initially.

However, as research continued, that small shadow of doubt shrank to the vanishing point. By 1976 an echo delay experiment placed on the moon by Apollo astronauts reduced the uncertainty down to 0.5%.[19] In 1979, measurements of the gravitational effects on radio signals further reduced the uncertainty to just 0.1%.[20] In 1980, a hydrogen maser clock (based on the laser principle and nearly 100 times more accurate than the best atomic clock) aboard a NASA rocket confirmed general relativity to the fifth place of the decimal (.00001).[21]

But all these tests were made in the context of the Sun's and Earth's gravity. What if the context were different?

Strong Field Tests

Compared to the gravity of black holes, neutron stars (i.e., stars that are solid crystals comprised of neutrons touching one another from the central cores out to their surfaces), and the universe in its earliest moment after creation, the gravity of the Sun and Earth are weaker by more than a hundred thousand times. Astrophysicists questioned for some time if departures from general relativity might be observed for very strong gravitational field events.

The first such tests to address this question were conducted on the binary pulsar PSR B1913+16.[22] A pulsar is a rapidly rotating neutron star whose magnetic axis is so offset from its rotation axis that powerful pulses of energy beam toward Earth every time it rotates. Most binary pulsars are systems in which an ordinary star orbits a pulsar. PSR B1913+16 is unusual in that the star orbiting the pulsar is also a neutron star. (Not all neutron stars emit powerful pulses.) A pulsar's gravitational pull on an ordinary star orbiting about it is very intense. The gravitational interaction between two neutron stars orbiting one another is far more intense yet.

In January 1992, an international team of astronomers led by Russell Hulse and Joseph Taylor published the results of ten years' high-quality observations not only on this pulsar but also on two others.[23] The team applied three separate tests of general relativity to each of the pulsars. In each case, general relativity passed with flying colors. In the case of PSR B1913+16, the observed results matched the values predicted by general relativity to an accuracy of better than 0.5%.

The 0.5% accuracy figure for general relativity is based on one set of experimental constraints only. General relativity predicts that, over time, two neutron stars orbiting one another will radiate so much gravitational energy that they will spiral inward toward one another causing their orbital periods to speed up—so much that it can be measured over decades rather than centuries or millennia.

Careful measurements of the orbital periods for PSR 1913+16 year by year provided an ever more stringent test of the theory of general relativity. With measurements extending throughout twenty years (1974–1993), general relativity was confirmed overall to an error of no more than one part in a hundred trillion. In the words of Roger Penrose, "This makes Einstein's general relativity, in this particular sense, the most accurately tested theory known to science!"[24] The rest of the scientific community agreed, awarding Hulse and Taylor the 1993 Nobel Prize in Physics for their breakthrough efforts.

Now, astronomers have accumulated 35 years of accurate measurements of the orbital changes for PSR 1913+16.[25] For the first time in any system, the relativistic shape correction to the elliptical orbit was affirmed. The astronomers also removed any doubt about the reality of gravitational radiation as predicted by general relativity. The orbital period decrease caused by gravitational wave damping compared to the general relativistic prediction they observed equals 0.9983 ± 0.0016 (between 99.67 and 99.99% agreement).[26]

In 2003, astronomers discovered a double pulsar binary, PSR J0737-3039

Figure 10.1: Double Pulsar Binary

This artist's impression of the double binary pulsar PSR J0737-3039 shows the collimated beams of radiation from each pulsar that result from the rapid rotation and strong magnetic fields of the two neutron stars. The two neutron stars are not shown to scale. If they were depicted as two marbles, they would be about 750 feet apart.

Credit: Michael Kramer, Jodrell Bank Observatory, University of Manchester

(see fig. 10.1). The two pulsars orbit one another with a period of just 2.454 hours. Over a five-year period, astronomers measured a spin precession of 25 degrees, a value in accord with the prediction from general relativity.[27] By 2025, PSR J0737-3039 will surpass PSR B1913+16 in its capacity to provide very high precision confirmations of general relativity.

General Relativity Confirmed in All Contexts

While measurements on binary pulsars did convince the community of physicists and astronomers of general relativity's reliability, there were still a few doubters among certain theologians and philosophers. They were waiting for general relativity to be proved in all relevant contexts.

General relativity had passed 13 independent experimental tests. What was lacking, however, were tests of the predicted but elusive Lense-Thirring effect, tests in and around black holes, and the observation of perfect or near-perfect (and therefore unambiguous) Einstein rings.

As Austrian physicists Joseph Lense and Hans Thirring pointed out in 1918, general relativity predicts that any spinning massive body will drag or twist the space-time fabric in its immediate neighborhood. Specifically, general relativity theory states that if a disk of material orbits a very dense body, like a neutron star or black hole, at an angle to the plane of the star or hole's spin axis, the dragging or twisting of space-time that is predicted will cause the disk to wobble like a child's top. In turn, the wobble (called Lense-Thirring precession) will generate oscillations in the intensity of the radiation emitted from the gas in the disk. The theory even predicts the rate at which the oscillations should occur, according to the spin characteristics of the particular neutron star or black hole.

In 2016, a team of four Polish astronomers derived jet energetics and timescales for the two pairs of extended and misaligned lobes emanating from the radio galaxy 3C 293. Their analysis demonstrated that Lense-Thirring precession generated by the supermassive black hole in 3C 293's nucleus (this black hole's mass exceeds several tens of millions of solar masses[28]) caused the observed jet dynamics.[29]

In the same year, an international team of eight astronomers reported on their observations of the iron emission line in the x-ray spectrum of the stellar mass black hole binary H1743-3222. They showed that the quasiperiodic oscillations in the iron line centroid energy is produced by Lense-Thirring precession.[30] One month earlier, a team of five Chinese astronomers showed that the quasiperiodic oscillations in the x-ray spectra of the black hole binary SWIFT J1842.5-1124 are consistent with the Lense-Thirring effect.[31] Four months earlier, three astronomers in the Netherlands showed that the quasiperiodic oscillations in the x-ray flux from the stellar mass black hole binary GRS 1915+105 are caused by different radii in the inner accretion flow of the black hole experiencing Lense-Thirring precession at different frequencies.[32] Ten months earlier, five European and Canadian astronomers' observations of the black hole binary SWIFT J1753.5-0127012 likewise showed quasiperiodic oscillations due to the Lense-Thirring effect.[33]

For solar system bodies, the predicted Lense-Thirring effect is extremely small. However, three laser-ranged, Earth-orbiting satellites, LAGEOS-1, LAGEOS-2, and LARES, have the necessary sensitivity to detect the tiny effect. Using 3.5 years of observations from the LARES satellite and several more years of observations from LAGEOS-1 and LAGEOS-2, a team of astronomers established that Earth's dragging of inertial space-time frames matched the value predicted by the Lense-Thirring effect to within 0.6%.[34] The Gravity Probe B mission, an Earth-orbiting satellite with four precision gyroscopes on board, measured a geodetic drift rate of -6,601.8 ± 18.3 milliarcseconds per year and a frame-dragging of -37.2 ± 7.2 milliarcseconds per year.[35] General relativity

Figure 10.2: Image of a Nearly Complete Einstein Ring at Optical Wavelengths

The gravity of the luminous foreground red galaxy, LRG 3-757, has gravitationally distorted the light of a much more distant blue galaxy.

Credit: NASA/ESA/Hubble Space Telescope (STScI/AURA)

predicted -6,606.1 milliarcseconds per year and -39.2 milliarcseconds per year, respectively.

Multiple studies now show that the Lense-Thirring effect as predicted by general relativity exists, with further affirmations on the way. What about the predicted Einstein rings?

Most people know that general relativity predicts that gravity will slightly bend the light of stars. A much more dramatic and definitive test of general relativity can be had when a massive galaxy lies exactly (or nearly exactly) on the line of sight between the observer's telescope and a distant quasar or compact galaxy. In this case, general relativity predicts the appearance of an Einstein ring centered on the image of the foreground galaxy. Now, many unambiguous, virtually complete Einstein rings have been seen at optical and infrared wavelengths.[36] The accompanying image in figure 10.2 was made by the Hubble Space Telescope, what physicist Andrew Watson termed a "dazzling demonstration of Einstein's theory at work."[37]

The list of gravitationally lensed galaxies and quasars now stands at several hundred.[38] Astronomers have even discovered several double Einstein rings.[39] One example is SDSS J0946+1006 (see fig. 10.3). In this case, the foreground galaxy, 3 billion light-years away, served as a gravitational lens for two distant

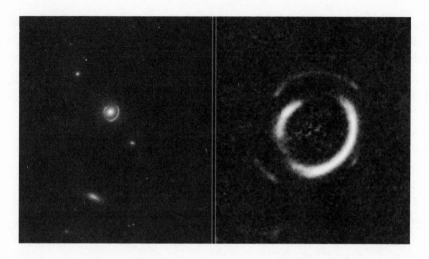

Figure 10.3: Double Einstein Ring Imaged by the Hubble Space Telescope
Credit: NASA/ESA/STScI/SLACS Team

galaxies, one of them 6 billion light-years away and the other 11 billion light-years away.

The previously elusive evidences for general relativity have now been supplied by these new astronomical observations. Even so, another powerful evidence recently surfaced.

Discovery of Gravity Waves

On February 11, 2016, the Laser Interferometer Gravitational Observatory (LIGO) research team announced that they had made the first direct detection of gravitational waves.[40] This remarkable achievement by the world's most sensitive detector (over a 4-kilometer laser baseline, LIGO can detect a distortion in space-time as small as 0.001 the diameter of an atomic nucleus) affirmed what many physicists consider the most significant prediction of general relativity—namely, that gravitational disturbances emit waves.

Because gravity is by far the weakest of the four fundamental forces of physics, physicists knew that, if gravity waves exist, they must be extremely feeble. Their only hope of detecting gravity waves is if they were lucky enough to observe an enormous gravitational disturbance. Such a disturbance happened on September 14, 2015, at 4:51 AM (ET). Two black holes with masses equal to 36 and 29 times the Sun's mass merged to form a black hole equal to 62 times the Sun's mass.[41] About 3 times the mass of the Sun was converted into gravitational waves within just a fifth of a second. LIGO detected these waves.

Later, LIGO detected gravitational waves from another merger event between two black holes.[42] This one occurred on Christmas Day, 2015, at 10:39 PM (ET). Two black holes with masses equal to 14 and 7.5 times the Sun's mass merged into a single black hole with a mass close to 21 times the Sun's mass. Since this merger occurred about three times closer, the LIGO team was able to observe the gravitational waves from the last 55 orbits of the two black holes before they finally merged.

LIGO in combination with another gravitational wave detector, Virgo, detected gravitational waves from two more merging events of black holes and on August 17, 2017 made the first detection of gravitational waves from the merging of two neutron stars.[43]

Unlike neutron stars, black holes contain no matter that might radiate light. Thus, since the previous four gravity wave detections were of the merging of two black holes, the events produced no emissions of light. In contrast, astronomers calculated that the merging of two neutron stars should spew debris that emits light at all wavelengths.

Astronomers using telescopes at 70 different observatories and space satellites quickly made follow-up observations of the August 17, 2017 gravitational wave event at gamma-ray, x-ray, ultraviolet, visible, infrared, and radio wavelengths.[44] These observations affirmed that neutron star merging events are responsible for most, if not nearly all, the r-process elements that exist on Earth and elsewhere in the universe. Half the elements heavier than iron are r-process elements, including such valuable and civilization-essential metals as silver, gold, platinum, palladium, osmium, thorium, and uranium.

The detection of gravitational wave events provided yet more evidence for a big bang creation event consistent with what the Bible has taught for thousands of years. It also revealed additional evidence for the fine-tuning design of the Creator (see ch. 15 and 17) for the benefit of human beings. It showed that Earth must be protected from the deadly radiation from nearby binary black hole and binary neutron star events during the era of humans and advanced animals yet be blessed with an abundance of such events at Earth's formation so as to adequately enrich Earth with the r-process elements necessary for life and civilization in particular.

So What?

Today it can be said that no theory of physics has ever been tested in so many different contexts, and so rigorously and exhaustively, as general relativity. The fact that general relativity has withstood all these tests so remarkably well implies that no basis remains for doubting any of the theological and philosophical conclusions dependent upon general relativity. Since general relativity accurately describes the dynamics of the universe in all contexts, the space-time theorems can be trusted. In other words, time really does have a beginning.

The law of causality (or the law of statistical correlation in which quantum or statistical mechanical effects are significant) says that effects emanate from causes, not the other way around. Thus, causes precede their effects. Time, then, can be defined as a dimension along which cause-and-effect phenomena occur.

While a few philosophers might object to this causal time definition, it is a definition that allows all time-dependent phenomena in the sciences to be treated consistently. It is the most common definition of time employed by the popular media and in everyday society. Since no physically living human transcends the space-time fabric of the universe (and, therefore, cannot observe time from outside or beyond time), no such human can boast an absolute or complete definition of time.

Such an absolute or complete time definition, however, is unnecessary. We simply need a consistent definition of time, and we need to use that definition consistently. So, whenever I refer to time in this book, I mean physical time, that is, time as defined by cause-and-effect operations.

The lack of physical time, thus, implies no cause and effect. If time's beginning is concurrent with the beginning of the universe, as the space-time theorems say, then the cause of the universe must be some entity operating in the equivalent of a time dimension completely independent of and preexistent to the time dimension of the cosmos. This conclusion is powerfully important to our understanding of who God is and who or what God isn't. It tells us that the Creator is transcendent, operating beyond the dimensional limits of the universe. It tells us that God is not the universe itself, nor is God contained within the universe. Pantheism and atheism do not square with the facts.

Pantheism claims there is no existence beyond the universe, that the universe is all there is, and that the universe has always existed. Atheism claims that the universe was not created and no entity exists independent of the matter, energy, and space-time dimensions of the universe. But all the evidence accumulated in the twentieth and twenty-first centuries tells us that a transcendent Creator *must* exist. Why? Because all the matter, energy, space dimensions, and even time, each suddenly and simultaneously came into being from some source beyond itself.

It is valid to refer to such a source, entity, or being as the Creator, for creating is defined as causing something—in this case everything in the universe—to come into existence. Matter, energy, space, and time are the effects caused by the Creator. Likewise, it is valid to refer to the Creator as transcendent, for the act of causing these effects must take place outside or independent of them.

Not only does science lead us to these conclusions, but so also does the Bible. It is the only holy book to do so.

 Discussion Questions _____

1. What problem does the author hope to solve by suggesting that scientists propose models that test for God-of-the-gaps or no-God-of-the-gaps. Is this possible?
2. Proof of the beginning of time probably ranks as the most "theologically significant theorem of all time." Why?
3. Discuss several recent confirmations of general relativity and how you think they will affect people's view of a cosmic beginning.
4. The author says that "all the data accumulated . . . tell[s] us that a transcendent Creator *must* exist." Discuss why some people do not accept this conclusion.

Chapter 11

A God Outside of Time, but Knowable

When atheist astronomer Geoffrey Burbidge complained that his peers were rushing off to join the "First Church of Christ of the Big Bang," he was on the right track. The space-time theorems of general relativity lead not just to a theistic conclusion but specifically to the God of the Bible.

Of all the holy books of the world's religions, only the Bible unambiguously states that time is finite, that time has a beginning, that God created time, that God is capable of cause-and-effect operations before the time dimension of the universe existed, and that God caused many effects before the time component of our universe existed. Some of the Bible verses making such statements are given in table 11.1.

Other holy books allude to extra dimensions, transdimensional phenomena, and transcendence, but these allusions are inconsistent. The god(s) and the doctrines these books proclaim are always shaped and limited in some way by the dimensions of length, width, height, and time.

The Bible alone describes God as a personal Creator who can act entirely independent of the cosmos and its 10 space-time dimensions. The God of the Bible is not subject to length, width, height, and time. He is the One who brought them into existence. Moreover, the Bible alone describes attributes of God that defy explanation in the limited context of four space-time dimensions. Some examples are the description of God as a Being who is singular and plural (the Trinity) and the simultaneity of human free will and divine predestination. God's extradimensional attributes are discussed briefly in chapter 18 and in detail in my book *Beyond the Cosmos*.[1]

The Hebrew phrase *shamayim erets* ("heavens and earth") when accompanied by definite articles, always refers to the entire physical universe, the totality of physical reality. The Hebrew word for "created" (*bara*) means "to make something brand-new or to make something out of nothing." Hebrews 11:3

Table 11.1: Some Bible Verses Teaching God's Extradimensional Capacities

In the beginning God created the heavens and the earth. (Genesis 1:1)
By faith we understand that the universe was formed at God's command, so that what is seen was not made out of what was visible. (Hebrews 11:3)

states that the universe we can detect was made through that which we cannot possibly detect. This means that the universe was made transcendently, that it came from a source independent of matter, energy, length, width, height, and time.

> This grace was given us in Christ Jesus before the beginning of time. (2 Timothy 1:9)
> . . . in the hope of eternal life, which God, who does not lie, promised before the beginning of time. (Titus 1:2)

These verses state that time has a beginning and that God was causing effects before the beginning of time.

> . . . you loved me before the creation of the world. (John 17:24)
> For he chose us in him before the creation of the world. (Ephesians 1:4)
> He was chosen before the creation of the world. (1 Peter 1:20)

The Greek word for "world" in these passages (*kosmos*) can refer to part of the earth, the whole of planet Earth, or the entire universe. Most scholars agree that the context of these verses implies the latter definition. Thus, God again is seen as causing effects before the creation of the universe, which would include our dimension of time.

> Through him all things were made; without him nothing was made that has been made. (John 1:3)
> For in him all things were created: things in heaven and on earth, visible and invisible, whether thrones or powers or rulers or authorities; all things have been created through him and for him. He is before all things, and in him all things hold together. (Colossians 1:16–17)

These verses declare that Jesus Christ in his pre-incarnate form created everything. Nothing was created that he did not create. He existed before anything was created. That is, Christ was not created.

> On the evening of that first day of the week, when the disciples were together, with the doors locked for fear of the Jewish leaders, Jesus came and stood among them. (John 20:19)
> They were startled and frightened, thinking they saw a ghost. He said to them, "Why are you troubled, and why do doubts rise in your minds? Look at my hands and my feet. It is I myself! Touch me and see; a ghost does not have flesh and bones, as you see I have."
> When he had said this, he showed them his hands and feet. And while they still did not believe it because of joy and amazement, he asked them, "Do you have anything here to eat?" They gave him a piece of broiled fish, and he took it and ate it in their presence. (Luke 24:37–43)

The disciples understood the impossibility of a physical body passing through physical barriers. That is why they concluded that the form of Jesus in front of them had to be ghostly or spiritual and not physical. But Jesus proved his physical reality by allowing the disciples to touch him and by eating food in front of them. Though it is impossible for three-dimensional physical objects to pass through three-dimensional physical barriers without one or the other being damaged, Jesus would have no problem doing this in extra dimensions. Six spatial dimensions would be adequate. He could simultaneously translate the first dimension of his physicality into the fourth dimension, the second into the fifth, and the third into the sixth. Then he could pass through the walls of the room and transfer his three-dimensional body from the fourth, fifth, and sixth dimensions back into the first, second, and third. This scenario is simply one out of nearly infinite different ways Jesus could have passed his physical body through walls. Since Jesus has and can create space-time dimensions at will, he can do the deed with any dimensional combination he desires, or he can decide to do it without any dimensions at all.

> In your relationships with one another, have the same mindset as Christ Jesus: Who, being in very nature God, did not

consider equality with God something to be used to his own advantage; rather, he made himself nothing by taking the very nature of a servant, being made in human likeness. And being found in appearance as a man, he humbled himself by becoming obedient to death—even death on a cross! Therefore God exalted him to the highest place and gave him the name that is above every name, that at the name of Jesus every knee should bow, in heaven and on earth and under the earth, and every tongue acknowledge that Jesus Christ is Lord, to the glory of God the Father. (Philippians 2:5–11)

This passage says that, in coming to Earth, Jesus Christ stripped himself of the extradimensional and transdimensional capacities he shared with God the Father and the Holy Spirit. These capacities were restored to him once he had fulfilled his mission of redeeming willing human beings from their sin.

Religions that view the Bible through the limited dimensionality of the universe inevitably deny portions of God's transcendence. Judaism accepts almost all the teaching of the Old Testament but rejects the New Testament. Islam and Mormonism "accept" both the Old Testament and New Testament but add other holy books to supersede them. Jehovah's Witnesses accept the Old and New Testaments but choose to change several hundred words in both to make it fit with their preconceived notions. Other cults such as Christian Science, Unity, and Religious Science simply ignore "unpleasant" or "paradoxical" passages in the Old and New Testaments.

The common denominator in all the alternatives to Christianity is a denial, at least in part, of God's transcendence and extradimensional attributes. For example, the tri-unity of God is taught only in the Christian faith.

Suffice it to say, Burbidge's conclusion stands. General relativity and the big bang lead to only one possible conclusion: a Creator matching the description of Jesus Christ as our Creator-God.

But Who Created God?

A question children often ask about God is, If God created us, who created God? A science-minded adult might phrase the question this way: If God created the universe and everything in it, including all matter, energy, and the 10 space-time dimensions, who created him?

The question itself yields an elegant proof for creation. The universe and everything in it is confined to a single, finite dimension of time. Time proceeds

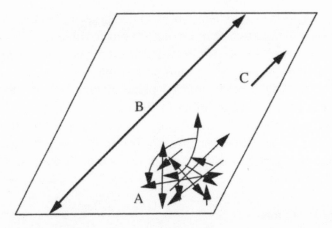

Figure 11.1: God's Time Frame Relative to Our Time Frame

If time were two-dimensional rather than one-dimensional, it would be some kind of plane rather than a line. In this case, an infinite number of time lines (*A*) would run in an infinite number of directions. This, according to general relativity and the Bible, is the *minimal* situation with the Creator. If the Creator were to so choose, he could move and operate for infinite time, forward and backward, on a time line (*B*) that never intersects or touches the time line of our universe (*C*).

Credit: Reasons to Believe

only and always forward. The flow of time can never be reversed. Nor can it be stopped. Because it has a beginning and can move in only one direction, cosmic time is really just half a dimension. The proof of creation lies in the mathematical observation that any entity confined to such a half-dimension of time must have some ultimate starting point or point of origination. That is, that entity must be created. This necessity for creation applies to the whole universe and ultimately to everything in it.

The necessity for God to be created, however, would apply only if God, too, were confined to half a dimension of time. He is not.

Again, by our definition, time is that realm or dimension in which cause-and-effect phenomena take place. According to the space-time theorems of general relativity, such effects as matter, energy, length, width, height, and time were caused independent of the time dimension of the universe. According to the New Testament (2 Timothy 1:9, Titus 1:2), such effects as grace and hope were caused independent of the time dimension of the universe (meaning before, outside of, or apart from our time dimension). So, both the Bible and general relativity speak of at least the equivalent of one additional time dimension for God, since effects existed before time in this universe began.

In the equivalent of two or more dimensions of time, an entity is free from the necessity of being created. If time were two-dimensional, for example, both a time length and a time width would be possible. Time would expand from a line into a plane (see fig. 11.1). In a plane of time, an infinite number of lines running in an infinite number of directions would be possible. If God were to so choose, he could move and operate along an infinite time line that never touches or crosses the time line of our universe. As John 1:3, Colossians 1:16–17, and Hebrews 7:3 say, he would have no beginning and no end. He would not be created.

Nontheistic Response

In 1989 John Maddox (then editor of the preeminent science journal *Nature*) wrote an editorial titled "Down with the Big Bang."[2] In it, Maddox predicted that since young-earth creationists have "impaled themselves on the hook of trying to disprove the relatively recent geological record," it will be only a matter of time before "the impatient creationists will have to retreat to the Big Bang" to support their belief in creation. Maddox conceded that creationists' beliefs have "ample justification" in the big bang. For this very reason he declared the big bang "thoroughly unacceptable" because it implies "an ultimate origin of our world" whose cause or Causer lies beyond the universe.[3] Here, Christians and theists are joined by nontheists in recognizing the theological implications of big bang cosmology and the space-time theorems.

What was Maddox's escape plan? He pinned his hopes on a 1989 paper by British astrophysicists, which shows that the universe might have begun as a line in space-time rather than as a point.[4]

A Point or a Line?

The space-time theorems of general relativity do imply that the universe originated from a singularity, but Maddox's definition of that singularity was inaccurate. A singularity is not an infinitely small point, as he suggests, but rather the whole of nine-dimensional space shrunken down to a size of zero volume.

Thus, it does not matter whether the universe expands from a point or a line. Both a point and a line have zero volume. For that matter, any one-, two-, three-, or N-dimensional shape for the origin of the universe that has zero volume yields a theistic conclusion. In all such cases the universe exhibits a big bang and an ultimate origin for all the cosmic space-time dimensions. Therefore, Maddox's argument fails. Based on his own words, Maddox's rejection of the big bang flows from his personal commitment to atheism rather than from scientific considerations.

Spontaneous Generation and Self-Organization?

In a *Free Inquiry* article, particle physicist Victor Stenger looked to a natural spontaneous generation process followed by some "natural processes of self-organization" as the way to avoid the need for God's participation.[5] Stenger's appeal to spontaneous self-generation at the moment the universe began, followed by billions of years of self-organization that continues right through to the present, is purely speculative. Not one example of significant self-generation or self-organization (one that involves order, complexity, function, and purpose) can be found in the entire realm of nature. Without causation nothing happens, and without organization by an intelligent being, systems tend toward lower and lower levels of complexity, function, and purpose.

Today, the best-known challenges to a Christian interpretation of the universe, at least for laypeople, come from the best-selling books by physicists Stephen Hawking and Lawrence Krauss. The next chapter briefly describes these challenges and explains why these challenges actually strengthen the case for the God of the Bible as the Originator and Designer of the cosmos.

 Discussion Questions _____

1. Table 11.1 lists some Bible verses "Teaching God's Extradimensional Capacities." Had you thought of God in this way before? Explain.
2. Discuss the answer to the "Who created God?" question as it relates to time.
3. What does former *Nature* editor John Maddox propose as an escape from the implications of big bang cosmology? Does it seem plausible?

Chapter 12

A Brief Look at
A Brief History of Time

S everal years ago I was invited to speak to a gathering of film and TV writers, directors, and producers. My idea was to present scientific evidences for the God of the Bible, but the group implored me to review and critique Stephen Hawking's book *A Brief History of Time*. A review of a science text for people in the film and TV industry? It seemed bizarre. But, come the night of the event, the place was packed with twice the number of people expected, and nearly everyone present had read the book.

What I learned that night is that British physicist Stephen Hawking has become a folk hero for many Americans and a cult figure for new agers. The folk hero status is easy to understand. Who can help but be stirred by the valor of a man who must force the communication of his brilliant mind through the constricting barriers of amyotrophic lateral sclerosis (ALS or Lou Gehrig's disease)? His status as a cult figure comes from his reputation for suggesting that theoretical physics renders God impersonal and unnecessary for our existence.

A Brief History of Time was Hawking's first book aimed at a popular audience. It is the best-selling science book of all time with more than ten million copies sold.[1]

Most of the book relates the universe's history to the latest discoveries about theories of gravity. It is engaging if for no other reason than one of the key history-makers tells the story.

Controversial Theology

A Brief History of Time is more than a popular-level text on gravitational theories. What makes Hawking's book unique and controversial are its philosophical and theological pronouncements.

In his final chapter, Hawking declares the goal of his life and work. He bends all his efforts toward answering these fundamental questions: "What is the nature of the universe? What is our place in it and where did it and we come from? Why is it the way it is?"[2] Hawking's dream is to answer these questions through physics alone. Thus far, he gives no reason for his refusal to acknowledge or accept answers already given elsewhere, specifically in the pages of the Bible. From his close contact with Christians—including his ex-wife Jane and physics colleague Don Page—we can assume he is aware, at least, that the Bible addresses these issues. Yet, he chooses to ignore its answers. In an interview for the *Sunday Times Magazine* (London), Jane Hawking said,

> There doesn't seem to be room in the minds of people who are working out these things for other sources of inspiration. You can't actually get an answer out of Stephen regarding philosophy beyond the realms of science. . . . I can never get an answer, I find it very upsetting.[3]

An Absent God

A Brief History of Time is based on a scientific paper that Hawking published with James Hartle.[4] The paper is a proposal on the state of the universe during the quantum gravity era (epoch when in big bang cosmology the universe is younger than 10^{-43} seconds, see ch. 9). Hartle and Hawking invoke imaginary time to complement real time so that, very near what might have been the beginning of the universe, time gives way to space such that there is only space and no time. The universe then would have no initial boundaries. As Carl Sagan summarizes in his introduction for *A Brief History of Time*, the Hartle-Hawking model represents an effort to posit "a universe with no edge in space, no beginning or end in time, and *nothing for a Creator to do*" (emphasis added).[5]

Thus, I was not surprised that in my debate with particle physicist Victor Stenger in 2008 at the International Skeptics Society Conference (on whether science establishes the existence of God), Stenger spent his allotted speaking time presenting the Hartle-Hawking model.[6]

One problem with the Hartle-Hawking model is that it predicted that the universe possesses a closed geometry. That is, the model predicts that the universe will eventually stop expanding and collapse under the force of its own gravity. As shown in chapter 5, there is insufficient matter in the universe to ever collapse it. Furthermore, dark energy dictates that the universe will *continue* to expand at an ever-accelerating rate.

Dark energy poses another problem for the Hartle-Hawking model. As

Leonard Susskind first pointed out,[7] in the Hartle-Hawking model, dark energy would imply that the present universe would be very nearly empty space-time. It would not be a universe that contains galaxy clusters, galaxies, stars, and planets. Later, Don Page expanded upon Susskind's critique.[8] His calculations showed that in the most plausible version of the Hartle-Hawking model, cosmic inflation would have expanded the present universe to be larger than $10^{10^{10^{122}}}$ megaparsecs. (1 megaparsec = 3.26 million light-years.) The present universe size measures only about 10^5 megaparsecs. Thus, Page showed that the model's empty space-time universe was about as empty as any physicist could conceivably imagine!

Page followed up his calculations with exhaustive attempts to rescue the Hartle-Hawking model from its empty cosmos dilemma. He found that none of his eight potential solutions offered a satisfactory resolution.[9]

A third problem for the Hartle-Hawking model is that it requires "imaginary time." The inclusion of imaginary time is ad hoc—nowhere throughout the entirety of the universe do we observe the operation of imaginary time or see a need for ever invoking imaginary time. Hawking and Hartle are appealing to a time dimension that transcends the universe we observe. Their appeal mirrors the same context as Christians citing a causal Agent beyond the observed space-time dimensions to explain the origin of the universe. As Hawking himself wrote in *A Brief History of Time*,

> Only if we could picture the universe in terms of imaginary time would there be no singularities [cosmic beginning]. . . . When one goes back to the real time in which we live, however, there will still appear to be singularities [a cosmic beginning].[10]

Hawking further conceded that the model he developed with Hartle was "just a proposal: it cannot be deduced from some other principle."[11]

The Grand Design

In 2010, Stephen Hawking and Caltech theoretical physicist Leonard Mlodinow published another best-selling science book for laypeople, *The Grand Design*.[12] The authors explicitly stated their theological agenda:

> This book is rooted in the concept of scientific determinism. . . . There are no miracles or exceptions to the laws of nature.[13]

In support of their scientific determinism and claim for complete lack of miracles, Hawking and Mlodinow make three bold assertions. They state, as scientific fact, that the discovery of extrasolar planets "makes the coincidences of our planetary conditions . . . far less compelling as evidence that the Earth was carefully designed just to please us humans."[14] Later in their book, they claim, "As Darwin and Wallace explained how the apparently miraculous design of living forms could appear without intervention by a supreme being, the multiverse concept can explain the fine-tuning of physical law without the need for a benevolent creator."[15]

Hawking and Mlodinow offered no defense or explanations of these three assertions. Apparently, they were counting on their great fame to convince readers. I will briefly explain here why Hawking and Mlodinow are wrong on the first two assumptions. In chapter 13, I will explain what the multiverse is and why it does not eliminate the need for a benevolent Creator.

Exoplanets

From 1988 to 1995, when the first eight exoplanets (planets beyond our solar system) were discovered,[16] astronomers predicted that subsequent discoveries of exoplanets would prove that the planets orbiting the Sun, including Earth, are common. Hawking and Mlodinow evidently thought this prediction was proven correct.

Today, the list of known exoplanets stands above 3,600.[17] While many "analogs" of the Sun's planets indeed have been found, there are none sufficiently similar to the Sun's planets for advanced life to be possible there. No known exoplanets are a candidate for anything other than the ephemeral existence of a few hardy microbes, and none make possible the existence of advanced life on another planet in the same planetary system. This may come as a surprise to some, especially those more exposed to *History* space documentaries than published scientific findings of planetary systems.

The planet that comes the closest to matching a solar system planet is Upsilon Andromedae e. Its distance from its host star is just 1% greater than Jupiter's distance from the Sun. Its mass is just 6+% greater than Jupiter's (because the inclination of Upsilon Andromedae e's orbit is not known, only a minimum mass has been determined). It also has a low eccentricity orbit (very nearly circular as opposed to highly elliptical), just like Jupiter. However, unlike Jupiter, Upsilon Andromedae e's mass does not dominate the mass of all the other planets in its planetary system. Two much larger planets reside in the Upsilon Andromedae system. Upsilon Andromedae c and d possess masses at least 14.6 times and 10.2 times greater than Jupiter's, respectively. These two planets orbit Upsilon Andromedae at 17% and 49% the distance that Jupiter orbits the Sun, respectively. Furthermore, they both have high eccentricity orbits. Moreover, the host star is 1.28 times more massive and 3.4 times more luminous than the Sun. The system includes a dim star orbiting the main star 750 times farther away than Earth orbits the Sun. Everything about these two planets and the host star rules out the possibility that another planet that may perhaps exist in the Upsilon Andromedae system could support advanced life.

The discovery of thousands of planets beyond our solar system has actually made the evidence for careful design "to please us humans" much more compelling. Thanks to exoplanetary research, astronomers now know that every planet and every comet-asteroid belt in our solar system plays an important role in making human existence possible on Earth.[18] That is, for advanced life to be possible, not only must an exact twin of Earth be found but also an exact twin of virtually all the bodies in the entire solar system. This requirement includes the need to find an exact twin of the Sun.[19]

For 60 years, astronomers have scoured the Milky Way Galaxy in their search to find an adequate twin of the Sun. While they found stars that are twins of one another, they have yet to find such a twin of the Sun.[20]

NASA's declaration that there might be tens of billions of habitable planets in our Milky Way Galaxy[21] presumes that the only criterion for habitability is that a planet is within the right range of distance from its host star so that liquid water could conceivably exist for some moment on the exoplanet's surface. However, for a planet to be truly habitable it must simultaneously reside in all nine of the known zones of habitability (see table 17.1 on p. 210).[22]

Only one planet out of the thousands discovered simultaneously resides in all nine known habitable zones. Earth not only does it all, it has done so for the past several billion years.

Origin of Life

All that Wallace and Darwin offered to explain how life originated without the need for a benevolent Creator was a hypothesis of a warm pond filled with life's building block molecules that spontaneously self-assembled into a simple life-form from which we all evolved. Much later, Carl Sagan acknowledged that Darwin and Wallace's pond must be expanded to at least the size of all Earth's oceans and that a minimum of a billion years would be needed for any self-assembly to be possible. Later still, origin-of-life researchers recognized more requirements. Earth's oceans must be packed with a dense concentration of all the required building block molecules, these molecules must be homochiral (all the ribose sugars right-handed in their configuration and all the amino acids left-handed), and Earth's oceans must be kept at optimal chemical and physical conditions for a very long time.

Over the past seven decades, origin-of-life researchers have discovered that none of these requirements for a naturalistic explanation of life's origin on Earth were met. Many necessary building block molecules were missing. For example, alanine, arginine, and tryptophan (the amino acids essential for making life-critical proteins) are missing outside of living organisms and the decay products of these organisms, not only on Earth but everywhere else astronomers have looked in the universe.[23] Similarly, ribose (the five-carbon sugar essential for linking nucleobases to make DNA and RNA) is missing.[24]

While lab experiments demonstrate that these molecules that are the fundamental building blocks of life molecules can be produced under conditions present in comets and interstellar molecular clouds,[25] the calculated production minus destruction rates yield abundances well below the present detection limits of several parts per billion. Abundances that low make naturalistic explanations for the origin of life impossible.

Outside of living organisms and their decay products, there are no natural sources of homochiral amino acids and ribose sugars.[26] The only example beyond a trivial excess of left-handed amino acids compared to right-handed ones was in the Tagish Lake meteorite, where an excess of about 43–59% aspartic acid was found.[27] However, in the same sample alanine was found to be racemic (possessing equal amounts of left- and right-handed molecules).[28] Assembly of these amino acids into proteins requires that all of them be 100% left-handed.

Life's origin on Earth or on any other conceivably habitable planet faces the oxygen-ultraviolet paradox. Even the tiniest amount of oxygen in the environment shuts down prebiotic chemistry. However, no oxygen in the environment means that there would be no shield to prevent the penetration of life-destroying ultraviolet radiation emanating from the host star. In the case of Earth, oxygen was present at a level to prevent a naturalistic origin of life.[29]

Life's origin on Earth was not a process drawn out over a billion plus years. It occurred in a geologic instant. The time interval between the first appearance of stable liquid water on Earth and the first appearance of stable life measures less than ten million years.[30] Furthermore, this origin occurred under hostile, not benign, environmental conditions. No building block molecules, no homochirality, the presence of oxygen, and little or no time not only rules out viable hypotheses for a naturalistic origin of life, it also rules out even the possibility of developing a scenario for a naturalistic origin of life. For readers interested in pursuing this subject at greater depth, our scientific team at Reasons to Believe has published four books about life's origin.[31]

Extraterrestrial Life

Despite the impossibility of a naturalistic origin of life, the remains of life will inevitably be discovered on several solar system bodies. Because life has been so abundant for so long on Earth (about 3.8 billion years), meteorites, comets, and asteroids striking Earth have exported Earth's soil throughout interplanetary space. Astronomers have calculated that 200 kilograms of Earth soil on average resides on every square kilometer of the Moon's surface.[32] The figure for the Martian surface is about 200 grams of Earth soil per square kilometer. Since every ton of Earth soil contains about 100 quadrillion microbes, astrobiologists, if they make a diligent search, should find evidence for the remains of life on the Moon, Mars, and nearly every other solar system body.

Given the intractable problems just noted for a naturalistic origin of life and given that impactors cannot deliver Earth life to other planetary systems in a form that could be recognized as the remains of life, life will exist beyond our solar system only if God created it there. From a biblical perspective, there is no doctrinal barrier preventing God from creating life elsewhere in the universe.[33] However, so far, all that astronomers observe elsewhere are conditions hostile to life, and especially conditions hostile to advanced life.[34]

Can We Know All?

The most fundamental clash between Hawking's philosophy and biblical Christianity (not to mention physical reality) is Hawking's belief that human beings can discover that "complete set of laws." By this, he means not just a complete and consistent unified field theory (a theory explaining how a single primal force splits into the strong and weak nuclear forces and the electromagnetic and gravitational forces) but "a complete understanding of the events around us, and of our own existence."[35] Elsewhere he has said that he wants to "know the mind of God."[36] Since the existence of the God of the Bible or the existence of singularities would guarantee that his goal could never be reached, it is understandable that he seeks to deny both.

Ironically, his goal is not just biblically impossible but was proven mathematically impossible by Kurt Gödel in 1930. According to Gödel's incompleteness theorem, "no nontrivial set of arithmetical propositions can have its proof of consistency within itself."[37] When applied to the cosmos, Gödel's theorem means it is intrinsically impossible to know from the universe that the universe can only be what it is.

Normal experience is sufficient to show most of us that our human limitations will never allow us to learn *everything* about ourselves and the universe. The nature quiz that God posed to Job some four thousand years ago would still stump even so brilliant and educated a man as Stephen Hawking (see Job 38–41). More ironically, Hawking's own words prove his goal impossible. He acknowledges two unavoidable limitations on our quest for more scientific knowledge:

1. The limitation of the Heisenberg uncertainty principle of quantum mechanics (the impossibility for the human observer to measure exactly both the position and the momentum of any quantum entity)
2. The impossibility of exact solutions to all but the very simplest of physical equations[38]

As Romans 1:19–22 affirms, even brilliant research scientists can waste their efforts, in this case on theoretically impossible lines of research, if they reject clear evidence pointing to God.

All This for Us

Stephen Hawking and many other scientists apparently find it impossible to believe that "this whole vast construction [the universe] exists simply for our sake."[39] As support for his incredulity, he says that "there does not seem to be any need for all those other galaxies, nor for the universe to be so uniform and similar in every direction on the large scale."[40] But, that statement ignores a growing body of research. The uniformity, homogeneity, size, and mass and dark energy densities of the universe must all be precisely as they are for human life to be possible at any time in the universe's history (see chs. 5 and 15).

Attacks by physicists and other scientists on the God of the Bible are not new. The Bible seems an affront to their intellectual prowess. This ancient "religious" document makes many pointed and challenging statements about cosmic origins, all of them testable and provable.

What an affront to pride. I know I felt it. The call to humility and submission in view of the awesomeness of what God created and wrote is more than some are willing to handle.

No society has seen as much scientific evidence for God as ours. But neither has any other society had access to so much learning, research, and technology. These are all things human beings tend to take credit for, especially those who consider themselves the masters of learning, research, and technology. This is what the apostle Paul meant when he commented that not many who are wise by the world's standards are counted as true believers (1 Corinthians 1:20–26).

 Discussion Questions _____

1. How does the Hartle-Hawking model fare in light of scientific evidence?
2. Discuss why "habitable zone" is not as easy as it sounds. How many habitable zones are there? What are the implications for actual habitability?
3. What obstacles does a naturalistic origin-of-life scenario face?
4. Discuss how to reach people who exhibit the hubris—while avoiding it ourselves—described at the end of the chapter.

Chapter 13

A Modern-Day Goliath

A couple decades ago, an alarm sounded like the one that echoed through
Israel's camp in the days of King Saul. The Goliath, this time, was quantum mechanics (a theory defining the energy relationships of particle-sized
physical phenomena in terms of discrete levels). Many prominent theologians
heralded this giant as "the greatest contemporary threat to Christianity."[1] Besides Stephen Hawking, several famous physicists and many new-age proponents have proliferated popular books exploiting the difficult and mysterious
nature of quantum mechanics to undermine the Christian view of origins.

These attacks seem to express again the defiant reaction to mounting evidence from physics and astronomy that the universe—all matter, energy, space,
and time—began in a creation event, and that the universe was strategically
designed for life, as the following chapters describe. This evidence is now sufficient to rule out all theological options but one—the Bible's. Obviously, this
unexpected turn of research proves discomfiting to those who reject the narrowness of the message of salvation through Jesus Christ alone.

In their insistence that the inescapable creator-designer cannot be the God
of the Bible, researchers grope for a replacement, any replacement. Four sets of
quantum possibilities, in addition to Sean Carroll's quantum eternity universe
and Stephen Hawking and James Hartle's "universe as a wave function" (discussed in chs. 10 and 12, respectively), are being proposed.

1. Quantum Tunneling
British astrophysicist Paul Davies, in his book *God and the New Physics*, written
in 1983, was the first to propose locking all cause-and-effect phenomena into
the time dimension of the universe. Because the act of creating represents cause
and effect, and thus a time-bound activity, the evidence for time's origin, said
Davies, argued against God's agency in the creation of the cosmos.[2]

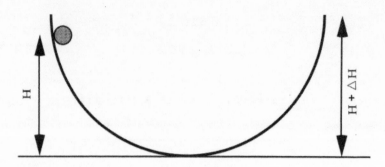

Figure 13.1: Quantum Tunneling

In classical physics a marble released from height H will roll down the side of a bowl and up the other side to the same height H, assuming the absence of friction. Since the lip of the bowl is at a height of H + ΔH, the marble will remain forever trapped inside the bowl. But the uncertainty principle of quantum mechanics states that for a quantum particle there must always exist a minimum uncertainty in the energy of the particle. This uncertainty implies that a quantum particle released from height H has a finite possibility of exceeding H + ΔH on the other side. The smaller ΔH is relative to H, the greater the possibility. Also, the faster the particle can travel from one side to the other (the less shallow the bowl), the greater the possibility. So quantum tunneling implies that a quantum mechanical particle can escape from the bowl, whereas a typical marble could not.

Credit: Reasons to Believe

Apparently, Davies is (or was) unaware that the Bible speaks of God's causing effects even before the beginning of the time dimension of our universe. As indicated in table 11.1, the Bible also speaks of the existence of dimensions beyond our time and space, extra dimensions in which God exists and operates.

Davies began by pointing out that virtual particles can pop into existence from "nothingness" through quantum tunneling (see fig. 13.1). The nothingness to which Davies referred was not absolute nothing. Rather, it was quantum fluctuations in the space-time fabric. An empty space-time fabric is not nothing. Virtual particles can be produced out of a quantum fluctuating space-time fabric, provided they are converted back into the quantum fluctuating space-time fabric before the human observer can possibly detect their appearance. This typically means that the particles so produced must disappear in less than a quintillionth (10^{-18}) of a second.

Davies next appealed to the grand unified theories of particle physics to suggest that, by the same means, the mass of the entire cosmos could have popped into existence. However, for a system as massive as the universe, the time for it to disappear back into quantum fluctuating space-time must be less than 10^{-103} seconds (102 zeros between the decimal point and the one), a moment a bit briefer than the measured age of the universe! (See "Hyper Quantum Mechanics?" later in this chapter for a response to a later attempt to bypass this limitation.)

Davies deserves credit for ongoing reconsiderations and revisions of his position. In a book published in 1984, *Superforce*, he argued that the laws of physics "seem themselves to be the product of exceedingly ingenious design."[3] In his 1988 book *The Cosmic Blueprint*, he posed this question: "If new organizational levels just pop into existence for no reason, why do we see such an orderly progression in the universe from featureless origin to rich diversity?"[4] He concluded that we have "powerful evidence that there is something going on behind it all" and the "impression of design is overwhelming."[5] In his 1999 book, *The Fifth Miracle*, Davies concludes that "the origin of life is virtually impossible" and that "you could be forgiven for concluding that a genome really is a miraculous object."[6] Davies seems to be moving toward some form of theism.

2. A Universe from Nothing

Famed astrophysicist Lawrence M. Krauss, in his book *A Universe from Nothing*,[7] claims to show why the latest physics proves that God is not necessary to explain the existence and features of the universe. Atheist biologist Richard Dawkins in the afterword writes, "Lawrence Krauss has delivered from physics 'the knockout blow' against the last remaining trump card of the theologian, 'Why there is something rather than nothing?'" In the flyleaf, the publisher writes that Krauss has provided an "antidote to outmoded philosophical and religious thinking," and a "game-changing entry into the debate about the existence of God."

Krauss's disciples may say that his book proves that God is dead, but Krauss himself backs away slightly from such a bold claim. Rather, he admits that on the basis of physics and logic "one cannot rule out such a deistic view of nature."[8] He claims this deistic view, however, "bears no logical connection to the personal deities of the world's great religions."[9] In other words, God may not be dead, but, according to Krauss, he certainly is not personal or presently active.

Universe = Nothing?

According to Krauss, one reason why God may not be personal is that the universe seems to add up to nothing. If the universe really adds up to nothing, why, Krauss implies, must we feel compelled to invoke Someone akin to the God of the Bible to explain its cause?

Krauss correctly explains that in a universe manifesting a flat geometry—and only in a flat geometry universe—the total Newtonian gravitational energy of each cosmic object is zero. The positive energy of motion is exactly canceled out by the negative energy of gravitational attraction. Therefore, the net energy of the universe is zero. Krauss claims that if the net energy of the universe is zero, then the universe is essentially nothing. That which is essentially nothing, he writes, does not need a big Something to explain its origin. Krauss also believes that the Heisenberg uncertainty principle does not put any limit on how "massive" the universe is, since the "net energy" of the universe is zero.

Little doubt remains today that we live in a universe that is very close to manifesting a flat geometry (see ch. 5). Consequently, Krauss does have a strong case for the total Newtonian gravitational energy of the universe being zero or very close to zero. However, the universe is more than Newtonian gravitational energy.

An analogy would be someone throwing a shot put straight up. There reaches a point in the trajectory where the upward kinetic energy exactly equals the downward gravitational energy. At that trajectory point the shot put is not moving either up or down. Its motion energy is zero. However, it would be wrong to conclude that the shot put is nothing. Even at that zero energy point, it is still a sphere of metal that weighs sixteen pounds. Likewise, even though the total Newtonian gravitational energy of the universe is zero, the universe still contains a huge amount of heat left over from the cosmic creation event and enormous quantities of dark energy, exotic dark matter, ordinary dark matter, and visible galaxies, stars, planets, dust, and gas. The universe does not reduce to absolutely nothing. (See the list of five different kinds of "nothing" later in this chapter.)

Hyper Quantum Mechanics?

Like Paul Davies, Krauss appealed to the analogy of virtual particle production to suggest how the universe might have popped into existence from "nothing." In *A Universe from Nothing*, Krauss never acknowledged the fatal flaws of the virtual particle production analogy for cosmic creation. However, he does hypothesize a second way that the universe could arise from nothing without divine agency.

The "nothing" in Krauss's second way is quite different from the virtual particle creation "nothing." Here, Krauss proposes that, in addition to the quantum mechanics that we observe to be constrained to space and time, there is an unobserved hyper quantum mechanics that exists beyond our universe. In his hypothesized hyper quantum mechanics, some dimension or dimensions of time entirely distinct from cosmic time would permit space-time bubbles, independent of the space or time dimensionality of our universe, to spontaneously pop into existence. However, if the hyper quantum mechanics is anything remotely like the quantum mechanics we observe operating in our universe, then the space-time bubbles that spontaneously appear must spontaneously disappear within very brief instants of time.

Krauss's appeal to a dimension or dimensions of time distinct from cosmic time is ironic. His appeal matches the Bible's declaration that the cause of the universe is an agent with the power to create independently of the one time dimension that currently governs the universe.

Krauss acknowledges that his appeal to some imagined hyper quantum mechanics to explain the universe's origin leads to a time-episode problem. He suggests the problem might be solved if the universe experiences a very aggressive inflationary expansion event *before* the hyper quantum mechanics would force the newly generated space-time bubble (our universe) to disappear.

As noted in the section above on quantum tunneling, Krauss's very aggressive inflationary expansion event would need to occur when, in the big bang model, the universe is much younger than 10^{-103} seconds. However, unlike inflationary big bang creation models (see ch. 5), Krauss's hyper quantum mechanics hypothesis does not provide a conceivable physical mechanism (such as symmetry breaking) for generating the very aggressive cosmic expansion. Nor does it eliminate the need for a subsequent aggressive cosmic inflation event. Furthermore, the hypothesis doesn't provide a viable (capable of explaining the possible existence of life) cosmic model wherein two time-separated aggressive inflationary expansion events produce a universe in which physical life is possible.

It is important to note here that all viable cosmic models require that an aggressive inflationary expansion event occur very early in cosmic history— between 10^{-35} and 10^{-33} seconds after the cosmic creation event (see ch. 5). Most inflationary big bang creation models predict that the act of inflation that occurs between 10^{-35} and 10^{-33} seconds will spawn a large number of space-time bubbles. These bubbles are different from the kind of space-time bubbles generated by Krauss's proposed hyper quantum mechanics. These bubbles are generated *after* our universe's creation event. Once formed by the inflation event, they subsequently never overlap. The lack of overlap means that it remains impossible for us humans to detect the existence of any of these bubbles.

Nevertheless, though we cannot prove their existence, we can determine that if they do exist, they still all require a transcendent causal Agent, One who is free to create and operate independent of space and time. The space-time theorem proved by Arvind Borde, Alan Guth, and Alexander Vilenkin[10] established that all viable inflationary big bang models are ones in which the universe and all of its bubbles (no matter how many space-time bubbles they predict are generated by the inflation event) are subject to a finite beginning in time, requiring a causal Agent beyond space and time to explain their existence. (Chs. 9, 10, and 12 explain why quantum gravity speculations offer no reasonable escape from the need for a cosmic beginning and Beginner.)

Stochastic Laws of Physics

Krauss ends his attempts to eliminate God as the universe's necessary Creator with the following proposal: "If the laws of nature are themselves stochastic and random, then there is no prescribed 'cause' for our universe."[11] What Krauss is suggesting by his appeal to "stochastic and random" laws of nature is that some process might exist that randomly produces all conceivable sets of physical laws and cosmic features. That being the case, then, according to Krauss, perhaps our universe's set of physical laws and cosmic features that make possible the existence of life may be the product of pure chance rather than divine design.

Krauss speculates a multiverse escape (appeal to an infinite number of universes where each universe is different from all others) from a cosmic Designer. Later in this chapter, I explain why such an escape fails.

Apart from problems with appealing to a multiverse, a major problem with Krauss's proposal is the question of where did the generator of stochastic and random laws of nature come from. That generator cannot be pure nothing. It must be something or Someone greater than the laws of nature and greater than any possible generator of laws of nature.

Nothing?

Throughout *A Universe from Nothing*, Krauss changes his definition of nothing. His definitions of nothing are actual somethings. So, what does "nothing" actually refer to? When physicists like Krauss write about nothing, they refer to one of the following five definitions of nothing, each of which really translates to something:

1. lack of matter or energy
2. lack of matter and energy

3. lack of matter, energy, and the four large expanding space-time dimensions of the universe
4. lack of matter, energy, and all the 10 space-time dimensions of the universe
5. lack of matter, energy, the 10 space-time dimensions of the universe, and any possible dimensions and/or sets of laws of physics existing beyond the universe's 10 space-time dimensions.

Note that all five of these "nothings" do not eliminate the need for something or Someone beyond that explains how the "lacks" become filled.

Where do all the somethings come from? A fundamental principle of cause and effect is that effects always come after their causes. An equally fundamental principle of cause and effect is that effects are never greater than their causes. These two principles undergird the entire enterprise of science. No human has ever observed them to be violated. They are a key component of the scientific method. Consequently, atheism and naturalism are self-defeating in that they demand that the living comes from that which is nonliving, the conscious comes from that which lacks consciousness, the personal comes from that which is impersonal, the mindful comes from that which has no mind, the emotional comes from that which lacks emotions, the willful comes from that which has no will, and the spiritual comes from that which is not spirit. To explain everything that we see existing in the universe, there must exist a causal Agent beyond the universe that is living, conscious, personal, mindful, emotional, volitional, spiritual, and orders of magnitude more intelligent, knowledgeable, powerful, caring, and loving than any of us human beings. The God of the Bible must exist!

Darwin Eradicated the Need for God?

Both Krauss and Dawkins, in *A Universe from Nothing*, credit Charles Darwin with eliminating the need for divine intervention.[12] Krauss refers to a workshop on the origin of life that was sponsored by the Origins Project he heads up at Arizona State University. He claims that the workshop demonstrated "plausible chemical mechanisms by which this [the origin of life] might be conceivable."[13]

I do not deny that biochemists are "homing in closer and closer every day to specific pathways that might generate biomolecules, including proteins ad RNA."[14] My colleague at Reasons to Believe Fazale "Fuz" Rana has demonstrated that fact beautifully in his book *Creating Life in the Lab*.[15] Fuz shows, however, that those chemical pathways are irrelevant to any conceivable naturalistic model for life's origin on Earth due to the conditions we know existed on Earth at the time of life's origin. The fact that biochemists have succeeded in demonstrating some of the necessary chemical pathways in their high-technology, well-funded laboratories simply proves that Someone much more intelligent, knowledgeable, and better funded (more powerful) than those biochemists must be responsible for life's origin on Earth.

Theology Impotent?

Like so many other famous nontheistic physicists,[16] Krauss declares that modern scientific advances have rendered philosophy and theology irrelevant. He writes, "Theology has made no contribution to knowledge in the past five hundred years. . . . No one has provided a counter example."[17] We at Reasons to Believe have provided many examples of the Bible accurately guiding and anticipating scientific research over the past 500 years. A few examples are:

- The Bible alone predicted all the fundamentals of big bang cosmology thousands of years before any scientist discovered any of these cosmic features (see ch. 3).
- The Bible predicted the invariability of the laws of physics.[18]
- The Bible predicted the order and the details of Earth's and life's natural history.[19]
- The Bible gave us the scientific method.[20]

Krauss endorses the Copernican principle "that there is nothing special about our place and time in the universe."[21] While it is true that we are not residing at the center of the Virgo Supercluster of galaxies, or at the center of the Local Group of galaxies, or at the center of the Milky Way Galaxy, or at the center of the solar system, our location is special nonetheless. We are living at the only location and time epoch within our solar system, galaxy, and cluster of galaxies where it would be possible for us to launch and sustain high-technology civilization. This specific location and time also happens to be the unique location and time where we can observe the vast reaches of the universe and directly witness the cosmic creation event. All this is explained and documented in my book *Why the Universe Is the Way It Is*.[22]

3. An Infinite Number of Possibilities and Chances (the Multiverse)

The full panoply of fundamental particles predicted by all particle physics theories has yet to be discovered. Until knowledge of all these particles is in hand, several theoreticians claim, we *might* not be able to close the door on alternate quantum physics.

Seizing the opportunity to speculate, these physicists hypothesize that either at the cosmic inflation event (see ch. 5) or sometime before the universe was 10^{-43} seconds old, different quantum physics allowed a seething space-time foam to form. This foam, they suggest, somehow budded an infinite number of baby universes. They further hypothesize that each baby universe would take on characteristics distinct from all the others, and that in the infinite number of universes every conceivable value of the constants of physics and every conceivable value of all the cosmic and particle physics characteristics would be represented.

An infinite number of universes featuring all conceivable values of the different cosmic and physical characteristics, these physicists state, could explain—without invoking a divine Creator—why one universe possesses so many properties that are so highly fine-tuned for the existence of physical life (see ch. 15). Their argument is that with an infinite number of universes, each with different physical characteristics, anything would be possible, even a universe as exquisitely fine-tuned or "apparently designed" as ours is for physical intelligent life.

Yet such an infinite number of universes is inadequate to explain away the fine-tuned nature of the universe. To explain away just one fine-tuned feature of the universe or one fine-tuned feature of one of its underlying physical laws or constants by chance one would need an infinite number of universes manifesting an infinite array of values for that feature. Additional such infinite number of universes are needed for each fine-tuned feature.

This appeal to multiple infinities of universes to explain away all the cosmic fine-tuning that makes life possible apart from a personal God is the atheistic version of the multiverse. (There are also theistic versions of the multiverse where God creates an infinite number of universes, and designs this infinite array of universes so as to efficiently produce one universe in which intelligent life can thrive.)

There are at least 10 reasons why the atheistic version of the multiverse does not eliminate the need for a personal, supernatural creating and designing God.[23] Here, I will discuss just five.

a. The timing is not coincidental.
The multiverse was not seriously proposed as an alternative to a personal God until nontheistic scientists had no other choice. For centuries, nontheists

had argued that design was not a pervasive feature of the universe. They also claimed that the observed designs were not all that remarkable and that many of the observed designs were far too inferior to be worthy of the handiwork of the Christian God. Our current knowledge and understanding of the universe (see chs. 15 and 17) no longer makes such arguments and claims credible. The evidence for ubiquitous, exquisite, and optimal design throughout the universe to make the existence of advanced life possible prompted Paul Davies to conclude in his book *The Cosmic Blueprint*,[24]

> [There] is for me powerful evidence that there is "something going on" behind it all. The impression of design is overwhelming.

When did nontheists propose that the multiverse was responsible for all the observed designs? Only when they could no longer credibly claim that less than an infinite number of rolls of the dice of natural processes could explain all the observed fine-tuned designs in the universe and Earth. Some of the reasons for their reluctance will be evident in what follows.

b. The multiverse explains too much.

The form of multiverse that nontheists propose not only explains away God's design, it explains away all human designs as well. For example, in an infinite number of an infinite number of universes, where all conceivable variations on the features of the universes are manifested, there could be an infinite number of planets just like Earth. On those infinite number of Earth-like planets there could be an infinite number of birch-like trees that shed pieces of white bark that are indistinguishable from 8.5 x 11 inch sheets of paper. These infinite number of pieces of white bark could fall upon soil containing chemicals that would imprint random ink-like markings on the pieces of bark. With an infinite number of pieces of such bark falling upon such soil, inevitably there will be a set of those pieces of bark that will possess imprinted markings that look identical to all the research papers published by all the nontheistic research scientists in the world.

As theoretical physicist Paul Steinhardt has pointed out, the problem with the atheistic version of the multiverse is that the hypothesis provides for all possible outcomes.[25] There is nothing that such a hypothesis could not conceivably explain. But, if a hypothesis can explain everything, then it really explains nothing. No experiment or observation could possibly falsify any of its explanations.

Using the same reasoning that nontheists apply to claim that the multiverse, not God, is responsible for all the designs we observe in the universe, we could also conclude that the multiverse, not scientists, is responsible for all the research papers published in the scientific literature. This analogy points out a major philosophical inconsistency in nontheists use of the multiverse to explain away God's design of the universe. One cannot use a different standard for testing the reality of divine design than one uses for testing the reality of human design. In other words, if one accepts the reality of human designs based on the physical evidences for those designs, then by the same kinds of investigation and deduction one must accept the reality of divine designs.

c. Overwhelming design evidence is seen on all observable size scales.

Scientists see overwhelming evidence for purposeful design of the natural realm for the specific benefit of life, and especially for human beings, on all observable size scales. It is not only the universe as a whole that reveals purposeful design. All the components of the universe do as well. No matter what the volume size scientists choose to investigate, they witness pervasive fine-tuned designs that make the flourishing of life and humans possible. Whether in our supercluster of galaxies, our local cluster of galaxies, the Milky Way Galaxy, our solar system, our planet, Earth's surface environment, plants and animals, individual cells, molecules, atoms, or fundamental particles, everywhere we look at each of these size scales we see overwhelming evidence for exquisite and pervasive fine-tuned designs.

At each of these size scales the evidence for purposeful design seems inexhaustible. The amount of design evidence discovered so far appears to be proportional to researchers' technological capabilities. As scientists' instruments expand their abilities to make detections and accurate measurements, the evidence for purposeful design mounts. This ongoing increase in design evidence is seen at all observable size scales. The more cosmic details astronomers discover, the more design evidence for the benefit of humans they uncover. Likewise, the more details astronomers learn about galaxies, stars, and planetary systems, the more design evidence they discover. The same consistently accumulating design evidence is witnessed by geophysicists, ecologists, microbiologists, molecular biologists, and particle physicists, as they expand their databases in their respective scientific disciplines.

Every instance where scientists have expanded the frontiers of scientific endeavor, they have uncovered much more evidence for purposeful design. It seems irrational and illogical to discount all this ubiquitous exquisite fine-tuning design by appealing to that which can never be detected or measured. If everywhere scientists can measure design they detect design, and if that evidence consistently mounts as scientists learn more, then surely the design is real.

A personal analogy might help. Every observation I make about my wife and two sons shows me that they are physical beings who really do exist. However, my measuring, observational, and experimental abilities have limits. There are certain aspects of their natures that are impossible for me to ascertain. Nevertheless, I do not appeal to that which is impossible for me to investigate to discount all the evidence I have accumulated.

d. Overwhelming design evidence is seen on all time scales.

In *The Cosmic Blueprint* Paul Davies posed this question, "If new organizational levels just pop into existence for no reason, why do we see such an orderly progression in the universe from featureless origin to rich diversity?"[26] Physicist Freeman Dyson, in his book *Disturbing the Universe*, wrote, "The more I examine the universe . . . the more evidence I find that the universe in some sense must have known we were coming."[27]

As astronomers look farther and farther away, they directly witness events at greater and greater times back in the history of the universe. What they note is that the universe is step-by-step progressively designed and prepared for the entry of human beings. Such detailed and complex preparation for such a highly specified purpose is the expected signature of an intelligent, powerful Planner. It is not the anticipated outcome of random chance.

e. The multiverse fails its one testable property.

Most scientists and philosophers assert that the multiverse is not testable. They draw this conclusion because Einstein's theory of general relativity states that once observers begin to exist in a universe, the space-time surface of that universe cannot overlap the space-time surface of any other possibly existing universes. This impossibility implies that if God made a trillion universes or only two, we could only discover information about the one universe in which we live. Thus, many scientists conclude that any discussion about the multiverse is not science. It is merely speculative metaphysics.

Despite our inability to detect the possible existence of other universes, there is a way to test the atheistic version of the multiverse model. A useful analogy is a coin-flipping experiment. If one observed a coin being flipped ten thousand consecutive times and always coming up heads on each of those ten thousand flips, one would be fully justified in concluding that the coin had been designed to only produce heads results. However, if one were making an appeal similar to multiverse speculations, one would surmise that an infinite number of coins were being flipped ten thousand consecutive times each by an infinite number of people and, therefore, reason that at least one of those coins would produce ten thousand consecutive heads outcomes.

Such an appeal to an infinite number of coins being flipped ten thousand consecutive times each by an infinite number of people is testable. It is testable even without any evidence for the additional coins.

One could take the one known coin that produced ten thousand consecutive heads outcomes and choose to examine it in more detail. For example, before betting on tails for the 10,001st flip, it would be prudent to first examine both sides of the coin. Even if that coin showed heads on one side and tails on the other, it would be wise to check the weight distribution of the coin. If examining the coin in more detail revealed evidence that it had been designed to always produce a heads outcome, one could reject the appeal to an infinite number of coins being flipped ten thousand times each in favor of the conclusion that there was a coin designer who manufactured the coin in such a way that it always produced a heads outcome.

One could apply this analogy to the universe. One could choose to examine the one and only observable universe in more detail than it has been examined before. If that more detailed examination sharply reduces the evidence of fine-tuned design for the specific benefit of humans, that outcome would favor the nontheistic model of the multiverse. On the other hand, if the more detailed examination dramatically increases the evidence of fine-tuned design for humanity's specific benefit, that outcome would favor the conclusion that an intelligent, powerful, and caring Designer manufactured the universe so that humans could thrive on Earth.

As chapter 15 describes and documents, throughout the 25-year history of the four editions of this book, the evidence of fine-tuned design of the universe, Milky Way Galaxy, solar system, and Earth for humanity's specific benefit has consistently risen in an extremely dramatic manner. This test strongly establishes the personal handiwork of a powerful, intelligent Creator who has a great love for human beings, and strongly repudiates atheistic versions of the multiverse.

4. Observer-Created Reality
In popular-level books on quantum mechanics, a clear distinction is seldom

made between the physics, philosophy, and religion of quantum mechanics. Therefore, let me briefly explain the differences:

- The *physics* of quantum mechanics tells us there are certain naturalistically inviolable principles operating on quantum entities. These principles allow the human observer to predict accurately the probability for the outcome of any particular quantum event (for example, an electron moving from one energy level to another).
- The *philosophy* of quantum mechanics is the attempt to describe the nature of cause and effect in quantum phenomena and, in particular, the role of human observers in such cause and effect.
- The *religion* of quantum mechanics is the attempt to discern who or what is ultimately behind cause and effect in quantum events.

In the 1920s and 1930s, the *physics* of quantum mechanics was questioned, most notably by Einstein.[28] But not anymore. The experimental evidence puts the physical principles of quantum mechanics beyond dispute.

A remaining problem, however, lies in the wedding of one philosophical interpretation of quantum mechanics to the physics. Danish physicist Niels Bohr cast such a large shadow over the early history of quantum mechanics research that his "Copenhagen interpretation" has been assumed by many to be one of its basic physics principles. But that isn't the case.

Niels Bohr, who operated from presuppositions equivalent to those found in Hinduism, declared that in the micro-world of quantum phenomena, reality in the absence of an observer does not exist. More to the point, he claimed that the act of observing creates the reality. Thus, he believed not only that a quantum event could not take place without an observer, but also that the observer, through his or her observations, actually brought about the quantum event.

Bohr arrived at his conclusions by noting a difference in a quantum particle before and after its detection by an observer. Before a specific quantum particle is detected, only a probability of where it might be located or of how energetic it is can be known. But after detection, the precise location or energy level is determined. This movement from imprecision to precision led Bohr and his associates at the Niels Bohr Institute in Copenhagen to believe that the observer actually gives reality to the quantum particle.

Since the founding of the Copenhagen interpretation of quantum mechanics, others, mainly non-physicists, have applied Bohr's conclusions about a quantum particle to the entire universe. If an observer can give reality to a

ALTERNATIVE PHILOSOPHIES OF QUANTUM MECHANICS

The flaws in the Copenhagen interpretation's philosophical aspects of quantum mechanics have proliferated a variety of alternatives. At last count, ten independent philosophical models have been developed and seriously proposed:[29]

1. A coherent reality exists independent of human thinking.
2. A common fundamental cause lies behind the cause-and-effect phenomena humans observe.
3. All possible outcomes will actually occur.
4. The act of observation dissolves the boundary between the observer and the observed.
5. The world obeys a nonhuman type of reasoning.
6. The world is composed of objects that possess attributes, whether or not the objects are observed.
7. The only observer who counts is the conscious observer.
8. The world is twofold, consisting of potentials and actualities.
9. The real essence of substances is beyond our knowledge.
10. The physical realm is the materialization of pure thought.

quantum particle, they say, then why not to the whole of the cosmos itself? Of course, these people assume that the observer in question is a human observer. From this assumption, it seems logical to conclude that human beings, not God, created the universe.

Some of the logical flaws in this line of reasoning are obvious; others are more subtle:

- There is no movement from imprecision to precision in quantum phenomena. In reality, the observer can choose where to put the imprecision. If the observer chooses to accurately measure the position of the quantum particle, the potential for any precision in measuring the particle's momentum is lost. Conversely, if the observer chooses to accurately measure the momentum of the quantum particle, the potential for any precision on the position of the particle will be irretrievably lost. This inevitable imprecision in quantum mechanical measurements is known as the Heisenberg uncertainty principle.

- While pure quantum events do exhibit effects that are significant and important, they result in no permanent change to any part of the universe.

- The observer does not give reality to the quantum entity. The observer can only choose what aspect of the reality to discern. Though in quantum entities, indefinite properties become definite to the observer through measurements, the observer cannot determine how and when the indefinite property becomes definite. That is, at some point in the measurement sequence, the pure quantum mechanical description becomes invalid and the physical system assumes a specific physical state. However, exactly where and when this transition occurs cannot be determined by human observers.

- Rather than showing us that human beings are more powerful than we otherwise thought, quantum mechanics shows us that we are weaker. In classical physics, no apparent limit exists on our ability to make accurate measurements. In quantum mechanics, a fundamental and easily determinable limit exists. In classical physics, we can see all aspects of causality. But in quantum mechanics, some aspect of causality always remains hidden from human investigation.

- Experiments in particle physics and relativity consistently reveal that the natural realm is correctly described by the condition that the human observer, as opposed to a detection instrument, is irrelevant.[30]

- The time duration between a quantum event and its observed result is always very brief; it's many orders of magnitude briefer than the period separating the beginning of the universe from the beginning of humans.

- For both the universe and human beings time is not reversible. Thus, no amount of human activity can ever affect events that occurred billions of years ago.

- There is nothing particularly special about human observers. Inanimate objects, like photoelectric detectors, are just as capable of detecting quantum mechanical events.

All these flaws punctuate what should be obvious to us all—humans are neither powerful nor wise enough to create a universe. To say that we created our own universe would imply that we can control time and restructure the past.

As time advances, the quantum mechanical alternatives to God become more and more absurd. Today, there are scientists and philosophers and mystics who are willing to claim that humans are the Creator.

The progression toward absurdity underscores two observations. First, the persistent rejection of God's existence and creative work, despite the build-up of evidence for both, suggests that the source of rejection is not purely intellectual. I realized this while reading an article in a humanist magazine. The article noted that "atheists, agnostics, humanists, freethinkers—call them what you will—are almost all former members of a Christian community or family."[31] It seems the issue for some of these atheists, agnostics, humanists, and freethinkers is not so much the deficiency of evidence for the Christian faith but rather the deficiencies of Christians they knew. They may be reacting to past hurts they incurred in their experiences with Christians or with people who call themselves Christians.

Second, the appeal to increasing absurdities in response to the evidences for the God of the Bible demonstrates again how secure these evidences must be. Nothing in our human experience can be proven absolutely. Our limitations in the space-time continuum of the cosmos guarantee this. But when a conclusion is opposed by increasingly absurd alternative explanations, that indicates something about the strength of the conclusion. For example, the Flat Earth Society still has "reasons" for rejecting the conclusion that Earth is spherical. But the reasons presented today are much more absurd than those presented 30 years ago and far more absurd than those presented 100 years ago. Thus, the history of their appeals for a flat Earth interpretation reflect the growing certainty about Earth's roughly spherical shape. Likewise, the history of appeals for a nontheistic interpretation for the physical realm reflect the growing certainty about the existence of the God of the Bible.

 Discussion Questions _____

1. Physicist Paul Davies has written several books addressing "nothingness" and "quantum tunneling." Discuss his apparent intellectual position on supernatural agency.

2. Lawrence Krauss holds to a "universe from nothing." Describe how five "nothings" do not rule out a Something beyond that accounts for all

the "lacks" in Krauss's proposal.

3. Is the atheistic version of the multiverse explanation compelling? Why or why not?

4. What points can be marshalled against a quantum-mechanical-alternative-to-God approach to the beginning of the universe?

Chapter 14

The Divine Watchmaker

The evidence for design in the natural realm has always been a popular argument for God's existence. Though in the past it has been criticized for its lack of rigor and thoroughness, the design argument has consistently proved itself to be the most compelling argument for God. That's because the design evidence is simple, concrete, and tangible.

Paley's Watchmaker Argument
A classic historical example of such tangible simplicity comes from the eighteenth-century British theologian-naturalist William Paley and is called "the Watchmaker argument."

> In crossing a heath, suppose I pitched my foot against a stone, and were asked how the *stone* came to be there; I might possibly answer, that, for anything I knew to the contrary it had lain there forever; nor would it, perhaps, be very easy to show the absurdity of this answer. But suppose I had found a *watch* upon the ground, and it should be inquired how the watch happened to be in that place, I should hardly think of the answer which I had before given, that for anything I knew, the watch might have always been there. . . . The watch must have had a maker—that there must have existed, at some time, and at some place or other, an artificer or artificers, who formed it for the purpose which we find it actually to answer, who comprehended its construction, and designed its use. . . . Every indication of contrivance, every manifestation of design, which existed in the watch, exists in the works of nature; with the difference, on the side of nature, of being greater or more, and that in a degree which exceeds all computation.[1]

No one of sound mind, Paley explains, would ever conclude that a watch was the product of bits of dust, dirt, and rock being shuffled together under natural processes. Even if the natural processes could operate for a very long time, there would still be no rational hope for a watch to be assembled. Yet, as all the naturalists of Paley's day admitted and all the biologists of today emphatically concur, the complexity and capability of living organisms far transcends anything we see in a watch. If a watch's complexity and capability demand an intelligent and creative maker, surely, Paley reasoned, the living organisms on our planet demand a Maker of far greater intelligence and creative ability.

Rebuttals by Hume, Darwin, and Gould

As persuasive as Paley's Watchmaker argument may seem, it has been largely rejected by secular scholars. The basis for the rejection stems from three rebuttals: one by philosopher David Hume, one by biologist Charles Darwin, and one by paleontologist Stephen Jay Gould.

Hume argued that the analogy between the watch and a living organism was not close enough. He claimed that a living organism only has the *appearance* of an engine, therefore, the complexity and capability of living organisms were only evidences for *apparent* design. As to where the apparent design of organisms came from, Hume hypothesized a universe composed of a finite number of particles all in perpetual, random motion for infinite time. In such a universe, Hume declared, the random shuffling of matter would eventually produce complex bioforms well adapted to their environment. To the casual observer such complexity and adaptation would bear the appearance of design.[2]

Darwin argued that observations within Earth's biosphere established three self-evident truths: (1) tremendous variations exist among populations of organisms, (2) these variations can be inherited, and (3) all organisms are involved in an intense competition for survival that favors the preservation by natural selection of superior variations. A fourth and a fifth can now be added to these three. The fourth: new variations to replace those extinguished through natural selection are generated by random changes, or mutations, in the genetic codes within organisms that are responsible for the inheritable characteristics. The fifth: lateral movement of a small part of one organism's genetic material into another organism. Many modern Darwinists therefore conclude that random mutations, lateral gene transfer, and natural selection can explain all the changes in life-forms that have occurred during the history of our planet.

In summarizing the claims of such radical Darwinists, biochemist Jacques Monod says, "Chance *alone* is at the source of every innovation, of all creation in the biosphere. Pure chance, absolutely free but blind, [lies] at the very root of the stupendous edifice of evolution."[3]

In his best-selling book *The Blind Watchmaker: Why the Evidence of Evolution Reveals a Universe without Design*, biologist and self-professed atheist Richard Dawkins declares,

> Natural selection, the blind, unconscious, automatic process which Darwin discovered, and which we now know is the explanation for the existence and apparently purposeful form of all life, has no purpose in mind. It has no mind and no mind's eye. It does not plan for the future. It has no vision, no foresight, no sight at all. If it can be said to play the role of watchmaker in nature, it is the *blind* watchmaker.[4]

This is the heart of the materialists' reply to Paley, the claim that the apparent design and purpose seen in Earth's life-forms is not real but rather the product of strictly natural processes.

Gould attempts to buttress the Darwinists' attack on Paley by pointing out a number of "bad designs" in nature.[5] He argues from his examples that living organisms developed by random tinkering, not as the result of any real design. Specifically, he gives the credit to opportunistic utilization of previously existing parts. In his most famous example, he claims that the panda's thumb is a clumsy adaptation of a wrist bone, not the work of a divine designer.

A Reply to Hume

Hume's attack on Paley's watch analogy is unfounded for the following reason: while no mechanical engine is an organism, all organisms are engines. An engine is any system capable of processing energy to perform work. All organisms do this. And they do a lot more. Thus, since no one would rationally argue that a working engine designed by another human could be chance-assembled by purely natural processes, it is far more ludicrous to suggest that strictly natural processes could assemble living organisms.

Hume made his argument before astronomers could measure the cosmos. He did not know his necessary condition for the natural assembly of bioforms, namely infinite time, was false. Neither did he know that suitable conditions for life chemistry have existed for only a brief portion of the universe's duration.

Hume also wrote before biologists could appreciate the incredible complexity and functionality of living organisms. Statistical mechanics tells us that if the means to preserve the initial and intermediate stages of assembly in organisms/machines are absent, then the greater the complexity and functionality of a system, the less advantageous additional time becomes for assembly by random processes (the parts wear out too soon). Moreover, assembly is not enough. Just as the assembled watch must first be wound up and the time set before it is able to function, so also something or Someone must set the assembled organism into operation.

Thanks to the invention of a new kind of microscope, Hume's claim that no strict analogy exists between a machine and an organism has been proved incorrect. For the last two decades, biochemists have possessed x-ray scanning electron microscopes so powerful they can map complex biological molecules down to the level of the individual atoms that make up the molecules.

Design that was hidden from view has now been exposed. One of the earliest molecules so mapped was the crystal structure of the F1-ATPase enzyme. The Japanese team that produced the map discovered nature's own rotary engine—no bigger than ten billionths by ten billionths by eight billionths of a meter.[6] This tiny motor includes the equivalent of an engine block, a drive shaft, and three pistons. It is a variable speed motor that runs at speeds between 0.5 and 4.0 revolutions per second.

Near the other end of the size spectrum is a map produced by a German research team of the yeast 26S proteasome molecule.[7] This molecule contains over two million protons and neutrons. Its map reveals that it serves as an intracellular waste-disposal and recycling system. Smaller molecules within the cell attach protein markers (called ubiquitin) to other protein molecules deemed waste material. (Apparently the cell's command center informs the marker molecules which proteins are ready for disposal.) Since these ready-for-disposal proteins resemble tangled balls of yarn, the first job of the 26S proteasome, after identifying a tagged protein, is to unfold, untwist, and unravel it. This function is performed by an apparatus at one end of the proteasome.

Once the targeted protein is straightened out, the proteasome slowly drags it into its core and cuts the protein into segments. These segments are precisely measured by a "ruler" inside the proteasome. The cut-up pieces are then ejected from the proteasome, and a "sanitation" fleet (other proteins) drives by to pick them up and sort them, separating the stuff that can be reused from the stuff that cannot.

To date, several hundred different biological molecules have been so mapped. Not only do biochemists now see strict analogies in these molecules to humanly designed machines, they are observing designs that are superior to our best human efforts. Nanomotors (motors that are just several billionths of a meter in diameter) designed and built by human engineers, for example, are ten times less efficient than the equivalently sized motors biochemists find in biological molecules.

The molecular biological machines biochemists have so far mapped do not work in isolation. They are strict analogies to factories. The biological machines cooperatively support one another in their tasks. Cells contain command-and-control systems that ensure each of the cell's machines operate at the just-right locations, at the just-right times, and at the just-right efficiency levels.[8] Thus, not only have all of Hume's rebuttals been refuted, Paley's design argument is now far too conservative.

The Origins Question

A major flaw in the attack by radical Darwinists on the Watchmaker argument is their failure to address the origin of life. The Darwinist mechanisms of natural selection and mutations are useless *until the first life-form is assembled.* Despite decades of intense research, origin-of-life scientists have yet to demonstrate the feasibility of any mechanism(s) assembling living organism from inorganic materials by strictly natural processes under early Earth's conditions. Here the analogy with Paley's watch remains quite close. Both have a high degree of complexity, and both move from zero functionality to complete functionality.

Another flaw is that, just like Hume, Darwin failed to understand that the geologic eras do not provide even remotely sufficient time for living organisms to change significantly by natural processes. While it is beyond dispute that life-forms have changed significantly over the course of Earth's history, only microevolutionary changes have been determined to occur by strictly natural processes.

Natural selection can move a species only a limited distance from the species' norm, and the greater the distance, the lower the probability for survival. A good example of these limitations is demonstrated in dog breeding. One cannot possibly breed a dog significantly smaller than a teacup poodle. Moreover, a teacup poodle requires an intense level of care just to survive. More tellingly, if all the dog breeds were allowed to mate with one another they would quickly revert to their wild dog ancestries.

For macroevolution to occur by strictly natural processes, multiple favorable mutations must take place simultaneously at a rate sufficient to overcome the natural extinction rate. This leads to insurmountable problems, problems I address more fully in my book *More Than a Theory*.[9]

Evolution Reversal

According to the fossil record, more and more species of life came into existence through the millennia before the appearance of modern humans. Through time, the number of species extinctions nearly balanced the number of introductions, but introductions remained slightly more numerous.

Everything changed, however, with the arrival of the human species. Since the first human being, the number of species going extinct has remained high while the number of new species appearing measures a virtual zero. Estimates of the current rate of extinction vary, from one species a day to five species an hour.[10] Though many believe that the influence of the human race is the predominant factor in that rate, environmental experts are willing to say that even if no humans existed, at least one species per year would still go extinct.[11] Meanwhile, as biologists Paul and Anne Ehrlich disclose, "The production of a new animal species in nature has yet to be documented." Furthermore, "in the vast majority of cases, the rate of change is so slow that it has not even been possible to detect an increase in the amount of differentiation."[12] Obviously, a tremendous imbalance between extinctions and speciation now exists.

The imbalance between speciation today and speciation in the fossil record era cannot be explained by radically different natural conditions. The conditions are known, and they are not significantly different. What is different is God's activity. The Bible declares that since God created Adam and Eve he has ceased from his work of creating new life-forms. But in the fossil record era (God's six days of creation), God was active in creating millions of species of life, introducing new species, and replacing and upgrading all those going extinct by natural processes.

What materialists fail to address is the reversal in the direction of biological evolution. Before humanity's appearance, life on Earth was becoming progressively complex and diverse (during God's days of creation). Since the appearance of human beings, life on Earth has become less complex and diverse (during God's seventh day of rest).

Much more could be added to the argument against the materialistic interpretation of life, such as the problems of mass extinction and mass speciation events, similarities in chemistry and form among Earth's species, the origin of sex, nonrandom mutations, results from long-term evolution experiments, missing horizontal branches in the fossil record trees, genetic decay, inconsistencies between molecular clock and fossil record dates, etc.[13] Modern research in astronomy, biology, and paleontology, far from discrediting Paley, fully exonerate him.

A Bad Design?

As for Gould's examples of bad design, three responses come to mind. First, his judging of certain biological components as bad is largely subjective. Others have disagreed with his evaluations. In particular, Peter Gordon takes issue with Gould's best-known example of the panda's thumb. Gordon argues that rather than the thumb being clumsy and jury-rigged, it is a functional, original design.[14] Gordon's conclusion has been established in a study by six Japanese biologists who used three-dimensional computed tomography and magnetic resonance imaging to demonstrate that certain bones of the giant panda's hand form a double pincer-like apparatus that allows the panda to "manipulate objects with great dexterity."[15]

Organisms are so complex that no biologist can claim to understand them completely. Thus, even biologists are in a poor position to judge the quality of the Creator's work.

Second, to believe in creation by God is not to claim that all the development in organisms is strictly divine. In addition to divine intervention, natural processes are obviously at work to change, at least to some degree, the form and function of organisms. Thus, the second law of thermodynamics, for example, would guarantee increasing degradation of the divine designs.

Third, Gould provides no new explanation for the design in the "previously existing parts." All he can muster are the already discredited Darwinist explanations.

A Better Argument

Far from being shattered, Paley's Watchmaker argument stands firm. Today it's possible to strengthen Paley's argument by looking at the whole in addition to the parts. Paley did the only thing he could do in the early 1800s: examine a tiny part of God's creation in search of evidence for him. However, that left unanswered the relationship of the whole to the parts and the parts to the whole. But these relationships can now be explored. The universe has now been measured and new understandings of the whole help us to comprehend more about the Creator.

Discussion Questions _____

1. Briefly explain the three rebuttals to Paley's Watchmaker argument given by Hume, Darwin, and Gould.
2. What are the counterarguments to these rebuttals?
3. If Paley were alive today, what evidence could he cite to buttress his Watchmaker analogy?

Chapter 15

A "Just-Right" Universe

No other generation has witnessed so many discoveries about the universe. No other generation has seen the measuring of the cosmos. For previous generations, the universe remained a profound mystery. But we are alive to see several of its mysteries solved.

Not only can we measure many characteristics of the universe throughout its history, but in these measurements we are discovering some of the attributes of the One who fashioned it all. Astronomy has provided us with new tools to probe the Creator's personality.

Building Blocks Problem

Before the measuring of the cosmos, nontheists assumed the availability of the appropriate building blocks for life. They posited that, with enough time, enough building blocks, the right natural processes, and even systems as complex as organisms could be assembled without the help of a supreme being. In chapters 4, 5, 6, 8, 9, and 10 we have seen there is not sufficient time. In this chapter we'll consider just how amazing it is that the universe provides the right building blocks and the right natural processes for life.

To put this situation in perspective, imagine the possibility of a Boeing 747 aircraft being completely assembled as a result of a tornado striking a junkyard. Now imagine how much more unlikely that possibility would be if bauxite (aluminum ore) is substituted for the junk parts. Finally, imagine the possibility if instead of bauxite, river silt is substituted. So, too, as one examines the building blocks necessary for life to come into existence, the possibility of that happening without Someone or something designing them stretches the imagination beyond the breaking point. Four major building blocks must be designed "just right" for life.

1. Getting the Right Molecules

For life to be possible, more than 40 different elements must be able to bond together to form molecules. Molecular bonding depends on two factors, the strength of the force of electromagnetism and the ratio of the electron mass to the proton mass.

If the electromagnetic force were significantly larger, atoms would hang on to electrons so tightly that no sharing of electrons with other atoms would be possible. But if the electromagnetic force were significantly weaker, atoms would not hang on to electrons at all, and again, the sharing of electrons among atoms, which makes molecules possible, would not take place. If more than just a few kinds of molecules are to exist, the electromagnetic force must be more delicately balanced yet.

The size and stability of electron orbits around the nuclei of atoms depend on the ratio of the electron mass to the proton mass. Unless this ratio is delicately balanced, the chemical bonding essential for life chemistry could never take place.

2. Getting the Right Atoms

Life molecules cannot result unless sufficient quantities of the elements essential for life are available, which means atoms of various sizes must be able to form. For that to happen, a delicate balance must exist among the constants of physics that govern the strong and weak nuclear forces, gravity, and the nuclear ground state energies (quantum energy levels important for the forming of elements from protons and neutrons) for several key elements.

In the case of the strong nuclear force—the force governing the degree to which protons and neutrons stick together in atomic nuclei—the balance is easy to see. If this force were too weak, multi-proton nuclei would not hold together. In that case, hydrogen would be the only element in the universe. On the other hand, if the strong nuclear force were of slightly greater strength than what we observe in the cosmos, protons and neutrons would have such an affinity for one another that not one would remain alone. They would all find themselves attached to many other protons and neutrons. In such a universe there would be no hydrogen, only heavy elements. Life chemistry is impossible without hydrogen; it is also impossible if hydrogen is the only element.

How delicate is the balance for the strong nuclear force? If the strong nuclear force were just 4% stronger, the diproton (an atom with two protons and no neutrons) would form. Diprotons would cause stars to so rapidly exhaust their nuclear fuel as to make any kind of physical life impossible. On the other hand, if the strong nuclear force were just 10% weaker, carbon, oxygen, and nitrogen would be unstable and again physical life would be impossible.[1]

Does this just apply to life as we know it? No, this holds true for any conceivable kind of life chemistry throughout the cosmos. This delicate condition must be met universally.

The strong nuclear force is both the strongest attractive force in nature and the strongest repulsive force in nature. The fact that it is attractive on one length scale and repulsive on a different length scale makes it highly unusual and counterintuitive. Nevertheless, without these weird properties, life would be impossible.

For life to be possible, it is critical that the strong nuclear force be attractive only over lengths no greater than 2.0 fermis and no less than 0.7 fermis (one fermi = a quadrillionth of a meter) and manifest the greatest attractive force at about 0.9 fermis.[2] At lengths shorter than 0.7 fermis, it is essential that the strong nuclear force be strongly repulsive. The reason is that protons and neutrons are packages of more fundamental particles called quarks and gluons. Each proton is a package made up of two up quarks and one down quark plus the relevant gluons, while each neutron contains two down quarks and one up quark with their relevant gluons. If the strong nuclear force were not strongly repulsive on length scales below 0.7 fermis, the proton and neutron packages of quarks and gluons would merge. Such mergers would mean no atoms, no molecules, and no chemistry would ever be possible anywhere or any time in the universe. As with the attractive effect of the strong nuclear force, the repulsive effect must be exquisitely fine-tuned, both in its length range of operation and the strength level of the repulsion.

In the case of the weak nuclear force—the force that governs, among other things, the rates of radioactive decay—if it were much stronger than what we observe, then the universe's matter would quickly be converted into heavy elements. But if it were much weaker, then the universe's matter would remain in the form of just the lightest elements. Either way, life-essential elements (such as carbon, oxygen, nitrogen, phosphorus) would either not exist at all or exist in amounts far too small for all the life-essential molecules to be built. Further, unless the weak nuclear force were delicately fine-tuned (to better than one part in ten thousand), those life-essential elements that are produced only in the cores of supergiant stars would never escape the boundaries of those cores (supernova explosions would become impossible).[3]

The strength of gravity's force determines how hot the nuclear furnaces in the cores of stars will burn. If the gravitational force were any stronger, stars would be so hot they would burn up relatively quickly—too quickly and too erratically for life. Additionally, a planet capable of sustaining life must be supported by a star that is both stable and long burning. However, if the gravitational force were any weaker, stars never would become hot enough to ignite nuclear fusion. In such a universe no elements heavier than hydrogen and helium would be produced.

In the late 1970s and early 1980s, Fred Hoyle discovered that an incredible fine-tuning of the nuclear ground state energies for helium, beryllium, carbon, and oxygen was necessary for any kind of life to exist. The ground state energies for these elements cannot be higher or lower with respect to each other by more than 4% without yielding a universe containing insufficient oxygen or carbon for life.[4] Hoyle, who has written extensively against theism[5] and Christianity in particular,[6] nevertheless concluded on the basis of this quadruple fine-tuning that "a superintellect has monkeyed with physics, as well as with chemistry and biology."[7]

In 2000, a team of astrophysicists from Austria, Germany, and Hungary demonstrated that the level of design for electromagnetism and the strong nuclear force is much greater than what physicists previously had determined.[8] The team began by noting that for any kind of conceivable physical life to be possible in the universe, certain minimum abundances of both the elements carbon and oxygen must exist. Next, they pointed out that the only astrophysical sources of significant quantities of carbon and oxygen are red giant stars. (Red giant stars are large stars that, through nuclear fusion, have consumed all their hydrogen fuel and subsequently fuse helium into heavier elements.)

The astrophysical team mathematically constructed models of red giant stars that adopted slightly different values of the strong nuclear force and electromagnetic force constants. They discovered that tiny adjustments in the values of either of these constants imply that red giant stars would produce too little carbon, too little oxygen, or too little of both oxygen and carbon. Specifically, they determined that if the value of the coupling constant for electromagnetism were 4% smaller or 4% larger than what we observe, then life would be impossible. In the case of the coupling constant for the strong nuclear force, if it were 0.5% smaller or larger, then life would be impossible.

These new limits on the strengths of the electromagnetic and strong nuclear forces provide much tighter constraints on quark masses and on the Higgs vacuum expectation value.[9] Without getting into the details of what quarks and the Higgs vacuum expectation value are all about, the new limits not only demonstrate an enhanced design for the physics of stars and planets but also an enhanced mathematical design of fundamental particle physics.

3. Getting the Right Nucleons

One must monkey with the physics of the universe to get enough of the right elements for life, and furthermore to get those elements to join together to form life molecules. One must also fine-tune the universe to get enough nucleons (protons and neutrons) to form the elements.

In the first moments after creation, the universe contained about 10 billion and 1 nucleons for every 10 billion antinucleons. The 10 billion antinucleons annihilated the 10 billion nucleons, generating an enormous amount of energy. All the galaxies and stars that make up the universe today were formed from the leftover nucleons. If the initial excess of nucleons over antinucleons were any less, there would not be enough matter for galaxies, stars, and heavy elements to form. If the excess were any greater, galaxies would form, but they would so efficiently condense and trap radiation that none of them would fragment to form stars and planets.

The neutron is 0.138% more massive than a proton. Because of this extra mass, neutrons require slightly more energy to make than protons. So as the universe cooled from the hot big bang creation event, it produced more protons than neutrons—in fact, about seven times as many.

If the neutron were just another 0.1% more massive, so few neutrons would remain from the cooling off of the big bang that there would not be enough of them to make the nuclei of all the life-essential heavy elements. The extra mass of the neutron relative to the proton also determines the rate at which neutrons decay into protons and protons build into neutrons (one neutron decays into one proton + one electron + one neutrino). If the neutron were 0.1% less massive, so many protons would be built up to make neutrons that all the stars in the universe would have rapidly collapsed into either neutron stars or black holes.[10] Thus for life to be possible in the universe, the neutron mass must be fine-tuned to better than 0.1%.

Another decay process involving protons must also be fine-tuned for life to exist. Protons are believed to decay into mesons (a type of fundamental particle). I say "believed to" because the decay rate is so slow that experimenters have yet to record a single decay event (average decay time for a single proton exceeds 4×10^{32} years, more than a billion trillion times the current age of the universe).

Nevertheless, theoreticians are convinced that protons must decay into mesons, and at a rate fairly close to the current experimental limits. Why? If protons decay any slower into mesons, the universe of today would not have enough nucleons to make the necessary galaxies, stars, and planets.[11] This is because the factors that determine this decay rate also determine the ratio of nucleons to antinucleons at the time of the creation event. Thus, if the decay rate were slower, the number of nucleons would have been too closely balanced by the number of antinucleons, which would have left too few nucleons after annihilation.

If, however, the decay rate of protons into mesons were faster, in addition to the problem of a too large ratio of nucleons to antinucleons, there would be a problem of maintaining life. Because a tremendous amount of energy is released in this particular decay process, the decay rate would destroy or harm life. Thus, the decay rate cannot be any greater than it is.

4. Getting the Right Electrons

Not only must the universe be fine-tuned to get enough nucleons, but a precise number of electrons must also exist. Unless the number of electrons is equivalent to the number of protons to an accuracy of one part in 10^{37} or better, electromagnetic forces in the universe would have overcome gravitational forces so that galaxies, stars, and planets never would have formed.

One part in 10^{37} is such an incredibly sensitive balance that it is hard to visualize. The following analogy might help: Cover the entire North American continent in dimes all the way up to the Moon, a height of about 239,000 miles. (In comparison, the money to pay for the US federal government debt would cover one square mile less than twenty feet deep with dimes.) Next, pile dimes from here to the Moon on a million other continents the same size as North America. Paint one dime red and mix it into the piles of dimes reaching to the Moon. Blindfold a friend and ask him to pick out one dime. The odds that he will pick the red dime are one in 10^{37}. And this is only one of the parameters so delicately balanced to allow life to form.

At whatever level we examine the building blocks of life—electrons, nucleons, atoms, or molecules—the physics of the universe must be meticulously fine-tuned. The universe must be exactly constructed to create the necessary electrons. It must be exquisitely crafted to produce the protons and neutrons required. It must be carefully fabricated to obtain the needed atoms. Unless it is skillfully fashioned, the atoms will not be able to assemble into complex enough molecules. Such precise balancing of all these factors is truly beyond our ability to comprehend. Yet with the measuring of the universe, even more astounding facts become apparent.

Cosmic Expansion

The first parameter of the universe to be measured was the universe's expansion rate. In comparing this rate to the physics of galaxy and star formation, astrophysicists found something amazing. If the universe expanded too rapidly, matter would disperse so efficiently that none of it would clump enough to form galaxies. If no galaxies form, no stars will form. If no stars form, no planets will form. If no planets form, there's no place for life. On the other hand, if the universe expanded too slowly, matter would clump so effectively that all of it, the whole universe in fact, would collapse into a super-dense lump before any solar-type stars could form.

The creation event itself imbues the universe with a certain rate of expansion. Subsequent to the creation event, the cosmic mass density and dark energy density modify the universe's expansion velocity in different ways. As described in chapter 5, for the universe to produce all the stars and planets necessary to explain the possibility of Earth sustaining physical life, the value of the cosmic mass density must be exquisitely fine-tuned. The dark energy density must be even more spectacularly fine-tuned. The original source or sources of dark energy must be at least 122 orders of magnitude larger than the amount astronomers now detect. This implies that somehow the source(s) must cancel one another so as to leave just one part in 10^{122}.[12]

As Lawrence Krauss and many other astrophysicists noted, this one part in 10^{122} is by far the most extreme fine-tuning yet discovered in physics.[13] An analogy that does not even come close to describing the precarious nature of this cosmic balance would be a billion pencils all simultaneously positioned upright on their sharpened points on a smooth glass surface with no vertical supports.

Relativity, Quantum Uncertainty, and Dimensionality

In addition to requiring exquisite fine-tuning of the forces and constants of physics, the existence of life demands still more. It demands that the fundamental particles, the energy, and the space-time dimensions of the universe enable the principles of quantum tunneling and special relativity to operate exactly as they do. Quantum tunneling must function no more or less efficiently than what we observe for hemoglobin to transport the right amount of oxygen to the cells of all vertebrate and most invertebrate species.[14] Likewise, relativistic corrections, not too great and not too small, are essential for copper and vanadium to fulfill their critical roles in the functioning of the nervous system and bone development of all the higher animals.[15]

For quantum tunneling to operate so that hemoglobin functions properly, the uncertainty in the Heisenberg uncertainty principle must be fine-tuned. The uncertainty we observe is very large. When scientists measure the momentum of a particle with the greatest precision currently possible, the position of the particle is now known to only about ± a third of a mile. However, if the uncertainty in the position becomes much greater or smaller than half a mile, hemoglobin will not function as it does and advanced life becomes impossible. (There are other life-essential proteins like hemoglobin that depend on fine-tuned quantum tunneling.[16]) Counter to Einstein's famous quote that "God does not play dice," this evidence demonstrates that, given God's goals, God must play dice, but he has exquisitely designed the dice for the benefit of physical life.

For relativity to operate so that certain proteins containing copper and vanadium will adequately support life means that the velocity of light must be fine-tuned. This is not the only reason why the velocity of light must be held constant and fixed at the value of 299,792.458 kilometers per second. Because of Einstein's equation, $E = mc^2$, even small changes in c (the velocity of light) lead to huge changes in E (the energy) or m (the mass). Thus, a slight change in light's velocity implies that starlight will either be too strong or too feeble for life, or that stars will produce the wrong elements for life.

As explained in chapter 4, stable orbits of planets about stars and of electrons about the nuclei of atoms are possible only in a universe described by three large and rapidly expanding dimensions of space. In addition, six extremely tiny space dimensions that are presently dormant but actively expanded during the first 10^{-43} seconds of the universe's history may be critical for quantum mechanics and gravity to coexist.[17] Therefore, physical life may require a different fine-tuning of the number of effective dimensions both in the present (namely four—three space plus one time) and possibly in the earliest moment of the universe's existence (namely ten—nine space plus one time).

Measuring the Universe's Age

The second parameter of the universe to be measured was its age. For many decades astronomers and others have wondered why God, assuming he exists, would wait billions of years to make life. Why did he not do it right away? Part of the answer is that, given the laws and constants of physics God chose to create, it takes billions of years just to fuse enough heavy elements in the nuclear furnaces of giant stars to make life chemistry possible.

Life could not happen any earlier in the universe than it did on Earth. Nor could it happen much later. As the universe ages, stars like the Sun—located in the right part of the galaxy for life (see ch. 17) and in a stable nuclear burning phase—become increasingly rare. If the universe were just a few billion years older, such stars would no longer exist.

A third measured parameter I have already discussed to some extent is entropy, or energy degradation. In chapter 4, I explained the evidence for the universe possessing an extreme amount of specific entropy. This high level of entropy is essential for life. Without it, systems as small as stars and planets would never form. But as extremely high as the entropy of the universe is, it could not be much higher. If it were higher, systems as large as galaxies would never form. Without galaxies, stars and planets cannot form.

Star Masses

A fourth measured parameter, another very sensitive one, is the ratio of the electromagnetic force constant to the gravitational force constant. If the electromagnetic force relative to gravity were increased by just one part in 10^{40}, the full range of small star sizes and types needed to make life possible would not form. And, if it were decreased by just one part in 10^{40}, the full range of large star sizes and types needed to make life possible would not form. For life to be possible in the universe, the full range of both large and small star sizes and types must exist. Large stars must exist because only their thermonuclear furnaces produce most of the life-essential elements. Small stars like the Sun must exist because only small stars burn long enough and stably enough to sustain a planet with life.[18]

Considering again the piles of dimes, one part in 10^{40} looks like this: a blindfolded person rummages through a billion sets of piles of dimes, each set are dimes as densely packed together as possible covering an area the size of North America and reaching as high as the Moon. Just one of the dimes is colored red. One part in 10^{40} is equivalent to the blindfolded person picking out the one red dime on the first try.

In the late 1980s and early 1990s, several other characteristics of the universe were measured successfully. Each of these, too, indicated a careful fine-tuning for the support of life. Currently, researchers have uncovered 140 characteristics that must take on narrowly defined values for life of any kind to possibly exist.[19] For readers wanting more than just the highlight reel of cosmic fine-tuning presented in these past few pages, they will find a list of 60 of these characteristics and the reasons they must be so narrowly defined in appendix A. A more complete list is available at reasons.org/finetuning.

Table 15.1: Cosmic Design Needed for Simple Life

In surveying the scientific literature over an 18-year time period, the scientific team at Reasons to Believe has demonstrated that the more astronomers and physicists learn about the universe, the more features of the universe and the laws of physics must be fine-tuned to make the existence of microbial life possible somewhere within the universe. A list of the specific fine-tuned features and scientific literature citations is available at reasons.org/finetuning.

survey date[20]	number of known fine-tuned features
1989	15
1991	17
1995	26
2001	35
2004	86
2006	140

The list of characteristics of the universe that must be finely tuned for life to be possible continues to grow. The more accurately and extensively astronomers measure the universe, the more finely tuned they discover it to be (see table 15.1). Also, as we have seen for many of the already measured characteristics, the degree of fine-tuning is utterly amazing—far beyond what human endeavors can accomplish.

For example, arguably the best machine built by man is the LIGO (Laser Interferometer Gravitational-Wave Observatory) instrument, a gravity wave detector engineered by California and Massachusetts Institutes of Technology physicists. It makes measurements accurate to one part in 10^{23}. By comparison, at least four different characteristics of the universe must be fine-tuned to better than one part in 10^{37} for physical life of any kind to exist (for comment on why life must be carbon-based, see "Another Kind of Life" on p. 208). My point is that the Entity who brought the universe into existence must be a personal Being, for only a person can design with anywhere near this degree of precision. Consider, too, that this personal Entity must be at least a hundred trillion times more "capable" than human beings.

God and the Astronomers
The discovery of this degree of design in the universe is having a profound

theological impact on astronomers. As we noted already, Hoyle concluded that "a superintellect has monkeyed with physics, as well as with chemistry and biology."[21] Hoyle also wrote,

> I do not believe that any scientist who examined the evidence would fail to draw the inference that the laws of nuclear physics have been deliberately designed.[22]

Davies has moved from promoting atheism[23] to conceding that "the laws [of physics] . . . seem themselves to be the product of exceedingly ingenious design."[24] He further testifies:

> [There] is for me powerful evidence that there is 'something going on' behind it all. The impression of design is overwhelming.[25]

> It seems as though somebody has fine-tuned nature's numbers to make the Universe.[26]

Astronomer George Greenstein, in his book *The Symbiotic Universe*, expressed these thoughts:

> As we survey all the evidence, the thought insistently arises that some supernatural agency—or, rather, Agency—must be involved. Is it possible that suddenly, without intending to, we have stumbled upon scientific proof of the existence of a Supreme Being? Was it God who stepped in and so providentially crafted the cosmos for our benefit?[27]

Theoretical physicist Tony Rothman in a popular-level article on the anthropic principle (the idea that the universe possesses narrowly defined characteristics that permit the possibility of a habitat for humans) concluded his essay with these words:

> The medieval theologian who gazed at the night sky through the eyes of Aristotle and saw angels moving the spheres in harmony has become the modern cosmologist who gazes at the same sky through the eyes of Einstein and sees the hand of

God not in angels but in the constants of nature. . . . When confronted with the order and beauty of the universe and the strange coincidences of nature, it's very tempting to take the leap of faith from science into religion. I am sure many physicists want to. I only wish they would admit it.[28]

In a review article on the anthropic principle published in the journal *Nature*, cosmologists Bernard Carr and Martin Rees state in their summary: "Nature does exhibit remarkable coincidences and these do warrant some explanation."[29] In a later article on the anthropic principle, Carr continued:

One would have to conclude either that the features of the universe invoked in support of the Anthropic Principle are only coincidences or that the universe was indeed tailor-made for life. I will leave it to the theologians to ascertain the identity of the tailor![30]

Physicist Freeman Dyson, in two books, concluded his treatments of the anthropic principle with,

The problem here is to try to formulate some statement of the ultimate purpose of the universe. In other words, the problem is to read the mind of God.[31]

I do not feel like an alien in this universe. The more I examine the universe and study the details of its architecture, the more evidence I find that the universe in some sense must have known that we were coming.[32]

Vera Kistiakowsky, professor emerita at MIT and past president of the Association of Women in Science, commented, "The exquisite order displayed by our scientific understanding of the physical world calls for the divine."[33] Arno Penzias, who shared the Nobel Prize for Physics for the discovery of the cosmic background radiation, remarked:

Astronomy leads us to a unique event, a universe which was created out of nothing, one with the very delicate balance needed to provide exactly the conditions required to permit life, and one which has an underlying (one might say "super-natural") plan.[34]

Years before communism's fall, Alexander Polyakov, a theoretician and fellow at Moscow's Landau Institute, declared:

We know that nature is described by the best of all possible mathematics because God created it. So there is a chance that the best of all possible mathematics will be created out of physicists' attempts to describe nature.[35]

China's famed astrophysicist Fang Lizhi and his coauthor, physicist Li Shuxian, recently wrote, "A question that has always been considered a topic of metaphysics or theology—the creation of the universe—has now become an area of active research in physics."[36]

In *A Brief History of Time* (the 1991 documentary about Stephen Hawking), Hawking's colleague and distinguished mathematician Roger Penrose commented, "I would say the universe has a purpose. It's not there just somehow by chance."[37] Hawking and Penrose's colleague George Ellis made the following statement in a paper delivered at the Second Venice Conference on Cosmology and Philosophy:

Amazing fine-tuning occurs in the laws that make this [complexity] possible. Realization of the complexity of what is accomplished makes it very difficult not to use the word "miraculous" without taking a stand as to the ontological status of that word.[38]

Stephen Hawking himself conceded:

It would be very difficult to explain why the universe should have begun in just this way, except as the act of a God who intended to create beings like us.[39]

Cosmologist Edward Harrison makes this deduction:

Here is the cosmological proof of the existence of God—the design argument of Paley—updated and refurbished. The fine-tuning of the universe provides prima facie evidence of deistic design. Take your choice: blind chance that requires multitudes of universes or design that requires only one. . . . Many scientists, when they admit their views, incline toward the teleological or design argument.[40]

Allan Sandage, winner of the Crafoord Prize in astronomy (equivalent to the Nobel Prize), remarked, "I find it quite improbable that such order came out of chaos. There has to be some organizing principle. God to me is a mystery but is the explanation for the miracle of existence, why there is something instead of nothing."[41] Robert Griffiths, who won the Dannie Heineman Prize for Mathematical Physics, observed, "If we need an atheist for a debate, I go to the philosophy department. The physics department isn't much use."[42] Perhaps astrophysicist Robert Jastrow, a self-proclaimed agnostic,[43] best described what has happened to his colleagues as they have measured the cosmos:

> For the scientist who has lived by his faith in the power of reason, the story ends like a bad dream. He has scaled the mountains of ignorance; he is about to conquer the highest peak; as he pulls himself over the final rock, he is greeted by a band of theologians who have been sitting there for centuries.[44]

In all my conversations with those researching the characteristics of the universe, and in all my readings of articles or books on the subject, not one person denies the conclusion that the cosmos appears to have been crafted to make it a fit habitat for life. Astronomers by nature tend to be independent and iconoclastic. If an opportunity for disagreement exists, they will seize it. But on the issue of the apparent fine-tuning of the cosmos for the benefit of life, and human beings in particular, the evidence is so compelling that I have yet to hear of any dissent.

Creator's Personality
Does the fine-tuning imply purposeful design? So many parameters must be fine-tuned and the degree of fine-tuning is so high, no other conclusion seems possible.

As Harrison pointed out, the evidence permits only two options: divine design or blind chance. Blind chance, as we saw in chapter 13 is problematic since conclusions based on chance should be derived from known, not hypothetical, sample sizes. The known sample size for the universe(s) is (and will always be) one since the space-time manifold for the universe is closed (meaning we cannot, even in principle, ever discover anything about other universes possibly existing).

Much more is going on, however, than mere talk by astronomers about cosmic design for sustenance of life. Words such as *somebody fine-tuned nature, superintellect, monkeyed, deliberately designed, overwhelming design, miraculous, hand of God, ultimate purpose, God's mind, exquisite order, very delicate balance, exceedingly ingenious, supernatural Agency, supernatural plan, tailormade, Supreme Being, and providentially crafted* obviously apply to a Person. Beyond just establishing that the Creator is a Person, the findings about design provide some evidence of what that Person is like.

One characteristic that stands out dramatically is his interest in and care for living things, particularly for human beings. We see this care in the vastness and quality of the resources devoted to allowing diverse life to exist and thrive .

For example, the baryon density (i.e., density of neutrons and protons) of the universe, as huge as it is, focuses on the needs of humans. How? The baryon density determines how efficiently nuclear fusion operates in the cosmos. The baryon density we measure translates into about a hundred-billion-trillion stars for the observable universe. As appendix A indicates, if the baryon density is too great, too much deuterium (an isotope of hydrogen with one proton and one neutron in the nucleus) is made in the first few minutes of the universe's existence. This extra deuterium will cause the stars to burn much too quickly and erratically for any of them to support a planet with life. On the other hand, if the baryon density is too small, so little deuterium and helium are made in the first few minutes that the heavier elements necessary for life will never form in stars.

What this means is that the approximately hundred-billion-trillion stars we observe in the universe—no more and no less—are needed for life to be possible in the universe. God invested heavily in living creatures. He constructed all these stars and carefully crafted them throughout the age of the universe so that at this brief moment in cosmic history humans could exist, have a pleasant place to live, and fulfill the purpose for which they were created.

Nontheistic Responses

When it comes to the finely tuned characteristics of the universe, nontheists find themselves in a difficult spot. The evidence is too weighty and concrete to brush aside. The evidence is inanimate. So, appeals to Darwinist hypotheses cannot be made. Appeals to near infinite time are thwarted by the proofs that the universe arose from an infinitesimally small volume only several billion years ago. The following five arguments seem to cover the range of nontheistic replies to the evidence for cosmic design that were not already addressed in chapter 13.

Argument 1: We would not be here to observe the universe unless the extremely unlikely did take place.

The evidence for design is merely coincidental. Our existence simply testifies that the extremely unlikely did, indeed, take place by chance. In other words, we would not be here to report on the characteristics of the universe unless chance produced these highly unlikely properties.

Rebuttal: This argument is fundamentally an appeal to infinite chances, which has already been answered (see ch. 13). Another response has been developed by philosopher Richard Swinburne[45] and summarized by another philosopher, William Lane Craig:

> Suppose a hundred sharpshooters are sent to execute a prisoner by firing squad and the prisoner survives. The prisoner should not be surprised that he does not observe that he is dead. After all, if he were dead, he could not observe his death. Nonetheless, he should be surprised that he observes that he is alive.[46]

To extend Craig and Swinburne's argument, the prisoner could conclude, since he is alive, that all the sharpshooters missed by some extremely unlikely chance. He may wish to attribute his survival to an incredible bit of good luck, but he would be far more rational to conclude that the guns were loaded with blanks or that the sharpshooters all deliberately missed. Someone must have purposed he should live. Likewise, the rational conclusion to draw from the incredible fine-tuning of the universe is that Someone purposed we should live.

Argument 2: The design of the universe is mere anthropomorphism.

Astrophysicist Joseph Silk, in an effort to communicate the physics of big bang cosmology to laypeople, mocks the conclusion that the universe has been fine-tuned for the support of life. He compares the "silliness" of the design idea with the folly of a flea's assumption that the dog on which it feeds has been designed precisely for its benefit. The flea's error, he suggests, becomes all too apparent once the dog is outfitted with a flea collar.[47]

Rebuttal: Silk's argument ignores some key issues. While the flea may be a little self-centered in assuming the dog was designed exclusively for it, there's no reason to deny that the dog was designed for a purpose, or for several purposes. (The myth that life is strictly the product of accidental natural processes is addressed in a full-length book I coauthored with biochemist Fazale Rana.[48]) The flea collar analogy may argue more strongly for design (e.g., population control) than for lack of it. More importantly, while we can imagine a wide range of hosts suitable for the support of the flea, each of them requires elements of design to facilitate the flea's survival. Though suitable hosts for the flea are relatively abundant, suitable universes for life are not. Astrophysicists have been unable to invent hypothetical universes significantly different from ours that could support human beings or, for that matter, any conceivable kind of physical, intelligent life.

Argument 3: Design arguments are outside the realm of science and, therefore, must be ignored.

The publications of the National Center for Science Education, among other similar groups, repeatedly assert that science is "empirically based and necessarily materialist; miracles cannot be allowed," and that "any theory with a supernatural foundation is not scientific."[49] Since the design arguments imply supernatural intervention, they can be justifiably ignored because they "cannot be considered scientific."[50]

Rebuttal: To affirm that science and theology are mutually exclusive may be convenient for materialists unwilling to defend their philosophy, but it is untenable. Science is rarely religiously neutral. Similarly, religious faith is rarely scientifically neutral. Both science and theology frequently address cause-and-effect dynamics and developmental processes in the natural realm. Both science and theology deal with the origin of the universe, the solar system, life, and humankind.

When it comes to causes, developmental processes, and origins, two possibilities always exist: natural or supernatural. To dogmatically insist that supernatural answers must never be considered is equivalent to demanding that all human beings follow only one religion, the religion of atheistic materialism. I find it ironic that in the name of religious freedom certain science education proponents insist on ridding our teaching and research institutions of any faith or worldview that dares to compete with their own.

Argument 4: Order can come out of chaos.

The idea that, under strictly natural conditions, order can and will arise out of chaos was first proposed by David Hume nearly 200 years ago. Hume made the claim without any evidential support. Recently, it has been revived by chemist and Nobel Laureate Ilya Prigogine in his book *Order Out of Chaos*.[51] Prigogine pointed to several chemical reactions in which order appears to arise from chaotic systems.

Rebuttal: The presumption of a natural self-ordering principle in chaotic systems arises from the fact that the more complex a system is, the greater the opportunity for departures from thermodynamic equilibrium in small portions of the system (and the greater the difficulty in determining what the thermodynamic equilibrium states actually are). According to the second law of thermodynamics, entropy increases in all systems, but entropy can decrease (i.e., order can increase) in part of a system, providing that an extra increase of entropy (i.e., disorder) occurs in a different part of the system. Because human investigators may be prone to underestimate the complexity of some systems, they occasionally are surprised by how far a small portion of a system can stray from thermodynamic equilibrium. However, the thermodynamic laws predict that these departures are temporary, and the greater the departure, the more rapidly the departures are corrected.

Without departures from thermodynamic equilibrium, raindrops and snowflakes, for example, would not form. But, raindrop and snowflake formation comes close to the self-ordering limits of natural process. Though snowflake patterns exhibit a high degree of order, their information content or level of design complexity remains very low. The distinction is roughly like the difference between the New Testament and a book containing the sentence "God is good" repeated 90,000 times. The latter shows considerable order but not much information. The former contains both a high degree of order and a high degree of information (or design). Prigogine's examples exhibit increases in order, but without significant increases in information content. Natural processes cannot explain the exceptionally high level of design complexity and information content in living organisms or in the structure of the universe that makes life possible.

Argument 5: As we continue to evolve, we will become the Creator-Designer.

In their book *The Anthropic Cosmological Principle*, astrophysicists John Barrow and Frank Tipler reviewed many new evidences for the design of the universe.[52] They went on to discuss versions of the anthropic principle like weak anthropic principle (conscious beings can only exist in an environment with characteristics that allow for their habitation), strong anthropic principle (nature must take on those characteristics to admit somewhere, sometime the existence of conscious beings), and more radical versions, including participatory anthropic principle (conscious observers are necessary to bring the universe into existence, and the universe is necessary to bring observers into existence). But what they favored was the final anthropic principle.

With final anthropic principle, the life that exists (past, present, and future) will continue to evolve with the inanimate resources of the universe until it all reaches a state that Barrow and Tipler call the "Omega Point."[53] This Omega Point, they say, is an Entity that has the properties of omnipotence, omnipresence, and omniscience, with the capacity to create in the past.[54] In other words, the Creator-God does not exist yet, but we (all life and all inanimate structures in the universe) are gradually evolving into God. When God is thus finally constructed, his power will be such that he can create the entire universe with all its characteristics of design billions of years ago.

In a later book, *The Physics of Immortality*,[55] Tipler proposed that evolution toward the Omega Point will occur through advancing computer technology. His idea leans on Moore's doubling-time law, which basically says that computer complexity and capability doubles every two years, while technological casing sizes shrink. By extrapolating this computer capability doubling time (currently, about eighteen months) some millions of years into the future, Tipler predicted that a future generation of human beings will be able not only to alter the entire universe and all the laws of physics but also to create a God who does not yet exist. Furthermore, we will be able to resurrect every human being who has ever lived by recovering the memories that once resided in each person's brain.

Rebuttal: It is hard to treat these final anthropic principle and Omega Point hypotheses seriously. In the *New York Review of Books*, noted critic Martin Gardner offered this evaluation of Barrow and Tipler's work:

> What should we make of this quartet of WAP, SAP, PAP, and FAP [anthropic principle hypothesis]? In my not so humble opinion I think the last principle is best called CRAP, the Completely Ridiculous Anthropic Principle.[56]

In *The Physics of Immortality*, Tipler grossly overestimated the role of human memory and the future capability of computers. Just as computers cannot function with memory banks only, so, too, the human mind and human consciousness do not operate by memory alone. While remarkable advances in computer technology are taking place now, the laws of physics impose predictable finite limits on future computer hardware. As Roger Penrose documented rigorously in *The Emperor's New Mind* and *Shadows of the Mind*, these limits do not even permit the duplication of human consciousness let alone the fantastic capabilities Tipler suggested.[57]

The cosmic model on which Tipler's whole premise rested is now out of date. It depends on the universe possessing enough matter to force the universe into a future stage of collapse. But, as we noted in chapter 5, measurements made in 1999 and 2000 establish that only three-tenths of the mass necessary to force a future collapse of the universe exists. Moreover, the measured value for the dark energy density term guarantees that the universe not only will expand forever, but also expand at an exponentially increasing rate.

But Tipler apparently wanted to alter much more than just the universe and the laws of physics. He believed, for example, that future computers will be able to expose people to game theory principles so effectively that all destructive thoughts and actions will be purged and villainy no longer occur, even for the likes of Adolf Hitler and Mata Hari.[58] In Tipler's religion at that time, the redemptive work of a Savior becomes unnecessary. Consider, however, that if Tipler's proposal were true, the better people comprehend game theory, the less propensity they would exhibit to commit evil. Unfortunately for Tipler, no such correlation is in evidence.

Tipler at that time not only banished hell but also redesigned heaven. Tipler's "heaven" would bring relational (more accurately, sexual) bliss to every man and woman. He produced an equation to "prove" that this computer-generated cosmic utopia would bring a woman to every man and a man to every woman, and be capable of delivering 100,000 times the joy and satisfaction of the most fulfilling partner each can imagine.[59] The popular appeal of such a notion documents the spiritual bankruptcy of our times. Evidently, many people have never tasted any greater delight than what sexual experience can bring.

In an article for the *Skeptical Inquirer*, Gardner again brandished his satiric knives:

> I leave it to the reader to decide whether they should opt for
> OPT (Omega Point Theology) as a new scientific religion superior to Scientology—one destined to elevate Tipler to the
> rank of a prophet greater than L. Ron Hubbard—or opt for

the view that OPT is a wild fantasy generated by too much reading of science fiction.[60]

To his credit, Frank Tipler has come to his senses. He has converted to Christianity. In 2007, he published his book *The Physics of Christianity*.[61]

In their persistent rejection of an eternal, transcendent Creator, some cosmologists (and others) are resorting to increasingly irrational options. There is a certain logic to it, however. If for personal or moral reasons the God of the Bible is unacceptable, then given all the evidence for transcendence and design, the alternatives are limited to flights of fancy.

Through time, as we unlock more of the secrets of the vast cosmos, men and women will be even more awed about how exquisitely designed the universe is. But where will that awe be aimed—at the created thing, or at the Creator? That is each person's choice.

 Discussion Questions _____

1. Do you find arguments for the extreme rarity of getting the right molecules, atoms, nucleons, and electrons in our universe persuasive? How can these types of evidences best be used?
2. If the universe's expansion rate is "by far the most extreme fine-tuning yet discovered in physics," why haven't all scientists accepted the same implications as the author?
3. With so many quotes from scientists affirming the anthropic principle, does it appear that a buildup of evidence in support of the universe's creation is winning the day? Why or why not?
4. All 60 fine-tuned parameters listed in Appendix A have been carefully crafted for our personal benefit and the purpose for which we were created. How does this strike you?
5. Describe the five nontheistic responses to cosmic fine-tuning arguments. What are the rebuttals?
6. Discuss astrophysicist Frank Tipler's bizarre proposal and change of heart.

Chapter 16

Responding to Nonempirical, Nontheistic Creation Models

Christian apologetics is typically perceived as the endeavor of refuting nonbelievers' arguments for God's nonexistence or nonoperation. There certainly is a place for refuting such arguments. For example, Paul in 2 Corinthians 10:5 says, "We demolish arguments and every pretension that sets itself up against the knowledge of God, and we take captive every thought to make it obedient to Christ." However, the biblical passage agreed by virtually all Bible scholars to be the marching orders for Christian witness exhorts all Christians to "always be prepared to give an answer to everyone who asks you to give the reason for the hope that you have. But do this with gentleness and respect, keeping a clear conscience."[1] This passage implies that Christians are to make the case for their Christian faith based on evidence and reason. Likewise, Christians should refute the arguments nonbelievers raise against God's existence with evidence and reason.

Nonempirical Appeals for Atheism

Today, the physical and historical evidence for the existence of the God of the Bible is so extensive and compelling that nonbelieving skeptics are increasingly resorting to nonempirical arguments to defend their unbelief. That is, they speculate about what we do not yet know or cannot possibly know about the universe and life to hypothesize that some exotic physics or biology might allow one to conceive of the universe and life existing apart from God. Others appeal to circular reasoning to defend a nontheistic worldview.

Appeal to the Unknown

An example of an appeal to the unknown are frequent attempts by nontheistic physicists and astronomers to point out that since we humans are ignorant, and always will be ignorant, about at least some of the conditions of the physical state of the universe between the moment of cosmic creation and 10^{-35} seconds after the cosmic creation event, it may be possible that during that tiny epoch of time physics operates very differently from what we see and measure. They presume or hope that the laws of physics and the cosmic physical state operated so differently during that tiny epoch that there really is not a cosmic beginning. If there is no cosmic beginning, they assert, then maybe there is no cosmic Beginner either.

As I explained in chapters 9–10 astronomers have found a way to observationally penetrate the conditions of the universe previous to 10^{-35} seconds, even previous to 10^{-43} seconds, after the big bang cosmic creation event. That penetration yielded good news for theists and bad news for atheists. Atheists, however, can and always will be able to appeal to shrinking regions of ignorance about the natural realm where they can speculate that perhaps radically altered physics in those regions might permit an escape from the personal cosmic Creator.

Circular Reasoning

An example of circular reasoning is found in a recent claim by physicists Ahmed Farag Ali and Saurya Das who had shown that the universe has no beginning, and thus no implied beginner.[2] Their claim employed "replacing classical geodesics with quantal (Bohmian) trajectories."[3] A geodesic is simply the shortest possible path between two points along a curved or flat space-time surface. In cosmology, a freely moving or falling particle always travels along a geodesic.

In standard cosmological models, geodesics may or may not cross one another or converge at points. Quantal Bohmian trajectories, by definition, are paths along which particles travel where it is impossible for the paths to ever cross each other or converge. Thus, Farag Ali and Das's starting assumption, namely that geodesics can be replaced wholesale by quantal Bohmian trajectories, rules out the possibility of a singularity occurring at any time or anywhere in the universe.

Farag Ali and Das's conclusion that their cosmological model "gets rid of the big bang singularity and predicts an infinite age of our universe"[4] is not a conclusion or scientific deduction. It's simply a restatement of their starting assumption. They presume a cosmic geometry that forbids the possibility of a cosmic beginning to show that there isn't a cosmic beginning.

Absolute Proof Trap

In presenting such nonempirical arguments, nontheists lay a trap for Christian evangelists and apologists. Fundamentally, these nontheists are saying to believers that they possess no case for the existence of the God of the Bible *until* they can refute all conceivable nonempirical arguments for God's nonexistence.

This approach presents Christians with an impossible challenge. A Christian would need to acquire complete knowledge not only about the physical universe but also about everything that could conceivably exist beyond the universe. Neither goal is possible. Since our powers of investigation are constrained by the universe's space-time dimensions, it is impossible for humans to ever gain a complete database about the properties of the universe let alone what lies beyond.

These constraints imply not only is it impossible for us to learn everything about the universe, but it is also impossible for us to learn everything about even the smallest component of the universe. In other words, we can never attain absolute proof about anything including our own existence. Our inability to ever gain absolute proof, however, does not mean that we cannot attain practical proof.

Practical versus Absolute Proof
What is practical versus absolute proof? Here's where an example may help.

When I first met my wife, Kathy, every observable indication seemed to confirm the reality of her existence. Everything she said matched what I would expect to emanate from a free-will being. Her body movements were consistent with a body fully subject to the laws of physics. Her senses operated in a manner consistent with a human body and analyzed by a brain.

Nevertheless, I could not be absolutely certain that she actually existed. If pressed with the question, I would have had to concede it was possible I was simply relating to a sophisticated hologram or that what I took to be physical evidence for her existence was illusionary. Maybe I was being exposed to elaborate illusions concocted by a very well-funded and technologically equipped team of magicians? All I had was a high probability of her existence. (Those familiar with films like *The Matrix* and *Total Recall* may appreciate this concept of questioning whether something is 100 percent real.)

Over the subsequent two years I had many opportunities to observe Kathy interacting with me and many others, as well as animals. This additional observational evidence gave me a much higher probability of her existence. Nevertheless, I still lacked absolute proof.

In the following year and a half, we began to date, got engaged, and got married. I had much more evidence that Kathy actually existed. I had more than enough evidence to commit to be her husband until death do us part. Still, however, I lacked absolute proof.

During my 39 years of marriage to Kathy, based on accumulating evidence, I have seen the probability for her existence steadily rise. The probability exceeds 99.99…99 percent. But, it is not 100 percent and, because of limitations in human capacity to gain all knowledge, it will never be 100 percent.

Likewise, no human being can ever be 100 percent certain that the God of the Bible exists. However, we can gather enough evidence to gain practical proof for God's existence. We can establish that the probability is very high and that the probability increases as we continue to explore the two books God has given us: the book of nature and the book of Scripture.

It is philosophically inconsistent to demand more evidence for God's existence than the evidence for a human being we interact with on a daily basis. Just as there came a time when I had enough evidence of Kathy's existence and of her character attributes that I decided to commit my life to her in marriage, there also came a time when the evidence for God's existence and of his character attributes became abundant enough that I decided to commit my life to him for all eternity. In both cases I lacked absolute proof, but I had more than enough practical proof.

God of the Gaps versus Naturalism of the Gaps

Nontheists often claim that Christians slip God into the scientific knowledge gaps. Specifically, they note that when scientists are unable to come up with a natural explanation for a phenomenon, Christians frequently use that inability to claim that God must have stepped in and supernaturally performed the deed. Nontheists will then point to several examples in the past where the apparent inability to explain a phenomenon by natural processes was satisfactorily resolved through additional scientific research.

There certainly have been many past instances where scientists' failures to provide a natural explanation were overcome by ongoing research efforts. However, it does not necessarily follow, as many nontheists insist, that every failure to provide a natural explanation eventually will be overcome through ongoing scientific research. Such insistence a priori assumes, but does not prove or establish in any way, either that God does not exist or that God will never intervene in the natural order of things. A classic way nontheists express this insistence is to assert that absence of evidence is never evidence of absence.

In addition to the God-of-the-gaps appeal there is the naturalism-of-the-gaps argument. Naturalism-of-the-gaps contrasts with God-of-the-gaps by consistently responding to any inability to explain a phenomenon by concluding that a natural process or some combination of natural processes must have done the deed. The logical fallacy committed here by nontheists is the presumption that gaps in our knowledge and understanding can only imply one possible conclusion.

Gaps in our knowledge and understanding can never be totally eliminated. They can, however, be made smaller, less numerous, and less problematic. They also can become larger, more numerous, and problematic. What happens to the gaps, in light of more extensive research, determines whether or not we are on the pathway toward more comprehensive knowledge and understanding, and ultimately truth.

Gaining knowledge and understanding gaps, thus, provide a powerful opportunity to test competing explanatory models. If a biblical creation model delivers a progressively more comprehensive and consistent explanation of the record of nature, where the gaps in knowledge and understanding grow smaller, less problematic, and fewer in number as scientists learn more, then such a demonstration establishes the veracity of that creation model. That model is all the more affirmed if the gaps in the nontheistic models concurrently become bigger, more problematic, and more numerous with increasing scientific research findings.

Investigating what happens to gaps as we learn more and more provides a means for shifting nonempirical appeals into the arena of the empirical. It takes appeals to the unknown into the realm of the known. It encourages skeptics to make their case on what is known and knowable rather than on what is unknown and unknowable.

Gaps and the Origin of Life

Origin-of-life research over the past seventy years yields one of the most dramatic examples of the theistic gaps growing smaller, less problematic, and fewer in number, while the nontheistic gaps have proceeded in the opposite directions. In 1953, Stanley Miller and Harold Urey performed a flask experiment that showed that glycine and alanine, the smallest and simplest of the amino acids, could be generated from inorganic substances.[5] Similar experiments were successful in producing a few more of the bioactive amino acids. In the 1970s, Sidney Fox successfully coaxed several amino acids to link together in a laboratory experiment.[6]

These experiments were hailed as proof that a naturalistic pathway existed for life to self-assemble from nonorganic substances. It was not long, however, before geochemists recognized that the conditions under which the Miller-Urey and Fox experiments were run resembled nothing like the conditions existing on Earth at the time of life's origin. Experiments run under actual conditions existing on early Earth yielded none of the building block molecules of proteins, DNA, or RNA.

Origin-of-life researchers committed to a naturalistic explanation did not give up. They began an exhaustive search for the isotope signatures for prebiotic molecules on early Earth. While they found abundant evidence for postbiotics, no matter how diligently and extensively they searched, they found none for prebiotics.

Geophysicists and chemists explained why no prebiotics were ever found. Even the tiniest amount of oxygen in Earth's atmosphere and oceans stymies the formation of prebiotic molecules.[7] However, with no oxygen at all, ultraviolet radiation from the youthful Sun would bathe Earth's surface. This ultraviolet radiation is just as catastrophic to prebiotic chemistry as oxygen. That is, if oxygen existed on early Earth, prebiotic building block molecules would be impossible. If oxygen did not exist, prebiotic building block molecules would be impossible. Without any prebiotic building block molecules, no conceivable naturalistic model or scenario for life's origin is possible.

With Earth ruled out, nontheistic origin-of-life researchers looked to outer space. They found 8 of the 20 bioactive amino acids in a few meteorites—at only a few parts per million[8] and the simplest amino acid, glycine, at less than a part per billion in a comet.[9] Completely missing were the basic (high pH) amino acids lysine and arginine.[10] Furthermore, no prebiotic synthesis experiment under any conceivable early Earth conditions has produced any lysine or arginine.

Dense molecular clouds in the spiral arms and core of our Milky Way Galaxy possess the highest abundance and diversity of carbonaceous molecules of any astrophysical source. Over 130 such molecules have been discovered in those locations so far. Completely missing, however, are any of the amino acids, nucleobases, or sugars that are the critical building block molecules for proteins, DNA, and RNA.[11] While chemical conditions within at least a few of the densest molecular clouds would permit the production of nucleobases and a handful of the simpler amino acids (perhaps even ribose), the amounts produced would evidently be below a few parts per hundred million, a density far too low to benefit any conceivable origin-of-life scenario.

The density of these building block molecules on early Earth is likely to be much lower. Many of the critical building block molecules cannot last outside of organisms and their decay products for more than just days, hours, or minutes. The known delivery times of these building block molecules to Earth are orders of magnitude greater.

Compounding the lack of building block molecules is the homochirality problem. Amino acids cannot be assembled into proteins unless all the amino acids share the same handedness. Likewise, nucleobases cannot be assembled into DNA or RNA unless all the ribose sugars between the nucleobases share the same handedness. Outside of living or recently dead organisms, amino acids and ribose sugars appear as random mixtures of left- and right-handed molecules. Furthermore, nowhere on Earth or anywhere else in the universe does a process operate to permit more than a trivial departure from random mixtures of handedness of these molecules.[12]

Further compounding the lack of building block molecules are the assembly challenges. The more (building block) isomers linked together on a mineral substrate (the one proven laboratory method for joining the building block molecules together), the harder for additional isomers to join the linkage, and the more difficult for the isomer chain to separate from the substrate. In the most recent laboratory experiments, chains of about 50 amino acids or nucleobases represent the upper limit, a number far short of what's needed for manufacturing the proteins, DNA, and RNA that life needs.

Accumulating knowledge and understanding about life's origin on Earth establishes that the absence of evidence for a naturalistic scenario for life's origin really is evidence of absence of any such possible scenario.

Then, there is the timing issue. The oldest known rocks on Earth show isotope evidence for a diverse ecosystem of unicellular life-forms.[13] This evidence implies that not just one but multiple species of life arose within a geological instant of time.

Lastly, there are the signatures of purpose in life's origin on Earth. Consider the remarkable abundance and diversity of microbes on Earth appearing as early as the laws of physics and the universe's gross features would allow. Without them, Earth's geologic and chemical transformation (propelled by that early life) would not have had sufficient time to attain survivable conditions for humans before the ever-brightening Sun became too bright.[14] Nothing less than the appearance of life at the earliest moment physics would permit and the maximum diversification and abundance of life from that time forward, for as long as physics would allow, could possibly account for the availability of resources for billions of humans, much less for development of the technologies that permit dissemination of the Gospel message to all peoples of the earth.

Do we know everything there is to know about the origin of life? No. However, the missing prebiotics on Earth, the lack of any conceivable source of prebiotic building block molecules, the short half-lives of the building block molecules, the oxygen-ultraviolet paradox, the homochirality problem, the assembly of the building block molecules problem, the extremely brief time window during which several distinct species of life simultaneously and abundantly appeared, and the signatures of divine purpose rule out the possibility of any rational naturalistic explanation for life's origin. The only reasonable explanation that remains is that a supernatural, super-intelligent Being created life. Readers wanting a more in depth treatment will find it in the book I coauthored with Fazale Rana titled *Origins of Life: Biblical and Evolutionary Models Face Off*.[15]

Creating Life in the Lab

Through studies of the physics and chemistry of the simplest existing cells, scientists have gained a comprehensive understanding of all the cell's operations. They also know in exquisite detail the structure of all the cell's molecular machinery and how the cell does everything that it does.

Given the current state of knowledge scientists possess about the simplest cells, theoretically they should have no trouble manufacturing a simple cell from chemical building blocks in the laboratory. However, in spite of all the technology, wealth, instrumentation, and highly intelligent and knowledgeable manpower at their disposal, scientists have been stymied in their attempts to make life in the lab. They have achieved phenomenal successes in reengineering unicellular life-forms, but are far from manufacturing life from scratch.[16]

Will biochemists eventually achieve their goal of creating life in the lab? If the technology, wealth, and intellectual resources available to achieve the goal keep increasing at an exponential rate, then possibly yes. Would that achievement prove that God is not necessary to explain the origin of life? What it would demonstrate is that a causal Agent much more intelligent, knowledgeable, richer, and powerful than the best that humanity can presently muster was responsible for life's origin.

One must not be surprised, however, that in spite of the overwhelmingly compelling case for a supernatural cause for life's origin, nontheists will persist in claiming that some hypothetical, unguided, mindless set of processes in the realm of the unknown or unknowable actually resulted in the origin of life. If these nontheists, though, are unable to articulate the processes that gave rise to life's origin, they have no reasonable case. Neither do they possess a reasonable case if the processes they *do* articulate become progressively more extreme or absurd as scientists learn more. Consider again, by way of analogy, flat-Earth proponents. They still have models and explanations for why Earth is flat rather than spherical, but their models and explanations have become more extreme and absurd with respect to our increase of knowledge about Earth.

While nontheists will always be able to appeal to some hypothetical, unguided, mindless processes in the realm of the unknown to possibly explain life's origin, the extremely high entropy measure (increasing the level of atomic and molecular disorder) of the universe combined with an analogy to humanity's best efforts to manufacture life in the lab more than sufficiently establish that a supernatural Creator must have brought life into existence.

Cause and Effect Principles

As already noted, the universe possesses an extremely high entropy measure. As Paul says in Romans 8:20–22, the entire universe is subject to a pervasive law of decay. This propensity toward dramatically increasing disorder implies that effects cannot be greater than their causes. Nontheists are forced to conclude that the living, the conscious, the personal, the mindful, the volitional, the emotional, and the spiritual arise from that which lacks life, consciousness, personality, mind, volition, emotions, and spirituality. However, everything we measure and observe strongly refutes this belief that something so dramatically greater naturally arises from something that lacks all those features.

Many years ago, I gave a talk to 300 nontheists sponsored by Atheists United. Before I presented my scientific evidences for God I asked the audience these two questions:

1. How many of you would believe in God and would be willing to consider submitting your life to him if you saw compelling scientific evidence for his existence and saw that evidence increasing as we learn more about the universe and the record of nature?
2. How many of you here will not believe in God until the scientific evidence eliminates all other conceivable alternate explanations for the universe and its life?

One-third of my audience raised their hands indicating an affirmative answer to question #1 while two-thirds raised their hands indicating an affirmative answer to question #2.

Nonbelievers in the first category can be reached through what we know and can know. We should not be surprised that nonbelievers in the second category insist on taking the debate into the realm of the unknown and the unknowable. As long as they remain in that realm, they will not and cannot be reached for Jesus Christ. The goal, as always, should be to gently and lovingly encourage them to leave the world of speculation about the unknowable, and walk the road to reality to meet the One who created us and everything we see and measure.

 Discussion Questions _____

1. What's the difference between "practical" and "absolute" proof? Do you think a skeptic will find this distinction persuasive?
2. In testing competing models (naturalistic vs. creation) for knowledge gaps, what does the evidence for the origin of life show?
3. For the two groups of nontheists identified at the end of the chapter, do you know of someone in the second category? Have you prayed that the Holy Spirit would generate a transformation?

Chapter 17

Earth: The Place for Life

The mind boggles in trying to grasp the minute detail the Designer wove together to make the universe suitable for life. That same beautiful intricacy is apparent as one looks closer to home—at our galaxy, our Sun, our neighboring planets, our Earth, our Moon, and more.

The first astronomers to provide evidence of these intricacies were Frank Drake, Carl Sagan, and Iosif Shklovsky. They developed the evidence out of their desire to estimate the number of planets in the universe with favorable environments for sustaining life. By 1966, Shklovsky and Sagan had determined it takes a certain kind of star with a planet located at the just-right distance from that star to provide the minimal conditions for life.[1] Working with just these two parameters, they estimated that 0.001% of all stars could have a planet capable of supporting advanced life.[2]

Much subsequent evidence has shown that Shklovsky and Sagan overestimated the range of permissible star types and the range of permissible planetary distances, and they also ignored dozens of other significant parameters. But their estimate of a million-plus possible intelligent life sites for our galaxy has persisted. It is this optimistic estimate that has fueled the search for extraterrestrial intelligent life.

In addition to much private money, more than $100 million in US taxpayer support has been devoted to the search for radio signals from extraterrestrial intelligent life.[3] With all the evidence for divine design (and against a naturalistic explanation) in the universe, one would think some caution (and some theology) would be in order before committing this much money. As we will see, the evidence for divine design mounts dramatically as we move from a large system, like the universe as a whole, to smaller systems such as our galaxy, our star, our planet, and life itself.

Figure 17.1: The Abell 370 Galaxy Cluster

Most galaxies reside in rich clusters of galaxies like Abell 370. In such clusters the densities and sizes of galaxies rule out the possible existence of advanced life. Every object in this image is a galaxy except for the two blue-white crossed spots in the lower left and upper right of the image, which are stars in our own galaxy.

Credit: NASA/ESA/Jennifer Lotz and the HFF Team (STScI)

The Right Galaxy Cluster

Our Milky Way Galaxy resides in a loose grouping of galaxies called the Local Group. The Local Group is located on the far outer edge of the Virgo supercluster of galaxies.

This location makes our galaxy exceptional. The vast majority of galaxies in the universe reside in rich clusters of galaxies (see fig. 17.1) making them subject to frequent near encounters, collisions, and mergers with other galaxies.[4] These near encounters, mergers, and collisions can be devastating for physical life, since they disturb the structure of the galaxy and send a star with a life-sustainable planet into a different orbit about the galaxy. That different orbit exposes the life-sustainable planet to deadly radiation or to encounters with other stars and dense molecular clouds that so disturb the accompanying system of planets, comets, and asteroids that it poses a serious risk for life on that planet.

For life to be possible, a galaxy cluster must be small enough where a

Figure 17.2: The Local Group Galaxy Cluster

The Andromeda Galaxy and its two prominent dwarf galaxy partners, M32 and NGC 205, are to the upper left. Below the Andromeda Galaxy is the dwarf spiral galaxy M33, the third largest galaxy in the Local Group. To the lower right is the MWG and above it the fourth and fifth largest galaxies in the Local Group: the Large and Small Magellanic Clouds, respectively. The other approximately 100 dwarf galaxies in the Local Group are too small and too faint to show up in this map.

Credit for the galaxy images: NASA/ESA/ESO/R. Hurt, Caltech-JPL, map by author

potentially life-sustaining galaxy in the cluster avoids "ram pressure stripping." This stripping, resulting from close encounters with other large galaxies, causes a galaxy to lose so much gas and dust that it cannot maintain the structure and symmetry of its spiral arms long enough for advanced life to possibly exist.

On the other hand, our galaxy cannot maintain its spiral structure without absorbing large amounts of gas and dust from dwarf galaxies in its immediate neighborhood. It is that spiral structure that allowed our Sun to form at the right time for life and to remain in a safe path in its orbit about the center of the Milky Way Galaxy.

Our galaxy resides in a galaxy cluster (see fig. 17.2) that has no giant galaxies. It has only two large galaxies, the Milky Way Galaxy (MWG) and the Andromeda Galaxy. The Andromeda Galaxy is far enough away to pose no threat to life in the MWG. About 100 dwarf galaxies accompany the Milky Way and Andromeda Galaxies. Two of the three largest dwarf galaxies, the Large and Small Magellanic Clouds, are in the precise locations to act as shepherds to funnel much smaller dwarf galaxies into the core of the MWG. This fine-tuned funneling is a major factor in explaining how the MWG maintained its highly symmetrical, unwarped, and hardly disturbed spiral structure throughout the past 10 billion years.[5] Since the MWG avoided collisions, mergers, and close fly-bys with large- and medium-sized galaxies over the past 10 billion years, while concurrently accreting a regular supply of small dwarf galaxies, it maintained the symmetrical pure disk that advanced life needs.[6]

While our galaxy avoided life-destroying encounters with other galaxies in the past, astronomers determined that life-destroying mergers are in the offing. About 4 billion years hence, the Large Magellanic Cloud will merge with the MWG.[7] About a billion years after that merger event the Andromeda Galaxy will merge with the Milky Way Galaxy.

The Right Galaxy

Not all galaxies are created equal in their capacity to support life. Popular media often give the impression that all galaxies are spirals like our galaxy. In reality, only 6% of the non-dwarf galaxies are spirals.[8] The other 94% are either ellipticals or irregulars.

In elliptical galaxies, star formation ceases before the interstellar medium becomes enriched enough with heavy elements. For life, stellar systems need to form late enough that they can incorporate this heavy-element-enriched material.

The problem with large irregular galaxies is they have active nuclei. These nuclei spew out life-destroying radiation and material. Meanwhile, most small irregular galaxies have insufficient quantities of the heavy elements essential for life.

Astronomers categorize galaxies as belonging to either the red or the blue population. Young stars tend to be hot and, therefore, blue-colored. Old stars tend to be cooler and, therefore, red-colored. Thus, galaxies aggressively forming new stars are blue, while galaxies in which star formation has ceased are red.

The MWG does not fit into either the red or blue category. It is green. While star formation has subsided in the MWG, it has not yet ended. Thus, our galaxy's population of large- and medium-sized stars contains both blue stars and stars aged enough to be yellow, plus a small number of red stars.

Green galaxies are rare, but exactly what advanced life requires to possibly exist. A galaxy dominated by blue stars will bathe its planets with too many too intense flares, plus too intense ultraviolet and x-ray radiation. A galaxy dominated by red stars will also bathe its planets with too many too intense flares,

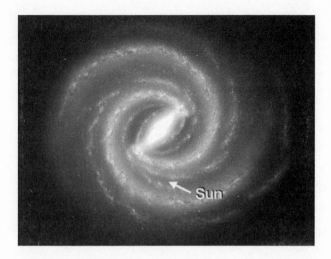

Figure 17.3: The Milky Way Galaxy

Astronomers produced this image of our galaxy by piecing together maps of different regions of our galaxy at radio, infrared, optical, and ultraviolet wavelengths. No other known galaxy has such symmetrical spiral arms with the just-right spacings advanced life requires. The Sun and its system of planets are presently half way between the Perseus and Sagittarius spiral arms.

Credit: NASA/JPL-Caltech, R. Hurt (SSC)

plus expose them to too many nova and supernova events. Another problem with a galaxy dominated by red stars is that it lacks the necessary level of ongoing star formation to sustain the galaxy's spiral structure for a long time. Another problem with a galaxy dominated by blue stars is that the aggressive formation of such stars inevitably causes major disturbances (warps, bends, spurs, and feathers) in the galaxy's spiral structure.

One reason why advanced life can exist in the MWG is that the galaxy's spiral arms are very stable, well separated, highly symmetrical, free of significant warps or bends, and relatively free of spurs and feathers (see fig. 17.3). In part, these spiral arm conditions are possible because the MWG is dominated by yellow stars complemented by significant populations of blue stars.

Our galaxy's mass and size is fine-tuned for life. A smaller galaxy will have its spiral structure more seriously disrupted by encounters with other galaxies. A larger galaxy will possess a much larger supermassive black hole in its nucleus. Large supermassive black holes generate relativistic jets of deadly radiation.

Advanced life is possible only on a planet orbiting a star that in turn orbits

Figure 17.4: NGC 4945, the Galaxy Most Similar to the Milky Way Galaxy

Though roughly the same size as the MWG, NGC 4945 has an active nucleus, much more prominent star-forming regions, and spiral arms far from symmetrical.

Credit: European Southern Observatory

the center of its galaxy near the co-rotation radius. The co-rotation radius is
that distance from the center of a galaxy where stars revolve around the galactic
center at the same rate that the spiral arms rotate. Newton's laws of motion determine the revolution rate of stars. Density waves determine the rotation rate
of the spiral arms. Only stars near the co-rotation radius avoid frequent crossings of spiral arms. Spiral arms host supergiant stars, giant molecular clouds,
and star-forming nebulae that bathe nearby planets with deadly radiation and
gravitationally disturb the asteroid and comet belts in a planetary system.

For a galaxy smaller than the MWG, the co-rotation distance is so close to
the galactic center it exposes planets at that distance to too much deadly radiation emitted from the galactic nucleus. For a galaxy larger than the MWG, the
co-rotation distance is so far from the galactic center it makes it highly unlikely
that planets there would possess the necessary abundance of heavy elements
that life requires. (The abundance of heavy elements in a spiral galaxy roughly
declines with distance from the galactic center.).

One unique feature of our galaxy is that it is significantly underluminous
for its mass and size.[9] Another unique feature is that its star-forming regions,

while numerous, are all small and dim. The underluminosity of the MWG and its star-forming regions shields Earth from damaging radiation exposure.

The MWG is a galaxy like no other. The known galaxy that comes the closest is NGC 4945 (see fig. 17.4). It is similar in size to the MWG and possesses a barred nucleus. However, x-ray observations reveal that the nucleus of NGC 4945 emits copious amounts of deadly radiation, probably powered by a supermassive black hole very much larger than the MWG.[10] Furthermore, its spiral structure is nowhere nearly as symmetrical as the MWG.

Interested readers will find a whole chapter on the fine-tuned features of the Local Group and the MWG in my book *Improbable Planet*.[11]

The Right Birthplace and the Right Move

What makes advanced life possible on Earth is the Sun's present location between two spiral arms just inside our galaxy's co-rotation distance. Almost all stars in our galaxy reside in the central bulge, the spiral arms, or the globular star clusters. In these three locations, star densities are high enough to disrupt the orbits of planets like Earth. Moreover, the presence of supergiant stars, neutron stars, black holes, or supernova remnants would expose Earth-like planets to radiation intense enough to damage their ionospheric and atmospheric layers.

A star *right at the co-rotation* distance would experience destructive mean motion resonances.[12] The safest place with the fewest spiral arm crossings is the Sun's present location *just inside the co-rotation distance*. The Sun's present orbital distance from the galactic center also fits where the stellar density and interstellar gas and dust are minimal.[13]

If the solar system had formed at its present location (about 26,000 light-years out from the galactic center), then it would lack the abundance of heavy elements advanced life needs, and would be oversaturated with light elements. Earth's mix of elements can be explained only if the solar system formed elsewhere—in a dense cluster of at least 10,000 stars formed at the radial distance with the highest concentration of heavy elements—about 12,000 light-years out from the galactic center.

In such a star cluster the solar system would have been exposed to Wolf-Rayet winds from supergiant stars that would have blasted away most of the solar system's lighter elements and lighter gases.[14] The solar system also would have been exposed to one or more neutron star merging events, several different kinds of supernovae, and asymptotic giant branch stars that would have endowed it with all the heavy elements at the just-right abundance levels that advanced life requires.[15]

Life is not possible in such a star cluster, however. The high density of stars prevents a planetary system from maintaining stable orbits for its planets and belts of asteroids and comets. Neighboring stars would also constantly blast a planetary system with radiation catastrophic for life.

At the just-right time, our solar system experienced a gravitational encounter with several large stars that strongly ejected it from the star cluster. The Sun and its system of nascent planets hurtled away from one of the most dangerous-for-life locations in the MWG. Fortuitously, another encounter with large stars halted its ejection velocity so that it settled into the safest-for-life orbit about the MWG's center.

The solar system's ejection journey was remarkable in a second way. As it traveled from our galaxy's most dangerous location to its safest, it miraculously avoided x-ray sources, giant stars, star clusters, star-forming nebulae, and giant molecular clouds.

The present orbit of the solar system about the galactic center stands out in yet another way. Most stars exhibit rather large up-and-down, back-and-forth, and side-to-side random motions away during their Newtonian orbital paths around the galactic center. The Sun's tiny up-and-down motions keep us from getting too exposed to deadly radiation from the galactic nucleus and from supernovae remnants.[16] The Sun's tiny back-and-forth and side-to-side motions also play a crucial role in keeping our solar system from getting too close to spiral arms and spurs.

Window to God's Glory

The Sun's unique location benefits us in yet another way. We get a clear view of the heavens. If we were in a spiral arm, 80–85% of the light from other galaxies would be absorbed by intervening gas and dust.[17] If we were near the galactic bulge, in or near a globular cluster, in or near an open star cluster, near a star-forming nebula, or anywhere but just inside the co-rotation distance, light from other stars or nebulae would make the night sky too bright. If not for our unique location, we would not have had the capacity to discover that we dwell in a spiral galaxy, that over a hundred billion other galaxies exist, that the universe is continually expanding, that there is cosmic background radiation left over from the cosmic creation event, and that our universe is traceable back to an exquisitely designed, transcendent creation event.

Situated where we are, however, we have what can be described as a window seat to the splendors of the universe. We are granted an unobstructed view—in a language understandable to all—of God's glory, power, and righteousness written in the heavens.[18]

Again, interested readers will find many more details on the amazing history of the solar system's birth and youth in my book *Improbable Planet.*[19]

The Right Star

Not only is a particular kind of galaxy cluster and galaxy essential for life, the star around which a life-bearing planet revolves must be just right. As we have seen, it must be located in the just-right part of the galaxy with the just-right orbit in that galaxy. Advanced life also requires a single star system. Zero or two-plus star systems will not do.

A planet ripped away from its star will be too cold for life. But if a planet small enough for life support orbits a binary or multiple star system, the extra star(s) will frequently pull the orbit out of one of the nine known habitable zones[20] essential for life support. The only possible exception would be a double-star system where one star with a very small mass either orbits extremely close to the bigger star or at an extreme distance from the bigger star.

As Shklovsky and Sagan first pointed out, a life-support planet must be maintained by a star of very specific mass. A star more massive than the Sun will burn too quickly and too erratically for life on the planet to be sustained. But the star cannot be any less massive either. Smaller mass stars experience more frequent and violent flares. Also, the smaller the mass of the star, the closer the planet must be to that star to maintain a temperature suitable for life chemistry. This causes another problem because the tidal interaction between a star and its planet increases dramatically (by the fourth power) as the distance separating them shrinks. Bringing the planet just a bit closer causes such a tremendous increase in tidal interaction that the planet's rotation period quickly lengthens from hours to months. This is the fate, for example, of both Mercury and Venus.

A rotation period of months means that one side of the planet will be blistering hot and the other side freezing cold. It also means no liquid water would exist on the planet, not even at the twilight edge between the blistering hot and freezing cold sides. Atmospheric transport would move any water from the day side to the night side, where it would freeze.[21]

The star must form at the just-right time in the history of the galaxy. If it forms too soon or too late, the mix of heavy elements suitable for life chemistry will not exist. For advanced life it must also be middle-aged. Only middle-aged stars maintain a sufficiently stable burning phase. Only stars in the very middle part of their middle-aged phase manifest flaring subdued enough to make advanced life sustainable.

Even the most stable stars in the most stable parts of their burning cycles experience changes in luminosity that can be detrimental for life. The Sun's luminosity, for example, has increased by 18 to 23% since life was first introduced on Earth.[22] Such a change is more than enough to exterminate life. But life survived on Earth because the increase in solar luminosity was exactly canceled out each step of the way by a decrease in the efficiency of the greenhouse effect in Earth's atmosphere. This decrease in greenhouse efficiency arose through the careful introduction of the just-right species of life, in the just-right quantities, at the just-right times. The slightest "evolutionary accident" would have caused a runaway freeze-up or runaway boiling (see "Climactic Runaways" on p. 209).

Here, materialists possess no reasonable explanation. How could strictly natural Darwinist-type processes possibly have anticipated the future physics of solar burning and responded by removing precisely the life-forms no longer adequate for removing the necessary greenhouse gases and replacing them with the precise life-forms to attain the just-right amounts of greenhouse gases? It takes a mind that knows in accurate detail the present and future physics of the Sun, the geochemistry of Earth, and the biology of Earth's life continually throughout the past 3.8 billion years to prevent Earth from experiencing a permanent sterilization event.

Another Kind of Life?
Everything written so far in this chapter assumes that physical life must be carbon-based. As physicist Robert Dicke observed 50 years ago, if you want physicists (or any other life-forms), you must have carbon.[23]

Arsenic, boron, and silicon are the only other elements on which complex molecules can be based, but arsenic and boron are relatively rare and, where concentrated, poisonous to life, and silicon can hold together no more than about a hundred amino acids. Only carbon yields the chemical bonding stability and bonding complexity that life requires. Given the constraints of physics and chemistry, we now know that physical life must be carbon-based.

The Right Planet
As biochemists now concede, for life molecules to operate so that organisms can live requires an environment where water vapor, liquid water, and frozen water are all stable and abundant. This means that a planet cannot be too close to its star or too far away. In the case of planet Earth, given its particular

CLIMATIC RUNAWAYS

Earth's biosphere is poised between a runaway freeze-up and a runaway evaporation. If the mean temperature of Earth's surface cools by even a few degrees, more snow and ice than normal will form. Snow and ice reflect solar energy much more efficiently than other surface materials. The reflection of more solar energy translates into lower surface temperatures, which in turn cause more snow and ice to form and subsequently still lower temperatures. Eventually, Earth's surface would be completely covered in ice and snow.

If the mean temperature of Earth's surface warms just a few degrees, more water vapor and carbon dioxide collect in the atmosphere. This extra water vapor and carbon dioxide create a better greenhouse effect in the atmosphere. This in turn causes the surface temperature to rise again, which releases even more water vapor and carbon dioxide into the atmosphere resulting in still higher surface temperatures. Eventually, Earth's water would exist entirely in the vapor state.

atmosphere, a change in the distance from the Sun as small as 2% would rid the planet of all life.[24]

The temperature of a planet and its surface gravity determine the escape velocity, a measure of which atmospheric gases dissipate to outer space and which are retained. For our planet to support life, it is essential for water vapor (molecular weight 18) to be retained, while molecules as heavy as methane (molecular weight 16) and ammonia (molecular weight 17) dissipate. Therefore, a change in surface gravity or temperature of just a few percent will make the difference.

While Earth has the just-right surface gravity and temperature,[25] ammonia and methane disappear much faster than their escape velocities would indicate. Chemical conditions in Earth's upper atmosphere—also indicative of fine-tuning—work efficiently to break down both molecules.[26]

In All Habitable Zones
A truly habitable planet must not only orbit its host star at a distance that permits liquid water on its surface, it must simultaneously reside in eight other known habitable zones. For example, life requires a minimum amount of

Table 17.1: Known Planetary Habitable Zones

1. liquid water habitable zone
2. ultraviolet habitable zone
3. photosynthetic habitable zone
4. ozone habitable zone
5. planetary rotation-rate habitable zone
6. planetary rotation axis tilt habitable zone
7. tidal habitable zone
8. astrosphere habitable zone
9. atmospheric electric field habitable zone

ultraviolet radiation. Without this radiation, many life-essential biochemical reactions and the synthesis of many life-essential biochemicals, such as those needed for DNA repair and the manufacture of vitamin D, cannot occur. Too much ultraviolet radiation, however, will destroy land-based life and surface-dwelling sea life.

Both the amount and wavelength of incident ultraviolet radiation on a life-supporting planet's surface must be exquisitely fine-tuned. For all stars the ultraviolet habitable zone is much narrower than the liquid water habitable zone. The ultraviolet habitable zone is especially narrow for vascular plants and animals. It is extremely narrow for the equivalent of human life. Even for primitive life (think microbes), fewer than 3% of the stars in the MWG offer any possibility that the ultraviolet and liquid water habitable zones would ever overlap.[27]

Table 17.1 lists all the presently known habitable zones. Of the 3,618 planets discovered so far by astronomers,[28] only one simultaneously resides in all nine of the known habitable zones. That planet is the one all readers are most familiar with. Readers interested in an in-depth description and documentation of the nine known habitable zones will find it in chapter 7 of my book *Improbable Planet*.[29]

The Right Planetary Companions
Late in 1993, planetary scientist George Wetherill (1925–2006), of the Carnegie Institution of Washington, DC, made an exciting discovery about our solar system. He noted that if Jupiter orbited any closer to the Sun or if it were slightly more massive, then its gravity would sufficiently disturb Earth's orbit as to rule

out the possibility of advanced life. On the other hand, his computer simulations of our solar system showed that without a Jupiter-sized planet positioned just where it is, Earth would be struck about a thousand times more frequently than it is already by comets and comet debris.[30] In other words, without Jupiter, impacts such as the one that wiped out the dinosaurs would be common.

Here is how the protection system works: Jupiter is two and a half times more massive than all the other planets combined. Because of its huge mass (thus huge gravity) and its location between Earth and the clouds of comets surrounding the solar system, Jupiter either draws comets (by gravity) to collide with itself, as it did in July 1994,[31] or, more commonly, it deflects comets (again by gravity) right out of the solar system. In Wetherill's words, if it were not for Jupiter, "we wouldn't be around to study the origin of the solar system."[32]

It also is critical that Jupiter isn't our only gravitational shield. Shielding is optimized when Jupiter is accompanied by a less massive gas giant planet orbiting the Sun farther away, plus two much smaller gas giant planets orbiting the Sun at yet greater distances.

We wouldn't be around if not for the very high regularity in Jupiter and Saturn's orbits. In July 1994, French astrophysicist Jacques Laskar also determined that if the outer planets were less orbitally regular, then the inner planets' motions would be chaotic, and Earth would suffer orbital changes extreme enough to disrupt its climatic stability.[33] In other words, Earth's climate would be unsuitable for life. (As it is, the tiny variations in Jupiter and Saturn's orbits may someday, but not soon, bounce lightweight Mercury right out of the solar system.) Thus, even the characteristics of Jupiter and Saturn's orbits must fit within certain narrowly defined ranges for life on Earth to be possible.

Two Brazilian astronomers showed that even tiny adjustments in the orbits of Jupiter, Saturn, Uranus, and Neptune would prove catastrophic for life in our solar system. Regions beyond the precise orbital positions of Jupiter, Saturn, Uranus, and Neptune abound in destructive mean motion resonances.[34] (When the orbital periods of bodies in the same system manifest a ratio of small integers, the bodies exert regular, periodic gravitational influences on each other and on other bodies in the system.) As it is, Uranus is close to a 7:1 resonance with Jupiter, a 2:1 resonance with Neptune, and a 3:1 resonance with Saturn. Meanwhile Jupiter and Saturn are very close to 5:2 resonance. If any of the gas giant planets' orbital positions were to shift ever so slightly, it would destabilize the orbit of one or more of the solar system planets, with catastrophic consequences for a long history of life on Earth.

Three Canadian astronomers further demonstrated that the orbital positions of Venus, Earth, and Mars must be fine-tuned so as to break up mean motion resonances that could be damaging for life on Earth. They showed that even the orbital features of the Earth-Moon system must be fine-tuned for this purpose.[35] The Earth-Moon system suppresses a resonance in Venus's orbit that is generated from the orbital patterns of Jupiter, Saturn, Uranus, and Neptune. Unless the Earth-Moon system is configured the way it is, both Venus's and Mercury's orbits would destabilize and generate destructive chaos throughout the inner solar system.

Every planet in our solar system contributes to making advanced life possible on Earth. The solar system's array of eight planets must be exactly the way it is.

The Right Collider and Right Moon

Our Moon is like no other. The ratio of its mass compared to the mass of its host planet Earth is about 50 times greater than the next closest known ratio of moon-to-host-planet mass. Plus, our Moon orbits Earth more closely than any other known large moon orbits its host planet.

Thanks to these unique features, Earth—unlike the other solar system planets—possesses a stable rotation axis tilt, which protects Earth from rapid and extreme climatic variations that otherwise would rule out advanced life. The Moon also slowed Earth's rotation rate down to the value at which advanced life could thrive and generated tides that efficiently recycle nutrients and wastes.

Only recently have astronomers had any clue how such a special Moon could form. Over the past 18 years, astronomer Robin Canup has developed progressively more sophisticated and detailed models demonstrating that the Moon resulted from a collision between a newly formed Earth (which, at that time, had a pervasive and very deep ocean) and a planet, Theia, about twice the mass of Mars (Mars = 0.107 Earth masses). This collision, Canup determined, took place with an impact angle of about 45 degrees and a very low impact velocity of less than 12 kilometers/second.[36] In addition to forming the Moon, this highly fine-tuned collision event brought about three more changes, each significant for advanced life: (1) it blasted away all or nearly all of Earth's water and atmosphere,[37] (2) it ejected light element material and delivered heavy elements, and (3) it transformed both the interior and exterior structure of Earth.

In a review article published in a December 2013 issue of *Nature*, Canup complained, "Current theories on the formation of the Moon owe too much to cosmic coincidences."[38] Indeed, the required "coincidences" continue to pile up. New research reveals that the Moon has a similar chemical composition to Earth's outer portions—a result Canup's initial models couldn't explain until modified. The revised model worked, showing that the total mass of the collider and primordial Earth was 4% larger than present-day Earth, the ratio of Theia's mass to the total mass lies between 0.40 and 0.45, and a fine-tuned orbital resonance with the Sun removed the just-right amount of angular momentum from the resultant Earth-Moon system.[39]

Astronomers Matija Cuk and Sarah Stewart found another way to explain the similar composition. In their model, an impactor about the mass of Mars collides with a fast-spinning (rotation rate = 2.3~2.7 hours) primordial Earth.[40] Earth's fast spin generates a Moon-forming disk of debris made primarily of primordial Earth's mantle material, thus explaining the similar chemical composition of the present-day Moon and Earth's present-day outer layers. As with Canup's most recent model, a fine-tuned orbital resonance between the Moon and the Sun is needed.

In an article published in the same issue as Canup's recent review, Stewart concludes, "In the new giant-impact models, lunar material is derived either from a range of depths in the proto-Earth's mantle or equally from the entire mantles of two colliding half-Earths."[41] Either way, while "each stage of lunar evolution is possible," she wonders, "With the nested levels of dependency in a multi-stage model, is the probability of the required sequence of events vanishingly small?"[42]

Canup suggests in her review that perhaps a small collider (Mars-sized) model can be retained without so much of the added fine-tuning of the Cuk-Stewart model if the collider's initial chemical composition were more Earth-like rather than Mars-like. However, extra fine-tuning may be needed to explain this required initial composition.

In yet another article in the same issue of *Nature*, Earth scientist Tim Elliott observes that the complexity and fine-tuning in lunar origin models appears to be accumulating at an exponential rate. The impact on lunar origin researchers, Elliott notes, is that "the sequence of conditions that currently seems necessary in these revised versions of lunar formation have led to philosophical disquiet."[43] What is the cause of this philosophical disquiet? May I submit that it stems from the fact that there is now more than sufficient evidence for the supernatural, super-intelligent design of the Earth-Moon system for humanity's specific benefit.

Table 17.2: Vital Poisons

The following elements are catastrophic for life, especially advanced life, if ingested in soluble form at either too high or too low a concentration level:[44]

boron	iron
fluorine	cobalt
sodium	nickel
magnesium	copper
phosphorus	zinc
sulfur	arsenic
chlorine	selenium
potassium	bromine
vanadium	molybdenum
chromium	tin
manganese	iodine

Vital Poisons

The Food and Drug Administration issues warnings about overdoing dietary supplements of chromium, molybdenum, selenium, and vanadium. Each of these elements, in sufficient quantity, becomes a deadly poison. On the other hand, a lack of any one of these elements will kill us. Each of them is essential for building proteins vital for our existence. There is a fine line, for example, between too little vanadium in the diet and too much. Molybdenum also plays a crucial and unique role in nitrogen fixation, the process by which nitrogen from the atmosphere gets fixed into chemicals that can be assimilated by plants. In fact, the nitrogen fixation necessary for life on the land would be impossible unless the just-right amount of molybdenum exists in the soil.

These four elements are not the only elements whose quantities must be fine-tuned for life's possible existence. We all know the devastating effects of iron deficiency. However, too much iron in the diet can prove just as damaging. Table 17.2 lists all the vital poison elements.

The Right Elemental Abundances

Earth has sustained a huge profusion and diversity of life throughout the past 3.8 billion years thanks to its unique inventory of elements and water. This unique inventory also explains in part why humans were able to success-fully launch and sustain global high-technology civilization. For most of the elements in the periodic table, Earth possesses a highly anomalous abundance level, an abundance level that is critical for long lasting life and the possibility of advanced life and advanced civilization. Table 17.3 lists Earth's most anomalous elemental abundance levels.

Extrasolar Planets

In 1995, astronomers first discovered a planet, 51 Pegasi b, outside of the solar system that was orbiting a nuclear burning star.[45] At that time, most astronomers presumed that once the list of discovered planets approached the hundreds or thousands, many, if not most, of those planets would manifest characteristics very similar to one of the planets in our solar system. They also assumed that we would find many planetary systems that would be carbon copies of our solar system.

Today, the list of discovered extrasolar planets stands at over 3,600.[46] Five orbit pulsars. The remainder orbit nuclear burning stars. The masses of the planets orbiting nuclear burning stars range from 2% of Earth's mass to more than 20 times the mass of Jupiter. For comparison, Mercury's mass equals 37% of Earth's mass, and Jupiter's mass is 318 times that of Earth's mass.

The only extrasolar planet that comes close to matching the characteristics of a solar system planet is Upsilon Andromedae e. As explained in chapter 12, while Upsilon Andromedae e comes close to matching several of the physical features of Jupiter, it lacks the characteristics of Jupiter that are crucial for the support of life in the solar system.

The extrasolar planetary systems discovered so far look nothing like our solar system. The norm for these systems is a population of hot and warm gas giant planets, ranging from the mass of Uranus (14.5 times Earth's mass) to many times the mass of Jupiter. These planets typically orbit their host stars significantly closer than Jupiter orbits the Sun. These systems also frequently contain one or more super-Earths, planets ranging in size from 1.5~10 times Earth's mass. Such super-Earths orbit their stars equal to or less than Earth's distance from the Sun. Furthermore, whereas the known extrasolar planetary systems are filled with many planets possessing high-eccentricity orbits, the solar system has only one—diminutive Mercury, which resides so close to the Sun it poses no risk of disturbing the other solar system planets.

Astronomers now have a good understanding of why the solar system is so exceptional. For most planetary systems, the larger planets form far from their host stars and migrate into close orbits. For the other known extrasolar planetary systems, the larger planets either do not migrate at all or migrate only

Table 17.3: Relative Abundances of Advanced-Life Critical Heavy Elements in Earth's Crust

The fractional abundance of magnesium (by mass) in Earth's crust is nearly identical to the fractional abundance of magnesium in the entire Milky Way Galaxy. (The light elements, hydrogen and helium, that escape Earth's gravity are not included). Thus, magnesium provides a helpful measuring stick for comparison purposes. For each element listed below, the number indicates how much more or less abundant it is in Earth's crust, relative to magnesium's abundance, as compared to its average abundance throughout the Milky Way Galaxy, relative to magnesium's abundance. Asterisks denote "vital poisons," essential elements that are toxic or lethal to humans if too much or too little is ingested. The water measure compares the amount of water in and on Earth, relative to the minimum amount planet formation models predict for a planet the mass of Earth orbiting a star identical to the Sun at the same distance from the Sun.[47]

carbon*	1,200 times less	zinc*	6 times more
nitrogen*	2,400 times less	arsenic*	5 times more
fluorine*	50 times more	selenium*	30 times less
sodium*	20 times more	yttrium	50 times more
aluminum	40 times more	zirconium	130 times more
phosphorus*	4 times more[48]	niobium	170 times more
sulfur*	60 times less[49]	molybdenum*	5 times more
chlorine*	3 times more	silver	3 times more
potassium*	90 times more	tin*	3 times more
calcium	20 times more	antinomy	10 times more
titanium	65 times more	iodine*	4 times more
vanadium*	9 times more	gold	5 times less
chromium*	5 times less	lead	170 times more
manganese*	3 times more	uranium	340 times more
nickel*	20 times less	thorium	610 times more
cobalt*	6 times less	water	250 times less
copper*	21 times more		

short distances toward their host stars. By contrast, the large planets in the solar system performed a "Grand Tack" migration.

Grand Tack

All standard planetary formation models, when applied to the solar system, are stymied by the "Mars Problem." While most solar system formation models can explain the masses and orbits of the solar system's four gas giant planets (Jupiter, Saturn, Uranus, and Neptune) as well as the masses and orbits of Mercury, Venus, and Earth, they predict that Mars should be as massive or a little more massive than Earth and that the Main Belt of asteroids should include a few bodies as massive or nearly as massive as Mars (Mars equals 0.11 Earth masses).

For over a decade a team of astronomers known as the Nice team, led by Alessandro Morbidelli of the Observatoire de la Côte d'Azur in Nice, France, toiled to solve the Mars Problem. The team's efforts culminated in the Grand Tack model.[50] This model proposed that the solar system originally had five gas giant planets: Jupiter, Saturn, Uranus, Neptune, and another Neptune-sized planet. In this scenario, Jupiter ejects the Neptune-sized planet into interstellar space or into the far outer reaches of the solar system as a result of Jupiter, Saturn, Uranus, and Neptune tacking by varying degrees. The Nice team used the sailing term "tacking" to refer to the migration of the solar system's gas giant planets first inward toward the Sun and then outward. Figure 17.5 shows the migration movements calculated by the Nice team that are needed to solve the Mars Problem and reproduce the orbital configurations of all five of the solar system's asteroid and comet belts.

The Grand Tack model also explains why the solar system is unique in possessing relatively underpopulated asteroid and comet belts. Other models show that aggressive inward migration of large planets in a planetary system totally eradicates comets and asteroids from the system. This eradication explains why astronomers have observed warm dust (the signature of the presence of comets and asteroids) around so few stars.[51] On the other hand, little or no inward migration of large planets would leave the primordial comet and asteroid belts intact. The Fomalhaut star provides an example with its Jupiter-sized planet that orbits at a distance six times greater than Neptune orbits the Sun and also hosts a population of asteroids and comets at least a hundred times greater than the Sun's.[52] The solar system is the only known planetary system that hosts asteroid and comet belts neither too big nor too small for sustaining advanced life in the same system.[53]

Many Fine-Tuned Characteristics

In appendix A and B we see that Earth is prepared for physical life through a variety of finely tuned characteristics of our galaxy cluster, galaxy, star, planet, planetary partners, collider, moon, and belts of asteroids and comets. This

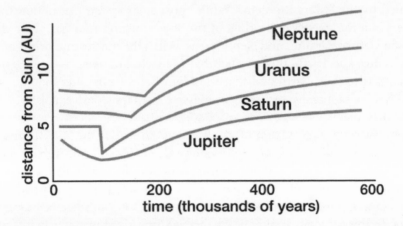

Figure 17.5: Grand Tack Migration

This illustration shows the Grand Tack migration pattern of the solar system's current gas giant planets. One astronomical unit (AU) = distance from Earth to the Sun.

Credit: Reasons to Believe

discussion by no means exhausts the list of characteristics that must be fine-tuned for physical life to exist. The astronomical and geophysical literature now includes discussions on hundreds of different characteristics that must take on narrowly defined values.

The list of design characteristics for our solar system grows longer with every year of new research. What were 2 parameters in 1966 grew to 8 by the end of the 1960s, to 23 by the end of the 1970s, to 30 by the end of the 1980s, to 123 in 2000, to over a thousand today. A sampling of 150 parameters that must be fine-tuned for the support of physical life is presented in appendix B.

Chances for Finding a Life-Support Planet

Each of the 150 parameters in appendix B (with nearly 400 in the more complete list) must be within certain limits to avoid disturbing a planet's capacity to support life. For some, including many of the stellar parameters, the limits have been measured very precisely. For others, including many of the planetary parameters, the limits are less precisely known. Trillions of stars are available for study, and star formation is quite well understood and observed. On the other hand, only 3,618 planets have been studied so far, and though astrophysicists have developed a good theory of planetary formation with significant observational confirmation, not all the details have yet been worked out.

Let's look at how confining these limits can be. Among the least confining would be the size and spatial distribution of a planet's continents. The limits here are loose, eliminating perhaps only 20% of all candidate planets that possess both surface oceans and surface continents. More confining would be parameters such as the planet's albedo (reflectivity), which eliminate about 90% of all candidates from contention. Most confining of all would be parameters such as the parent star's mass and the planet's distance from its parent star, which eliminate 99.9% of all candidates.

Of course, not all the listed parameters are strictly independent of the others. Dependency factors reduce the degree of confinement. On the other hand, all these parameters must be kept within specific limits for the total time span needed to support life on a candidate planet. This increases the degree of confinement.

An attempt at calculating the possibility that a randomly selected planet in our universe will possess the capacity to support microbial physical life for at least 3 billion years (the minimum requirement for making the existence of vascular plants and animals possible) is presented in the Design Compendium maintained on the Reasons to Believe website (reasons.org/finetuning). Although I have tried to be optimistic (that is, conservative) in assigning the probabilities and the dependency factors, I readily admit many of the estimates may need to be modified.

Future research should provide us with much more accurate probabilities. If past research is any indication, however, the number of parameters that must be fine-tuned will increase and the probabilities decrease. Indeed, the parameter list has grown from 41 to 128 between the second edition of this book (1995) and the third edition (2001), and from 128 in the third edition to 676 in the RTB Design Compendium (compiled in 2007 and edited in 2009). Meanwhile, the probability for finding a planet or rock anywhere in the universe with the capacity to support long-lasting microbial physical life, independent of divine miraculous intervention, has shrunk from 10^{-53} to 10^{-144} to 10^{-556}.

With considerable security, therefore, we can draw the conclusion that even with a hundred billion trillion stars in the observable universe, the probability of finding, without divine intervention, a single planet capable of supporting physical life is much less than one in a quadrillion, quadrillion quadrillion, quadrillion, quadrillion, quadrillion, quadrillion quadrillion, quadrillion, quadrillion, quadrillion, quadrillion quadrillion, quadrillion, quadrillion, quadrillion, quadrillion quadrillion, quadrillion, quadrillion, quadrillion, quadrillion, quadrillion

quadrillion, quadrillion, quadrillion, quadrillion, quadrillion quadrillion, quadrillion, quadrillion, quadrillion, quadrillion quadrillion, quadrillion, quadrillion, quadrillion, quadrillion. The odds actually are much, much higher that one of Earth's inhabitants will be killed by a sudden reversal in the second law of thermodynamics.[54]

Life-form Type

The environmental requirements for life to exist depend quite strongly on the life-form in question. The conditions for primitive life to exist, for example, are not nearly as demanding as they are for advanced life. Also, it makes a big difference how active the life-form is and how long it remains in its environment. On this basis, there are six distinct zones or regions in which life can exist. In order of the broadest to the narrowest they are as follows:

1. for unicellular, low metabolism life that persists for a brief time period
2. for unicellular, low metabolism life that persists for a long time period
3. for unicellular, high metabolism life that persists for a brief time period
4. for unicellular, high metabolism life that persists for a long time period
5. for advanced life that survives for a brief time period
6. for advanced life that survives for a long time period
7. for human life or the equivalent that survives for a brief time period

Complicating factors, however, are that unicellular, low metabolism life is more easily subject to radiation damage and has a very low molecular repair rate. The origin-of-life problem is also much more difficult for low metabolism life.[55] The RTB Design Compendium gives probability estimates for the features required:

a) microbial life lasting for at least 90 days: probability $= 10^{-333}$
    microbial life lasting for at least 3 billion years: probability $= 10^{-556}$
b) intelligent physical life maintaining a global high-technology
    civilization: probability $= 10^{-1032}$

The RTB Design Compendium includes extensive scientific literature citations that support the probability estimates. Thus, the probability of finding a life-site within the observable universe capable of sustaining the equivalent of human civilization, without invoking the intervention of a super-intelligent, supernatural Being, is much less than one chance in $10^{10^{32}}$!

These factors seem to indicate that the Local Group galaxy cluster, the Milky Way Galaxy, the Sun, each of the ten planets of the primordial solar system, the planet that collided with the primordial Earth, Earth, the Moon, and the solar system's five belts of asteroids and comets, in addition to the universe, have undergone divine design. It seems apparent that personal intervention on the part of the Creator takes place not just at the origin of the universe but throughout the history of the universe and the solar system. In other words, Earth seems more than simply "the pick of the litter," the planet selected from the Creator's searching through the vastness of the cosmos for life's best home. Rather, the remoteness of the probability of finding a planet fit for life suggests that the Creator personally and specially designed and constructed our galaxy cluster, our galaxy, our Sun, each of the Sun's planets and belts of asteroids and comets, Earth's collider, the Moon, and Earth for life.

If divine design is essential to explain the properties of simpler systems such as the universe, our galaxy, and the solar system, then God's involvement is even more essential to explain systems as complex as organisms, including human beings. I and my colleague Fazale Rana have described this much enhanced complexity in six other books and explained how it compels God's involvement.[56]

 Discussion Questions

1. Green galaxies are rare, and yet required for life. What are the problems for life in galaxies dominated by red stars or blue stars?

2. Describe some of the benefits of the Sun's unique location. Are we doing all we can to maximize our "window seat to the splendors of the universe"?

3. It is fair to assume that most people are unaware of the nine planetary habitable zones. How does this knowledge affect your conversations about exoplanets in the news?

4. The author tracks several remarkable admissions from lunar researchers who speak of fine-tuning and "philosophical disquiet." Do you see an entry point of discussion with people who hold this position and, if so, how would you approach it?

5. How does the Grand Tack model explain the solar system's formation and ability to sustain advanced life?

6. The list of parameters that must be fine-tuned for long-lasting microbial life to exist on a planet has grown to at least 676 and the probability for finding life on another planet has shrunk to 10^{-556}. What would be a good strategy for discussing these numbers with skeptics?

Chapter 18

Extradimensional and Transdimensional Powers

As we have seen in previous chapters, the recent measurements of the cosmos have revealed not only the existence of God but also his transcendence, his personality, and even his care and love for human beings. These discoveries lead to some important conclusions about the awesome power available to God and consequently the extent of his ability to bless humankind.

Because human beings can visualize phenomena only in dimensions that they can experience, in their attempts to describe God, they characterize him as a Being confined to a four-dimensional box. One reason we know the Bible comes from a supernatural source is that, just like the implications from the recent measurements of the cosmos, it claims that God is not so confined—he transcends the space-time dimensions of the universe. In its unique insistence that God moves and operates in dimensions independent of length, width, height, and time, the Bible not only insists on transdimensional and extradimensional capacities for God, but it also specifically describes how he functions in these extra dimensions (see table 11.1).

The Bible is unique, too, in describing certain attributes of God, such as the Trinity—in which God is depicted simultaneously as singular and plural, three Persons but one essence. It also portrays God as predetermining everything for us while simultaneously giving us freedom of choice. These concepts are provable contradictions if God is confined to just four dimensions, but each can be resolved by a God who both fills all 10 cosmic space-time dimensions and transcends them. Let us examine the Trinity and the nearness of God as specific examples.

The Trinity: An Absurdity?
Ironically, adherents of non-Christian religions—like Islam and the Jehovah's Witnesses—often appeal to limited dimensionality as a proof against

Christianity. Often I have encountered apologists from such faiths who state categorically Christianity is false since the Trinity is mathematically absurd.

My initial response is to agree. The Trinity is a mathematical absurdity in the context of a god limited in his operations to just the four dimensions of length, width, height, and time. Then I share with them the evidence from general relativity, the big bang, and particle physics for the existence of more dimensions besides the four we experience. Since God created and controls all these dimensions, he must be able to operate in them. The new physics proves, too, that he can create space-time dimensions at will and that he transcends all the space-time dimensions he has created or could create. A Trinitarian nature is no problem for such a Being. Neither is it a problem for him to predetermine (from his perspective transcendent of the space-time dimensions of the universe) all of our actions, words, and thoughts from before he created the universe 13.8 billion years ago, while at the present moment (from within the confines of those space-time dimensions) granting us the freedom to choose those actions, words, and thoughts.

Given the time and the interest, I can demonstrate to those skeptical about the Trinity how the God who both fills and transcends 10 space-time dimensions can manifest such characteristics and capabilities as the simultaneity of God's predetermination and human free choice, God's capacity to be both dead and alive, and several other paradoxical Christian doctrines. Indeed, this was the theme of my book *Beyond the Cosmos*.[1] The key point, however, is that we would expect human-invented theologies to be constrained by the limitations of human perspective, while a theological message from a transcendent Being should at least in some ways transcend the limits of human perspective and visualization.

Nearness of God
The Bible declares forthrightly that God is very close to each and every one of us.[2] But, it just as forthrightly states that God is invisible.[3] The apostle Paul says that no one has ever seen God, nor can see him.[4] Evidently, it is impossible for us to make physical contact with God. How, then, can God be so close and yet be beyond physical contact?

An analogy that might help was developed partly by Edwin Abbott, a nineteenth-century schoolmaster and preacher who published the book *Flatland: A Romance of Many Dimensions* in 1884.[5] Imagine a universe where only two dimensions of space exist rather than three. In such a universe, flatlanders would be confined to a plane of length and width with no possibility of operating in the dimension of height. A three-dimensional being then could approach the plane of the flatlanders and place his hand just a tenth of a millimeter above the two-dimensional bodies of two flatlanders separated from one another by just one centimeter. Since the three-dimensional being is slightly above the plane of the flatlanders, there is no possibility that the flatlanders can see him. And yet, the three-dimensional being is a hundred times closer to each of the flatlanders than they are to one another.

As with the flatlanders, so it is with human beings. God is closer to each of us than we ever can be to one another. But because God's proximity to us takes place in dimensions or realms we cannot tangibly experience, we cannot possibly see him.

The only way we could see God is if he were to place a portion of his being into our space-time fabric. This would be analogous to the three-dimensional being poking his finger through the plane of the flatlanders. If one of the flatlanders were to investigate, he would draw the conclusion that this visitor to their realm is a small circle. But what if the three-dimensional being were to separately reveal three of his fingers to the friend of that flatlander? The friend then would draw the conclusion that the visitor to their realm was not one small circle but rather three small circles. We could then imagine a theological debate between the two flatlanders that would end up with the first flatlander founding the Church of the One Circle while the second would establish the Church of the Three Circles.

This analogy may appear amusing, but it fairly represents what non-Christians have done with the Trinity or Tri-Unity of God. Some have accepted God's singularity but rejected his plurality while others accept his plurality and reject his singularity. Only Christians accept that God is simultaneously singular and plural.

Good That He Goes Away?

Just hours before Jesus was arrested by his enemies to be crucified, he told his disciples he would be leaving them.[6] He informed them that he would be returning to his Father. As he said these things, his disciples' hearts were filled with sorrow.[7] It's easy to understand their feelings but not so easy to understand his words of reassurance: "It is for your good that I am going away."[8]

How could Jesus's going away be good? And how does this statement fit with his promise to be with them always? Paul's letter to the Philippians sheds some light:

[Christ Jesus], being in very nature God,
    did not consider equality with God something to be grasped,
but made himself nothing,
    taking the very nature of a servant,
    being made in human likeness.
And being found in appearance as a man,
    he humbled himself
    and became obedient to death—even death on a cross!
Therefore God exalted him to the highest place
    and gave him the name that is above every name.[9]

Jesus Christ was fully God, sharing in all the power, all the authority, and all the extradimensional capabilities God possesses. But for our sake, Christ lowered himself and accepted the weakness and limitations of a human. He came into our dimensions to show us God, whom we could never otherwise picture, to give us an example of humility, and to pay the price for our redemption. After fulfilling his purpose in coming, Jesus once again took up all the power, authority, and transdimensional and extradimensional capacities that were rightfully his as God.

It is easy to empathize with the disciples' grief. Who would want to give up the tangible nearness of Jesus, seeing his face, hearing his words, feeling his touch, walking at his side? But as a human, Jesus could be in only one place at a time, holding one conversation at a time, performing one miracle at a time, etc. He needed rest, too.

Imagine all that he could gain by giving up his physical presence and regaining his extradimensional nearness. As he told his disciples, they would do greater miracles than the ones he had performed in front of them.[10] Further, he would never leave them, never fall asleep on them, never walk away to take care of someone else's need.[11] He could live in them, as well as beside them. The same powerful promise is made to all people who give their lives to Jesus Christ.

Discussion Questions _____

1. How does God's extradimensional power help our human limitations when it comes to difficult-to-understand doctrines such as the Trinity?
2. In the great "emptying" passage, Jesus humbled himself to the point of death on behalf of people he loved. What does this tell you about a God who possesses extra/transdimensional power and yet shows this kind of restraint?

Chapter 19

The Point

Several years ago, I spoke at a prestigious American university to a group of about 40 science professors. I presented much of the information that appears in the pages of this book. Afterward, I conversed with four physics professors and asked for their response.

One of the four said he could not deny the truth of my message. The others nodded in agreement. I asked if they could see, then, the rationality of turning over their lives to Jesus Christ. Another of the four spoke up, saying, yes, they could see it, but they weren't yet ready to be that rational.

This statement was not a brush-off. Each man went on to name his reasons for resistance. One confessed his unwillingness to give up sexual immorality. The others spoke of deep wounds inflicted long ago by people who called themselves Christians. What each of them needed and showed willingness to receive was compassion—not to mention further dialogue.

Other professors expressed their need for more time to assimilate the information, check references, and investigate the Bible for themselves. I could empathize. After all, it took me two years of study to become willing to entrust my life to God's care and keeping (see ch. 2).

The beauty of the scientific (and other) evidences God has allowed us to discover about him is that these meet the needs of two large segments of society: (1) those whose barriers to personal faith in Christ are intellectual, that is, barriers of misinformation and misunderstanding; and (2) those whose barriers to faith come from personal pain or stubborn rebellion lurking under the cover of intellectual objections.

Drawing Near to God

It is awesome and wonderful to behold the character of the Creator in what he has made, but not everyone seems to see it. In the elegant architecture of the universe, a galaxy cluster, a galaxy, the Sun, the planets, Earth, the Moon, a human being, or even the simplest living thing, some people are struck by the wisdom, power, and care of the Creator, while others see an amazing coincidence or the work of some unidentified extraterrestrials.

The book of Hebrews declares, "Anyone who comes to [God] must believe that he exists and that he rewards those who earnestly seek him."[1] In a sense, this verse sets forth a test of the heart. The person who wants to draw near to God must be (and will be) humble-hearted enough not only to see and accept his existence but also to see and trust his goodness, his love.

Israel's King David said, "The Lord is close to the brokenhearted." And "The Lord is near to all who call on him, to all who call on him in truth."[2]

Drawing near to God, calling on him "in truth," begins with humbly acknowledging *who we are*—his creation and no one else's, foolishly inclined to place ourselves or others in God's place of authority over our lives—and *who he is*—the Divine Maker and Provider of all things, including a way across the gulf that divides us from him.

Nature itself shows us these truths. But the Bible brings us the details and clarifies specifically how God bridges that gulf to bring us to himself in a personal, everlasting relationship.

His care for us and desire to draw us near are best demonstrated in Christ's coming to Earth to pay the death penalty for our rebellious nature. The Bible says that we "who once were far away have been brought near by the blood of Christ."[3]

The way has been made, it has been made clear, and it has been proven by the resurrection of Jesus Christ—a testable fact of history.[4] But knowing the way and knowing God are not one and the same thing.

The crucial difference lies in our moving beyond acceptance of facts to acceptance of him. Acceptance of his life in exchange for ours, of his death in exchange for ours, of his goodness in exchange for ours, of his authority in exchange for ours, even of his faithfulness in exchange for ours—this will be our step toward him. The Bible assures us that if we draw near to him, he will draw near to us.[5]

Why Extra Evidence to This Generation?

One question I hear often is, "Why has our generation been singled out to receive such an abundance of evidences for God and his Word?" Why have we been given so much more proof than previous generations?

The answer I see from the Bible is that God measures out evidence in direct proportion to the level of resistance to his truth. Where the resistance is relatively low, less hard evidence for the God of the Bible is necessary to overcome it. But where resistance, namely arrogance, is high, so also is the quantity and quality of evidence he provides to overcome it.

Let's consider our world today. We have the most wealth, the most discretionary time, the most education, and the most technology of any previous generation. And how do we respond to these blessings? The loudest voices say that we humans deserve all the credit. The loudest voices say that humanity is deity. Given such arrogance, no wonder evidences are being flooded upon us.

Though the opposition seems great, God has equipped us to overcome it. He says, "See, I have placed before you an open door that no one can shut."[6] Let's make good use of these evidences to build our own faith and the faith of others while he is still holding that door open.

 Discussion Questions _____

1. The author identifies two barriers to faith—intellectual and personal—that prevent people from embracing Christ. How will this book help you address the former? The latter?
2. What have you learned from reading this book? What will you do with the knowledge you've gained?

Evidence for the Fine-Tuning
of the Universe[1]

More than a hundred different parameters for the universe must have values falling within narrowly defined ranges for physical life of any conceivable kind to exist. This appendix includes just a partial list. A more complete list with scientific literature citations is available at reasons.org/finetuning.

1. strong nuclear force constant
    if larger: no hydrogen; nuclei essential for life would be unstable
    if smaller: no elements other than hydrogen
2. weak nuclear force constant
    if larger: too much hydrogen converted to helium in big bang, hence too much heavy-element material made by star burning; no expulsion of heavy elements from stars
    if smaller: too little helium produced from big bang, hence too little heavy-element material made by star burning; no expulsion of heavy elements from stars
3. gravitational force constant
    if larger: stars would be too hot and would burn up too quickly and too unevenly
    if smaller: stars would remain so cool that nuclear fusion would never ignite, hence no heavy-element production
4. electromagnetic force constant
    if larger: insufficient chemical bonding; elements more massive than boron would be too unstable
    if smaller: insufficient chemical bonding; inadequate quantities of either carbon or oxygen
5. ratio of electromagnetic force constant to gravitational force constant
    if larger: no stars of less than 1.4 solar masses, hence short stellar life

spans and uneven stellar luminosities

 if smaller: no stars of more than 0.8 solar masses, hence no heavy element production

6. ratio of electron to proton mass
    if larger: insufficient chemical bonding for stable molecules to be possible
    if smaller: insufficient chemical bonding for stable molecules to be possible

7. ratio of numbers of protons to electrons
    if larger: electromagnetism would dominate gravity, preventing galaxy, star, and planet formation
    if smaller: electromagnetism would dominate gravity, preventing galaxy, star, and planet formation

8. expansion rate of the universe
    if larger: no galaxy formation
    if smaller: universe would collapse prior to star formation

9. entropy level of the universe
    if larger: no star condensation within the proto-galaxies
    if smaller: no proto-galaxy formation

10. baryon or nucleon density of the universe
     if larger: too much deuterium from big bang, hence stars burn too rapidly
     if smaller: insufficient helium from big bang, hence too few heavy elements forming

11. velocity of light
     if faster: stars would be too luminous
     if slower: stars would not be luminous enough

12. age of the universe
     if older: no solar-type stars in a stable burning phase in the right part of the galaxy
     if younger: solar-type stars in a stable burning phase would not yet have formed

13. initial uniformity of cosmic radiation
     if smoother: stars, star clusters, and galaxies would not have formed
     if coarser: universe by now would be mostly black holes and empty space

14. fine structure constant (a number, 0.0073, used to describe the fine structure splitting of spectral lines)

if larger: DNA would be unable to function; no stars more than 0.7 solar masses

if larger than 0.06: matter would be unstable in large magnetic fields

if smaller: DNA would be unable to function; no stars less than 1.8 solar masses

15. average distance between galaxies

if larger: insufficient gas would be infused into our galaxy to sustain star formation over an adequate time span

if smaller: the Sun's orbit would be too radically disturbed

16. average distance between stars

if larger: heavy element density too thin for rocky planets to form

if smaller: planetary orbits would become destabilized

17. decay rate of the proton

if greater: life would be exterminated by the release of radiation

if smaller: insufficient matter in the universe for life

18. ^{12}Carbon (^{12}C) to ^{16}Oxygen (^{16}O) energy level ratio

if larger: insufficient oxygen

if smaller: insufficient carbon

19. ground state energy level for ^{4}Helium (^{4}He)

if higher: insufficient carbon and oxygen

If lower: insufficient carbon and oxygen

20. decay rate of ^{8}Beryllium (^{8}Be)

if faster: no element production beyond beryllium and, hence, no life chemistry possible

if slower: heavy element fusion would generate catastrophic explosions in all the stars

21. mass excess of the neutron over the proton

if greater: neutron decay would leave too few neutrons to form the heavy elements essential for life

if smaller: neutron decay would produce so many neutrons as to cause all stars to collapse rapidly into neutron stars or black holes

22. initial excess of nucleons over antinucleons

if greater: too much radiation for planets to form

if smaller: not enough matter for galaxies or stars to form

23. polarity of the water molecule

if greater: heat of fusion and vaporization would be too great for life to exist

if smaller: heat of fusion and vaporization would be too small for life's existence; liquid water would become too inferior a solvent for life chemistry to proceed; ice would not float, leading to a runaway freeze-up

24. supernova explosions

if too far away: not enough heavy element ashes for the formation of rocky planets

if too close: radiation would exterminate life on the planet; planet formation would be disrupted

if too frequent: life on the planet would be exterminated

if too infrequent: not enough heavy element ashes for the formation of rocky planets

if too soon: not enough heavy element ashes for the formation of rocky planets

if too late: life on the planet would be exterminated by radiation

25. white dwarf binaries

if too many: disruption of planetary orbits from stellar density; life on the planet would be exterminated

if too few: insufficient fluorine produced for life chemistry to proceed

if too soon: not enough heavy elements made for efficient fluorine production

if too late: fluorine made too late for incorporation in proto-planet

26. ratio of exotic to ordinary matter

if larger: universe would collapse before solar-type stars could form

if smaller: galaxies would not form

27. galaxy clusters

if too dense: galaxy collisions and mergers would disrupt star and planet orbits; too much radiation

if too sparse: insufficient infusion of gas into galaxies to sustain star formation for a long enough time

28. number of effective dimensions in the early universe

if larger: quantum mechanics, gravity, and relativity could not coexist and life would be impossible

if smaller: quantum mechanics, gravity, and relativity could not coexist and life would be impossible

29. number of effective dimensions in the present universe

if larger: electron, planet, and star orbits would become unstable

if smaller: electron, planet, and star orbits would become unstable

30. mass values for the active neutrinos

if larger: galaxy clusters and galaxies would be too dense
if smaller: galaxy clusters, galaxies, and stars would not form

31. big bang ripples
    if smaller: galaxies would not form; universe expands too rapidly
    if larger: galaxy clusters and galaxies would be too dense; black holes would dominate; universe collapses too quickly

32. total mass density
    if larger: universe would expand too slowly, resulting in unstable orbits and too much radiation; random velocities between galaxies and galaxy clusters would be too large
    if smaller: universe would expand too quickly for solar-type stars to form

33. dark energy density
    if larger: universe would expand too quickly for solar-type stars to form
    if smaller: universe would expand too slowly, resulting in unstable orbits and too much radiation

34. size of the relativistic dilation factor
    if larger: certain life-essential chemical reactions would not function properly
    if smaller: certain life-essential chemical reactions would not function properly

35. uncertainty magnitude in the Heisenberg uncertainty principle
    if larger: certain life-essential elements would be unstable; certain life-essential chemical reactions would not function properly
    if smaller: oxygen transport to body cells would be inadequate; certain life-essential elements would be unstable; certain life-essential chemical reactions would not function properly

36. density of neutrinos
    if larger: galaxy clusters and galaxies would be too dense; supernova eruptions would be too violent
    if smaller: galaxy clusters, galaxies, and stars would not form; inadequate supernova eruptions resulting in too few heavy elements dispersed into the interstellar medium

37. ratio of proton to electron charge
    if larger: inadequate chemical bonding
    if smaller: inadequate chemical bonding

38. ratio of cosmic mass density to dark energy density

if larger: galaxies, stars, and planets needed for life would form at the wrong time or the wrong location or both

if smaller: galaxies, stars, and planets needed for life would form at the wrong time or the wrong location or both

39. initial homogeneity of the universe

if greater: no galaxies or stars form

if lesser: black holes form before any stars form; no nuclear-burning stars

40. number of neutrino species

if less than 3:   big bang fuses insufficient helium from hydrogen, resulting in inadequate life-essential elements

if more than 4:   big bang fuses too much helium from hydrogen, resulting in inadequate life-essential elements

41. ratio of ordinary matter to exotic matter

if larger: rotation curves of spiral galaxies would not be flat enough; galaxy clusters would not be in virial equilibrium

if smaller: insufficient star formation

42. density of giant galaxies during early cosmic history

if larger: galaxy cluster suitable for advanced life will never form

if smaller: galaxy cluster suitable for advanced life will never form

43. epoch for peak of hypernova eruptions events

if earlier: density of heavy elements will be too high at best epoch for life

if later: density of heavy elements will be too low at best epoch for life

44. epoch for peak of supernova eruptions events

if earlier: density of heavy elements will be too high at best epoch for life

if later: density of heavy elements will be too low at best epoch for life

45. number of different kinds of supernovae

if lower: some of the elements essential for life will be missing

46. number of supernova eruption events

if too many: too much heavy element production for life to exist

if too few: inadequate production of heavy elements for life to exist

47. decay rate of an isolated neutron

if faster: big bang would fuse too little hydrogen into helium, resulting in inadequate life-essential elements *if slower:*   big bang would fuse too much hydrogen into helium, resulting in inadequate life-essential elements

48. density of metal-free population III stars in early universe

if higher: cosmic metallicity at optimal time for life will be too high; too much gas will be blown out of primordial galaxies

if lower: cosmic metallicity at optimal time for life will be too low; too little gas will be blown out of primordial galaxies

49. average mass of metal-free population III stars

if larger: these stars will not scatter any of their heavy elements into interstellar space

if smaller: these stars will scatter an insufficient quantity of heavy elements into interstellar space

50. water's heat of vaporization

if larger: liquid water would evaporate too slowly

if smaller: liquid water would evaporate too rapidly

51. hypernova eruptions

if too many: relative abundances of heavy elements on rocky planets would be inappropriate for life; too many collision events in planetary systems

if too few: not enough heavy element ashes present for the formation of rocky planets

if too soon: leads to a galaxy evolution history that would disturb the possibility of advanced life; not enough heavy element ashes present for the formation of rocky planets

if too late: leads to a galaxy evolution history that would disturb the possibility of advanced life; relative abundances of heavy elements on rocky planets would be inappropriate for life; too many collision events in planetary systems

52. H_3^+ production amount

if too large: planets will form at wrong time and place for life

if too small: simple molecules essential to planet formation and life chemistry will not form

53. density of quasars

if larger: too much cosmic dust forms; too many stars form too late, disrupting the formation of a solar-type star at right time and right conditions for life

if smaller: insufficient production and ejection of cosmic dust into the intergalactic medium; ongoing star formation impeded;

deadly radiation unblocked

54. density of giant galaxies in the early universe

   if larger: too large a quantity of metals ejected into the intergalactic medium, providing future stars with too high of a metallicity for a life-support planet at the right time in cosmic history

   if smaller: insufficient metals ejected into the intergalactic medium, depriving future generations of stars of the metal abundances necessary for a life-support planet at the right time in cosmic history

55. masses of stars that become hypernovae

   if too massive: all the metals produced by the hypernova eruptions collapse into black holes resulting from the eruptions, leaving none of the metals available for future generations of stars

   if not massive enough: insufficient metals are ejected into the interstellar medium for future star generations to make stars and planets suitable for the support of life

56. density of gamma-ray burst events

   if larger: frequency and intensity of mass extinction events will be too high

   if smaller: not enough production of copper, scandium, titanium, and zinc

57. intensity of primordial cosmic superwinds

   if too low: inadequate star formation late in cosmic history

   if too great: inadequate star formation early in cosmic history

58. smoking quasars

   if too many: early star formation will be too vigorous, resulting in too few stars and planets being able to form late in cosmic history

   if too few: inadequate primordial dust production for stimulating future star formation

59. level of supersonic turbulence in the infant universe

   if too low: first stars will be the wrong type and quantity to produce the necessary mix of elements, gas, and dust so that a future star and planetary system capable of supporting life will appear at the right time in cosmic history

   if too high: first stars will be the wrong type and quantity to produce the necessary mix of elements, gas, and dust so that a future star and planetary system capable of supporting life will appear at the right time in cosmic history

60. rate at which the triple-alpha process (combining of three helium nuclei to make one carbon nucleus) runs inside the nuclear furnaces of stars

if too high: stars would manufacture too much carbon and other heavy elements; stars may be too bright

if too low: stars would not manufacture enough carbon and other heavy elements to make advanced life possible before cosmic conditions would rule out the possibility of advanced life; stars may be too dim

Evidence for the Fine-Tuning of the Milky Way Galaxy, Solar System, and Earth

The following parameters of a planet, its moon, its star, and its galaxy must have values falling within narrowly defined ranges for life of any kind to exist. A more complete list with breakdowns for different kinds of life with scientific literature citations is available at reasons.org/finetuning.

1. galaxy cluster type
   if too sparse: insufficient infusion of gas to sustain star formation for a long enough time
   if too rich: galaxy collisions and mergers would disrupt solar orbit
2. galaxy mass
   if too small: starburst episodes would occur too late in the history of the galaxy; galaxy would absorb too few dwarf and super-dwarf galaxies, thereby failing to sustain star formation over a long enough time; structure of galaxy may become too distorted by gravitational encounters with nearby large- and medium-sized galaxies
   if too large: starburst episodes would occur too early in the history of the galaxy; galaxy would absorb too many medium-sized, dwarf, and ultra-dwarf galaxies, making radiation from the supermassive black hole in the galaxy's core too deadly and disturbing the galaxy's spiral structure too radically
3. galaxy type
   if too elliptical: star formation would cease before sufficient heavy element build-up for life chemistry
   if too irregular: radiation exposure would be too severe on occasion and not all the heavy elements for life chemistry would be available

4. galaxy-mass distribution

   if too much in the central bulge: a life-supportable planet would be exposed to too much radiation

   if too much in the spiral arms: a life-supportable planet would be destabilized by the gravity and radiation from adjacent spiral arms

5. galaxy location

   if too close to a rich galaxy cluster: galaxy would be gravitationally disrupted

   if too close to a very large galaxy or galaxies: galaxy would be gravitationally disrupted

   if too far from dwarf galaxies: insufficient infall of gas and dust to sustain ongoing star formation

6. proximity of solar nebula to a supernova eruption

   if closer: nebula would be blown apart

   if farther: insufficient heavy elements for life would be absorbed

7. timing of solar nebula formation relative to a supernova eruption at even the right distance

   if earlier: nebula would be blown apart (because it would not have sufficiently collapsed to hold together)

   if later: nebula would not absorb enough heavy elements

8. number of stars in parent star birth aggregate

   if too few: insufficient input of certain heavy elements into the solar nebula

   if too many: planetary formation and planetary orbits would be too radically disturbed

9. star formation history in parent star vicinity

   if too much too soon: planet formation and planetary orbits would be too radically disturbed

10. birth date of the star-planetary system

    if too early: quantity of heavy elements would be too low for large rocky planets to form

    if too late: star would not yet have reached stable burning phase; ratios of potassium-40, uranium-235, -238, and thorium-232 to iron would be too low for long-lived plate tectonics to be sustained on a rocky planet

11. parent star distance from center of galaxy

if closer: galactic radiation would be too great; stellar density would disturb planetary orbits; wrong abundances of silicon, sulfur, and magnesium relative to iron for appropriate planet core characteristics

if farther: quantity of heavy elements would be insufficient to make rocky planets; wrong abundances of silicon, sulfur, and magnesium relative to iron for appropriate planet core characteristics

12. z-axis heights of star's orbit

if too great: exposure to harmful radiation from the galactic bulge and nearby spiral arms would be too great when it gets too far above or below the galactic plane

13. parent star age

if younger: luminosity of star would change too quickly

if older: luminosity of star would change too quickly

14. parent star mass

if less: range of planet distances for life would be too narrow; tidal forces would disrupt planet rotational period; stellar flare activity would be too great, ultraviolet radiation would be too variable for plants

if greater: luminosity of star would change too quickly; star would burn too rapidly

15. parent star metallicity

if too small: insufficient heavy elements for life chemistry would exist

if too great: life would be poisoned by certain heavy element concentrations

16. parent star color

if redder: photosynthetic response would be insufficient

if bluer: photosynthetic response would be insufficient

17. galactic tides

if too weak: too low of a comet ejection rate from giant planet region and beyond

if too strong: too high of a comet ejection rate from giant planet region and beyond

18. flux of cosmic-ray protons (one way cloud droplets are seeded)

if too small: inadequate cloud formation in planet's troposphere

if too large: too much cloud formation in planet's troposphere

19. solar wind

if too weak: too many cosmic-ray protons reach planet's troposphere causing too much cloud formation; too much incident deadly cosmic radiation

if too strong: too few cosmic-ray protons reach planet's troposphere causing too little cloud formation; too much incident deadly solar radiation

20. parent star luminosity relative to speciation of life

if increases too soon: runaway greenhouse effect would develop

if increases too late: runaway glaciation would develop

21. surface gravity (escape velocity)

if stronger: planet's atmosphere would retain too much ammonia and methane

if weaker: planet's atmosphere would lose too much water

22. distance from parent star

if farther: planet would be too cool for a stable, efficient water cycle

if closer: planet would be too warm for a stable, efficient water cycle

23. inclination of orbit

if too great: seasonal differences on the planet would be too extreme

if too small: small seasonal differences would limit abundance and diversity of life

24. orbital eccentricity

if too great: seasonal temperature differences would be too extreme

25. axial tilt

if greater: latitudinal surface temperature differences would be too great

if less: latitudinal surface temperature differences would be too great

26. rate of change of axial tilt

if greater: climatic changes would be too extreme; surface temperature differences could become too extreme

27. rotation period

if longer: diurnal temperature differences would be too great

if shorter: atmospheric jet streams would become too laminar and average wind speeds would increase too much

28. planet's magnetic field

if stronger: electromagnetic storms would be too severe; too few cosmic-ray protons would reach planet's troposphere, inhibiting adequate cloud formation

if weaker: ozone shield would be inadequately protected from hard stellar and solar radiation; time between magnetic reversals would be too brief for the long term maintenance of advanced life civilization

29. thickness of crust

if thicker: too much oxygen would be transferred from the atmosphere to the crust and the volcanic and tectonic activity necessary for continental buildup would be too weak

if thinner: volcanic and tectonic activity would be too great

30. albedo (ratio of reflected light to total amount falling on surface)

if greater: runaway glaciation would develop

if less: runaway greenhouse effect would develop

31. asteroidal and cometary collision rate

if greater: too many species would become extinct

if less: crust would be too depleted of materials essential for life

32. oxygen to nitrogen ratio in atmosphere

if larger: advanced life functions would proceed too quickly

if smaller: advanced life functions would proceed too slowly

33. carbon dioxide level in atmosphere

if greater: runaway greenhouse effect would develop

if less: plants would be unable to maintain efficient photosynthesis

34. water vapor level in atmosphere

if greater: runaway greenhouse effect would develop

if less: precipitation would be too meager for life on the land

35. ozone level in stratosphere

if greater: surface temperatures would be too low; insufficient long wavelength ultraviolet radiation at the surface for life-critical biochemistry to operate

if less: surface temperatures would be too high; too much deadly ultraviolet radiation at planet surface

36. oxygen quantity in atmosphere

if greater: plants and hydrocarbons would burn up too easily

if less: advanced animals would have too little to breathe

37. nitrogen quantity in atmosphere

if greater: too much buffering of oxygen for advanced animal respiration; too much nitrogen fixation for support of diverse plant species; greenhouse effect would be too enhanced

if less: too little buffering of oxygen for advanced animal respiration; too little nitrogen fixation for support of diverse plant species; insufficient enhancement of greenhouse effect

38. ratio of potassium-40, uranium-235, -238, and thorium-232 to iron for the planet

   if too low: inadequate levels of plate tectonic and volcanic activity

   if too high: radiation, earthquakes, and volcanic activity at levels too high for advanced life

39. rate of planet's interior heat loss

   if too low: inadequate energy to drive the required levels of plate tectonic and volcanic activity

   if too high: plate tectonic and volcanic activity shuts down too quickly

40. seismic activity

   if greater: too many life-forms would be destroyed; continents would grow too large; vertical relief on the continents would become too great; too much erosion of silicates would remove too much carbon dioxide from the atmosphere

   if less: nutrients on ocean floors from river runoff would not be recycled to continents through tectonics; too little erosion of silicates would remove insufficient carbon dioxide from the atmosphere; continents would not grow large enough; vertical relief on the continents would be inadequate for the proper distribution of rainfall, snow pack, and erosion

41. volcanic activity

   if lower: insufficient amounts of carbon dioxide and water vapor would be returned to the atmosphere; soil mineralization would become too degraded for life

   if higher: advanced life, at least, would be destroyed

42. timing of the initiation of continent formation

   if too early: silicate-carbonate cycle would be destabilized

   if too late: silicate-carbonate cycle would be destabilized

43. soil mineralization

   if too nutrient-poor: no possibility of life or complexity of life would be limited

   if too nutrient-rich: no possibility of life or complexity of life would be limited

44. gravitational interaction with a moon

   if much greater: axial tilt variations would make life impossible

   if greater: tidal effects on the oceans, atmosphere, and rotational period would be too severe

   if much less: axial tilt instabililty would make advanced life impossible *if less:*   orbital obliquity changes would cause climatic instabilities; movement of nutrients and life from the oceans to the continents and vice versa would be insufficient; magnetic field would be too weak

45. Jupiter's distance

if greater: too many asteroid and comet collisions would occur on Earth

if less: Earth's orbit would become unstable; Jupiter's presence would too radically disturb or prevent the formation of Earth

46. Jupiter's mass

if greater: Earth's orbit would become unstable; Jupiter's presence would too radically disturb or prevent the formation of Earth

if less: too many asteroid and comet collisions would occur on Earth

47. inward drift in major planet distances

if greater: Earth's orbit would become unstable

if less: too many asteroid and comet collisions would occur on Earth

48. major planet eccentricities

if greater: orbit of life-supportable planet would be pulled out of life-support zone; too many asteroid and comet collisions

49. major planet orbital instabilities and mean motion resonances

if greater: orbit of life-supportable planet would be pulled out of life-support zone; too many asteroid and comet collisions

50. mass of Neptune

if too small: not enough Kuiper Belt objects (asteroids and comets beyond Neptune) would be scattered out of the solar system

if too large: chaotic resonances among the gas giant planets would occur

51. Kuiper Belt of asteroids (beyond Neptune)

if not massive enough: Neptune's orbit remains too eccentric, which destabilizes the orbits of other solar system planets

if too massive: too many chaotic resonances and collisions would occur in the solar system

52. separation distances among inner terrestrial planets

if too small: orbits of all inner planets would become unstable in less than 100,000,000 million years

if too large: orbits of the inner planets most distant from star would become chaotic

53. continental relief

if smaller: insufficient variation in climate and weather; rate of silicate weathering would be too small *if greater:*   too much variation in climate and weather; rate of silicate weathering would be too great

54. chlorine quantity in atmosphere
   if smaller: erosion rates, acidity of rivers, lakes, and soils, and certain metabolic rates would be insufficient for most life-forms
   if greater: erosion rates, acidity of rivers, lakes, and soils, and certain metabolic rates would be too high for most life-forms

55. iron quantity in oceans and soils
   if smaller: quantity and diversity of life would be too limited to support advanced life; if very small, no life would be possible
   if larger: iron poisoning of at least advanced life would result

56. tropospheric ozone quantity
   if smaller: insufficient cleansing of biochemical smogs
   if larger: respiratory failure of advanced animals, reduced crop yields, and destruction of ozone-sensitive species

57. mesospheric ozone quantity
   if smaller: circulation and chemistry of mesospheric gases so disturbed as to upset relative abundances of life-essential gases in lower atmosphere
   if greater: circulation and chemistry of mesospheric gases so disturbed as to upset relative abundances of life-essential gases in lower atmosphere

58. quantity and extent of forest fires
   if smaller: growth inhibitors in the soils would accumulate; soil nitrification would be insufficient; insufficient charcoal production for adequate soil water retention and absorption of certain growth inhibitors; inadequate coverage of the planet by grasslands and savannas
   if greater: too many plant and animal life-forms would be destroyed; too many forests would convert to savannas and grasslands; less carbon dioxide would be removed from the atmosphere, resulting in global warming; less rainfall

59. quantity and extent of grass fires
   if smaller: growth inhibitors in the soils would accumulate; soil nitrification would be insufficient; insufficient charcoal production for adequate soil water retention and absorption of certain growth inhibitors
   if greater: too many plant and animal life-forms would be destroyed;

too many savannas and grasslands would be converted to deserts; less rainfall

60. quantity of soil sulfur

if smaller: plants would become deficient in certain proteins and die

if larger: plants would die from sulfur toxins; acidity of water and soil would become too great for life; nitrogen cycles would be disturbed

61. density of quasars in host galaxy's vicinity

if smaller: insufficient production and ejection of cosmic dust into the intergalactic medium; ongoing star formation impeded; deadly radiation unblocked

if larger: too much cosmic dust forms; too many stars form too soon, disrupting the formation of a solar-type star at the right time and under the right conditions for life

62. density of giant galaxies in host galaxy vicinity

if smaller: insufficient metals ejected into the intergalactic medium, depriving future generations of stars of the metal abundances necessary for a life-support planet at the right time in cosmic history

if larger: too large a quantity of metals ejected into the intergalactic medium, providing future stars with too high of a metallicity for a life-support planet at the right time in cosmic history

63. giant star density in galaxy

if smaller: insufficient production of galactic dust; ongoing star formation impeded; deadly radiation unblocked

if larger: too much galactic dust forms; too many stars form too early, disrupting the formation of a solar-type star at the right time and under the right conditions for life

64. rate of sedimentary loading at crustal subduction zones

if smaller: too few instabilities to trigger the movement of crustal plates into the mantle thereby disrupting carbonate-silicate cycle

if larger: too many instabilities triggering too many crustal plates to move down into the mantle thereby disrupting carbonate-silicate cycle

65. poleward heat transport in planet's atmosphere

if smaller: disruption of climates and ecosystems; lowered biomass and species diversity; decreased storm activity and precipitation

if larger: disruption of climates and ecosystems; lowered biomass and species diversity; increased storm activity

66. polycyclic aromatic hydrocarbon abundance in solar nebula

if smaller: planet formation process would be too inefficient; insufficient early production of asteroids, which would prevent a planet like Earth from receiving adequate delivery of heavy elements and carbonaceous material for life, advanced life in particular

if larger: planet formation process would too efficient; early production of asteroids would be too great, resulting in too many collision events for a planet arising out of the nebula that could support life

67. phosphorus and iron absorption by banded iron formations

if smaller: overproduction of cyanobacteria would have consumed too much carbon dioxide and released too much oxygen into Earth's atmosphere thereby overcompensating for the increase in the Sun's luminosity (too much reduction in atmospheric greenhouse efficiency)

if larger: underproduction of cyanobacteria would have consumed too little carbon dioxide and released too little oxygen into Earth's atmosphere thereby undercompensating for the increase in the Sun's luminosity (too little reduction in atmospheric greenhouse efficiency)

68. silicate dust annealing by nebular shocks

if too little: rocky planets with efficient plate tectonics cannot form

if too much: too many collisions in planetary system; orbital instabilities in planetary system too severe

69. size of galactic central bulge

if smaller: inadequate production of life-essential heavy elements; inadequate infusion of gas and dust into the spiral arms, preventing solar type stars from forming at the right locations late enough in the galaxy's history

if larger: radiation from the bulge region would kill life on a life-support planet and generate the wrong kinds of spiral arms

70. solar magnetic activity level

if smaller: solar wind would inadequately repel or dampen cosmic rays

if greater: solar luminosity fluctuations would be too large; solar flares would be too frequent and intense

71. quantity of geobacteraceae

if smaller or nonexistent: polycyclic aromatic hydrocarbons accumulate in the surface environment thereby contaminating the environment for other life-forms

if greater: could crowd out other important bacterial species

72. quantity of aerobic photoheterotrophic bacteria

if smaller: inadequate recycling of both organic and inorganic carbon in the oceans

if greater: could crowd out other important bacterial species

73. average rainfall and snowfall precipitation

if too small: inadequate water supplies for land-based life; inadequate erosion of landmasses to sustain the carbonate-silicate cycle; inadequate erosion to sustain certain species of ocean life that are vital for the existence of all life

if too large: too much erosion of landmasses, which upsets the carbonate-silicate cycle and hastens the extinction of many species of life vital for life's existence

74. distance from nearest black hole

if too close: radiation would prove deadly for life

75. density of black holes in vicinity of potential life-support planet

if too high: radiation would prove deadly for life

76. water absorption capacity of planet's lower mantle

if too low: too much water on planet's surface; no continental landmasses; too little plate tectonic activity; carbonate-silicate cycle disrupted

if too high: too little water on planet's surface; too little plate tectonic activity; carbonate-silicate cycle disrupted

77. ratio of inner dark halo mass to stellar mass for galaxy

if too low: co-rotation distance is too close to the galactic center exposing the life-support planet to too much radiation and too many gravitational disturbances

if too high: co-rotation distance is too far from the galactic center, making it very unlikely that the solar system would be ejected that far from its birth star cluster

78. star rotation rate

if too slow: too weak of a magnetic field, resulting in not enough protection from cosmic rays for the life-support planet

if too fast: too much chromospheric emission, causing radiation problems for the life-support planet

79. aerosol particle density emitted from forests
    if too low: too little cloud condensation, which reduces precipitation, lowers the albedo (planetary reflectivity), and disturbs climates on a global scale
    if too high: too much cloud condensation, which increases precipitation, raises the albedo (planetary reflectivity), and disturbs climate on a global scale; too much smog

80. density of interstellar and interplanetary dust particles in vicinity of life-support planet
    if too low: inadequate delivery of life-essential materials; undercompensates for the luminosity of the host star
    if too high: disturbs climate too radically on life-support planet; overcompensates for the luminosity of the host star

81. thickness of mid-mantle boundary
    if too thin: mantle convection eddies become too strong; tectonic activity and silicate production become too great
    if too thick: mantle convection eddies become too weak; tectonic activity and silicate production become too small

82. galaxy cluster density
    if too low: insufficient infall of gas, dust, and dwarf galaxies into a large galaxy that eventually could form a life-supportable planet
    if too high: gravitational influences from nearby galaxies would disturb orbit of the star with a life-supportable planet thereby exposing that planet to either deadly radiation or gravitational disturbances from other stars in that galaxy

83. star formation rate in solar neighborhood during past 4 billion years
    if too high: life on Earth would be exposed to deadly radiation or Earth's orbit would be disturbed

84. cosmic-ray luminosity of Milky Way Galaxy
    if too low: not enough production of boron
    if too high: life spans for advanced life too short; too much destruction of planet's ozone layer; overproduction of boron

85. air turbulence in troposphere
    if too low: inadequate formation of water droplets
    if too great: rainfall distribution would be too uneven; storms would be too severe

86. quantity of phytoplankton
    if too low: inadequate production of molecular oxygen and inadequate

production of maritime sulfate aerosols (cloud condensation nuclei); inadequate consumption of carbon dioxide

if too great: too much cooling of sea surface waters and possibly too much reduction of ozone quantity in lower stratosphere; too much consumption of carbon dioxide

87. quantity of iodocarbon-emitting marine organisms

if too low: inadequate marine cloud cover; inadequate precipitation

if too great: too much marine cloud cover; too much cooling of Earth's surface

88. mantle plume production

if too low: inadequate volcanic and island production rate

if too great: too much destruction and atmospheric disturbance from volcanic eruptions

89. quantity of magnetars (proto-neutron stars with very strong magnetic fields)

if too few during galaxy's history: inadequate quantities of r-process elements synthesized

if too many during galaxy's history: too great a quantity of r-process elements synthesized; too great of a high-energy cosmic-ray production

90. frequency of gamma-ray bursts in galaxy

if too low: inadequate production of copper, titanium, and zinc; insufficient hemisphere-wide mass extinction events

if too great: too much production of copper and zinc; too many hemisphere-wide mass extinction events

91. parent star magnetic field

if too low: solar wind and solar magnetosphere would not be adequate to thwart a significant amount of cosmic rays

if too great: too high of an x-ray flux would be generated

92. level of outward migration of Neptune

if too low: total mass of Kuiper Belt objects would be too great; Kuiper Belt too close to the Sun; Neptune's orbit not be circular enough and distant enough to guarantee long-term stability of inner solar system planets' orbits

if too great: Kuiper Belt too distant and contain too little mass to play any significant role in contributing volatiles to life-support planet or to contributing to mass extinction events; Neptune would be too distant to play a role in contributing to the long-term stability of inner solar system planets' orbits

93. Q-value (rigidity) of Earth during its early history

if too low: final obliquity (axial tilt) of Earth becomes too high; rotational braking of Earth too low

if too great: final obliquity of Earth becomes too low; rotational braking of Earth is too great

94. parent star distance from galaxy's co-rotation circle

if too close: a strong mean motion resonance would destabilize the parent star's galactic orbit

if too far: planetary system would experience too many crossings of the spiral arms

95. frequency of late impacts by large asteroids and comets

if too low: too few mass extinction events; inadequate rich ore deposits of ferrous and heavy metals

if too many: too many mass extinction events; disturbances of planet's crust too radical

96. size of the carbon sink in the deep mantle of the planet

if too small: carbon dioxide level in planet's atmosphere would be too high

if too large: carbon dioxide level in planet's atmosphere would be too low; biomass would be too small

97. growth rate of central spheroid for the galaxy

if too small: inadequate flow of heavy elements into the spiral disk; inadequate outward drift of stars from the inner to the central portions of the spiral disk

if too large: inadequate spiral disk for late-born stars

98. amount of gas infalling into the central core of the galaxy

if too little: galaxy's nuclear bulge becomes too large

if too much: galaxy's nuclear bulge fails to become large enough

99. level of cooling of gas infalling into the central core of the galaxy

if too low: galaxy's nuclear bulge becomes too large

if too high: galaxy's nuclear bulge fails to become large enough

100. ratio of dual water molecules, $(H_2O)_2$, to single water molecules, H_2O, in the troposphere

if too low: inadequate raindrop formation; inadequate rainfall

if too high: distribution of rainfall over planet's surface too uneven

101. quantity of volatiles on and in Earth-sized planet in the habitable zone

if too low: inadequate ingredients for the support of life; atmosphere would be too thin; oceans would be too shallow or nonexistent

if too high: no possibility for a means to compensate for luminosity changes in star; atmosphere would be too thick; oceans would be too deep

102. level of spiral substructure in spiral galaxy

if too low: galaxy would not be old enough to sustain advanced life

if too high: gravitational chaos would disturb planetary system's orbit about center of galaxy and thereby expose the planetary system to deadly radiation or disturbances by gas or dust clouds or both

103. mass ratio of inner gas giant planet to outer gas giant planet

if greater by 50%: resonances would generate non-coplanar planetary orbits, which would destabilize orbit of life-support planet

if lesser by 25%: mass of the inner gas giant planet necessary to adequately protect life-support planet from asteroidal and cometary collisions would be large enough to gravitationally disturb the orbit of the life-support planet

104. timing of late heavy bombardment

if too early: bombardment of Earth would be too intense; too much mass accretion; too severe a disruption of mantle and core; too much core growth

if too late: bombardment of Earth would not be intense enough; too little oxygen would be delivered to the core; too little core growth; too little life history time

105. degree of continental landmass barrier to oceans along rotation axis

if too low: rotation rate of planet slows down too slowly

if too high: rotation rate of planet slows down too quickly

106. lifetimes of methane in different atmospheric layers

if too short: greenhouse gas input to atmosphere inadequate to prevent runaway freezing of planetary surface

if too long: greenhouse gas input to atmosphere launches a runaway evaporation of planet's surface water

107. release rate of biogenic bromides into the atmosphere

if too low: tropospheric ozone and nitrogen oxides abundances in the atmosphere would be too high for healthy land life;

greenhouse effect of the atmosphere may be too high to compensate for changes in solar luminosity; too much ultraviolet radiation blocked out, causing plant growth to suffer

if too high: tropospheric ozone in the atmosphere would be too low to maintain a clean enough atmosphere for healthy land life; greenhouse effect of the atmosphere may be too low to compensate for changes in solar luminosity; ozone abundance in stratosphere would become too low to block out enough UV radiation to protect surface life

108. height of the tallest trees

if too low: inadequate interception and capture of water from rolling fog; inadequate buildup of soil nutrients and biodeposits; loss of quality timber for sustaining human civilization

if too high: inadequate tree growth efficiency; greater level of tree damage

109. mass of ordinary dark matter halo surrounding the galaxy

if too small: spiral structure cannot be maintained long term; galaxy would grow too rapidly; galaxy structure would become too disturbed

if too large: spiral structure cannot be maintained long term; galaxy would not grow rapidly enough; galaxy structure would become too disturbed

110. mass of exotic dark matter halo surrounding the galaxy

if too small: spiral structure cannot be maintained long term; galaxy would grow too rapidly; galaxy structure would become too disturbed

if too large: spiral structure cannot be maintained long term; galaxy would not grow rapidly enough; galaxy structure would become too disturbed

111. density of ultra-dwarf galaxies (or supermassive globular clusters) in vicinity of the galaxy

if too low: spiral structure would not be adequately sustained; heavy element flow into galactic habitable zone would be inadequate; galactic structure stability would not be adequately maintained

if too high: galactic core would produce too much deadly radiation; too many heavy elements would be funneled into the galactic habitable zone; galactic structure stability would not be

adequately maintained
112. formation rate of molecular hydrogen on dust grain surfaces when the galaxy is young
    if too low: too few stars would form during the early history of the galaxy, which would delay the possible formation of a planetary system capable of sustaining advanced life past the narrow epoch in the galaxy's history during which advanced life could exist
    if too high: too many stars would form during the early history of the galaxy, which would lead to the shutdown of star formation and spiral structure before the epoch during which a planetary system capable of sustaining advanced life could form
113. intensity of far ultraviolet radiation from nearby stars when circumsolar disk was condensing into planets
    if too much weaker: Saturn, Uranus, Neptune, and Kuiper Belt would have been much more massive, making advanced life on Earth impossible
    if too much stronger: Uranus, Neptune, and the Kuiper Belt would never have formed and Saturn would have been smaller, making advanced life on Earth impossible
114. amount of methane generated in upper mantle of planet
    if too small: inadequate delivery of methane to planet's atmosphere, causing too little solar heat to be trapped by the atmosphere
    if too large: too great a delivery of methane to planet's atmosphere, causing too much solar heat to be trapped by the atmosphere
115. level of biogenic mixing of seafloor sediments
    if too low: too low of a level of marine sediment oxygen resulting in a too low biomass and nutrient budget for marine coastal ecosystems; disruption of biogeochemical cycles
116. production of organic aerosols in the atmosphere
    if too small: depending on the particular aerosol, either too little solar radiation is reflected into space or too little solar radiation is absorbed into the troposphere
    if too large: depending on the particular aerosol, either too much solar radiation is reflected into space or too much solar radiation is absorbed into the troposphere
117. total mass of primordial Kuiper Belt of asteroids and comets
    if too small: inadequate outward drift of Jupiter, Saturn, Uranus, and

>
> Neptune; inadequate circularization of the orbits of Jupiter, Saturn, Uranus, and Neptune; late heavy bombardment of Earth would not be intense enough to bring about the necessary chemical transformation of Earth's crust, mantle, and core; inadequate delivery of water and other volatiles to Earth
>
> *if too large:* too much outward drift of Jupiter, Saturn, Uranus, and Neptune; late heavy bombardment of Earth would be too intense; too much delivery of water and other volatiles to Earth

118. quantity of sub-seafloor hypersaline anoxic bacteria

> *if too small:* inadequate sulfate reduction and methanogenesis to sustain the global chemical cycles essential for sustaining advanced life and human civilization; inadequate supply of concentrated metal ores for sustaining human civilization
>
> *if too large:* too high of a level of sulfate reduction and methanogenesis to sustain the global chemical cycles essential for sustaining advanced life and human civilization

119. mass of moon orbiting life-support planet

> *if too small:* inadequate ocean tides; planet's rotation rate would not slow down fast enough to make advanced life possible; a mass lower than about a third of the Moon's would not be adequate to stabilize the tilt of the planet's rotation axis
>
> *if too large:* a mass higher by 2% of the Moon's mass would destabilize the tilt of the planet's rotation axis; ocean tides would be too great, causing too much erosion and disturbing continental shelf life; planet's rotation rate would slow down so quickly as to make advanced life impossible

120. density of galaxies in the local volume around life-support galaxy

> *if too low:* inadequate growth in the galaxy; inadequate buildup of heavy elements in the galaxy; star formation would be too anemic and history of star formation activity would be too short
>
> *if too high:* galaxy would suffer catastrophic gravitational disturbances and star formation events would be too violent and too frequent; galaxy would grow too large and too quickly; astronomers' view of the universe would be significantly blocked

121. surface level air pressure for life-support planet

> *if too small:* lung operation in animals would be too inefficient, eliminating the possibility of high respiration rate animals; wind

velocities would be too high and air streams too laminar, causing devastating storms and much more uneven rainfall distribution; less lift for aircraft, making air transport more dangerous and costly

if too great: lung operation would be too inefficient, eliminating the possibility of high respiration rate animals; wind velocities would be too low, resulting in much lower rainfall on continental landmasses; too much air resistance, making air transport slower, more costly, and more dangerous

122. level and frequency of ocean microseisms

if too low: inadequate precipitation; inadequate redistribution of continental shelf nutrients

if too high: storm intensities would become too great; preciptiation levels would be too high; too much disturbance of the continental shelf environment and ecosystems

123. depth of Earth's primordial ocean

if too shallow: early planet-sized collider would have eradicated too much of Earth's light element material and would have too radically altered or destroyed the primordial Earth; no moon would form or the moon's size or composition would be too radically disturbed

if too deep: early planet-sized collider would have ejected too little of Earth's light element material into interplanetary space; no moon would form or the moon's size or composition would be too radically disturbed

124. rate of quartz re-precipitation on Earth

if too low: cycling of silicon would be so disturbed as to affect the production of free oxygen by phytoplankton and the removal of carbon dioxide from the atmosphere by the weathering of silicates

if too high: cycling of silicon would be so disturbed as to affect the production of free oxygen by phytoplankton and the removal of carbon dioxide from the atmosphere by the weathering of silicates

125. rate of release of cellular particles (fur fiber, dandruff, pollen, spores, bacteria, phages, etc.) and viruses into the atmosphere

if too low: inadequate production of aerosol particles that are especially effective as cloud condensation nuclei, thereby resulting in too little rain, hail, snow, and fog

if too high: too much production of aerosol particles that are especially effective as cloud condensation nuclei, thereby casing too much precipitation or precipitation that is too unevenly distributed

126. rate of leaf litter deposition upon soils

if too low: inadequate amounts of nutrients delivered to soils; inadequate amounts of silica delivered to soils; serious disruption of silica cycling

if too high: soils and the ecosystems within them become too deprived of light, oxygen, and carbon dioxide; inadequate nitrogen fixation in soils

127. date of star formation shutdown in the galaxy

if too soon: no possibility of planets forming with the mix of heavy elements to support advanced life

if too late: probability too high that a nearby supernova eruption or an encounter with a dense molecular cloud or a young bright star would prove deleterious to life on the life-support planet

128. degree of confinement to the galactic plane for the galaxy's light-emitting ordinary matter

if less: spiral structure would either collapse or become unstable

if more: inadequate infusion of gas and dust into the spiral arms, preventing solar-type stars from forming at the right locations late enough in the galaxy's history

129. average albedo of Earth's surface life

if less: would cause runaway evaporation of Earth's frozen and liquid water

if more: would cause runaway freeze-up of Earth's water vapor and liquid water

130. collision velocity and mass of planet colliding with primordial Earth

if either is too low: insufficient amount of Earth's light element material would be removed; infusion of heavy element material into Earth's core would be too small; no moon would form or too small of a moon would form

*if either is too high:*Earth would suffer too much destruction; too much of Earth's light element material would have been removed; no moon would form or the moon's size and/or composition would be too radically disturbed

131. photo erosion by nearby giant stars during planetary formation phase
    if smaller: too few volatiles would be removed from the protoplanetary disk
    if larger: too many volatiles would be removed from the protoplanetary disk; too radical of a truncation of the outer part of the planetary disk and hence inadequate formation of gas giant planets that are distant from the star
132. surface density of the protoplanetary disk
    if smaller: number of protoplanets produced would be too many; average protoplanet mass would be too small
    if larger: number of protoplanets produced would be too few; average protoplanet mass would be too large
133. quantity of terrestrial lightning
    if less: too small or too unstable of a charge-depleted zone would exist in the Van Allen radiation belts surrounding Earth, making efficient communication satellite operation impossible; too few forest and grass fires would be generated; inadequate nitrogen fixation
    if more: Earth's Van Allen radiation belts would become so weak that too much hard radiation would penetrate Earth's surface to the detriment of life; too many forest and grass fires would be generated
134. timing of solar system's last crossing of a spiral arm
    if earlier: humanity would now be too close to a spiral arm and thus would face more cosmic rays, a colder climate, a weaker ozone shield, and a high probability of encountering a large molecular cloud
    if later: humanity would now be too close to a spiral arm and thus would face more cosmic rays, a colder climate, a weaker ozone shield, and a high probability of encountering a large molecular cloud; inadequate time for the buildup of resources provided by previous generations of advanced life
135. amount of iron-60 injected into Earth's primordial core from a nearby type II supernova eruption
    if less: inadequate differentiation of Earth's interior layers, which prevents any long-term support of plate tectonics and a strong magnetic field
    if more: Earth's plate tectonics would become too destructive; Earth's

interior structure would become inappropriate for the support of life and advanced life in particular

136. level of oxidizing activity in the soil
   if smaller: inadequate oxygenation of the soil for healthy root growth and the support of animal life in the soils; inadequate nutrients for land life
   if larger: organic matter would too rapidly decompose

137. level of water-soluble heavy metals in soils
   if lower: inadequate trace element nutrients available for life, especially for advanced life
   if higher: soluble metals would be at toxic levels for life, especially advanced life; catastrophic drop in soil microorganism diversity would occur

138. quantity of methanotrophic symbionts in wetlands
   if lower: inadequate consumption and conversion of methane gas and inadequate delivery of carbon to mosses, causing too much methane and carbon dioxide to be released to the atmosphere, resulting in a global warming catastrophe
   if higher: too much consumption and conversion of methane gas and too much delivery of carbon to mosses, causing too little methane and carbon dioxide to be released to the atmosphere, resulting in a global cooling catastrophe

139. ratio of asteroids to comets for the late heavy bombardment of Earth
   if lower: inadequate delivery of heavy elements to Earth; too many volatiles delivered to Earth; melting of Earth would not be sufficient to adequately transform Earth's interior
   if higher: inadequate delivery of volatiles to Earth; bombardment would be too destructive; chemical transformation of Earth's interior would become inappropriate for the long-term support of advanced life

140. quantity and diversity of viruses in the oceans
   if lower: inadequate breakdown of particulate nutrients into usable forms for bacteria and microbial communities
   if higher: too much devastation of bacteria, microorganisms, and larger life-forms in the oceans

141. quantity of amommox bacteria (bacteria exploiting anaerobic ammonium oxidation reactions) in the oceans
   if lower: food chain base in oxygen-depleted marine environments

would be driven to a level too low

if higher: consumption of fixed nitrogen by these bacteria would deprive photosynthetic life of an important nutrient

142. quantity of soluble silicon and silica in the oceans

if lower: too severe a limitation on the growth of marine diatoms, which would remove an important source from the food chain and an important contributor to both nitrogen fixation and marine aerosol production

if higher: silicon and silica absorption by certain marine organisms could reach toxic levels for those organisms; diatom growth could become too predominant and thus damage the ecosystem

143. quantity of phosphorous and phosphates in the oceans

if lower: too severe a limitation on the growth of nitrogen-fixing marine bacteria

if higher: growth of algae blooms could result in toxin release levels detrimental to virtually all other life-forms

144. availability of light to upper layers of the oceans

if lower: inadequate phytoplankton growth in low-iron content waters

if higher: phytoplankton growth in high iron content waters would become too aggressive and thus upset that part of marine ecosystem; certain phytoplankton blooms would release too many toxins that could prove deadly to other life-forms

145. amount of summer ground foliage in the arctic

if smaller: lower reflectivity warms the arctic, possibly leading to climate instabilities

if larger: higher reflectivity cools the arctic, possibly leading to climate instabilities

146. quantity of dissolved calcium in lakes and rivers

if smaller: inadequate removal of carbon dioxide from the atmosphere, leading to climatic instabilities and possible runaway freezing

if larger: too much removal of carbon dioxide from the atmosphere, leading to climatic instabilities and possible runaway evaporation of Earth's liquid water and ice

147. mass of the potential life-support planet

if smaller: planet would retain too light of an atmosphere and too small of an atmospheric pressure; planet's gravity would not be adequate to retain water vapor over a long period of time;

pressure in planet's mantle would be too low, resulting in a loss of mantle conductivity and consequently a level of plate tectonics too weak and too short lived

if greater: planet would retain too heavy of an atmosphere and too great of an atmospheric pressure; gravitational loss of low molecular weight gases from the atmosphere would be too low; tectonic activity level would be too short lived

148. quantity of clay production on continental landmasses

if smaller: inadequate conditioning of soil for advanced plants; inadequate removal of carbon dioxide from the atmosphere; inadequate oxygenation of the atmosphere

if greater: inadequate aeration of soil for advanced plants; too much removal of carbon dioxide from the atmosphere

149. date for opening of the Drake Passage (between South America and Antarctica)

if earlier: Earth's surface would have been cooled down prematurely relative to the gradual increasing luminosity of the Sun

if later: Earth's surface would have been cooled down too late relative to the gradual increasing luminosity of the Sun

150. frequency of giant volcanic eruptions

if lower: inadequate delivery of interior gases to the atmosphere; insufficient buildup of islands and continental landmasses; insufficient buildup of surface crustal nutrients

if higher: too much and too frequent destruction of life

Notes

Chapter 1 – The Awe-Inspiring Night Sky

1. George Roche, *A World without Heroes: The Modern Tragedy* (Hillsdale, MI: Hillsdale College Press, 1987), 120.
2. Hugh Ross, "Biblical Forecasts of Scientific Discoveries," *Reasons to Believe*, reasons.org/explore/publications/tnrtb/read/tnrtb/1976/01/01/biblical-forecasts-of-scientific-discoveries.

Chapter 2 – My Skeptical Inquiry

1. The details of this calculation are presented in my paper titled "Fulfilled Prophecy: Evidence for the Reliability of the Bible," *Reasons to Believe*, reasons.org/explore/publications/tnrtb/read/tnrtb/2003/08/22/fulfilled-prophecy-evidence-for-the-reliability-of-the-bible.
2. A detailed account of my personal search for truth is given in *Meet Hugh Ross* (Covina, CA: Reasons to Believe, 2013), DVD.
3. *Meet Hugh Ross* (Covina, CA: Reasons to Believe, 2013), DVD.

Chapter 3 – Big Bang: The Bible Taught It First!

1. Arno A. Penzias and Robert W. Wilson, "A Measurement of Excess Antenna Temperature at 4080 Mc/s," *Astrophysical Journal* 142 (July 1965): 419–41, doi:10.1086/148307.
2. George Gamow, "Expanding Universe and the Origin of Elements," *Physical Review* 70 (October 1, 1946): 572–73, doi:10.1103/PhysRev.70.572.2.
3. Vesto Slipher, "The Radial Velocity of the Andromeda Nebula," *Lowell Observatory Bulletin* 1 (September 1912), 56–57.
4. Edwin Hubble, "A Relation between Distance and Radial Velocity among Extra-Galactic Nebulae," *Proceedings of the National Academy of Sciences, USA* 15 (March 15, 1929): 168–73, doi:10.1073/pnas.15.3.168.

5. Georges Lemaître, "A Homogeneous Universe of Constant Mass and Increasing Radius Accounting for the Radial Velocity of Extra-Galactic Nebulae," *Monthly Notices of the Royal Astronomical Society* 91 (March 13, 1931): 483–90, doi:10.1093/mnras/91.5.483. The original paper appears in French in *Annales de la Société Scientifique de Bruxelles, Tome XLVII, Serie A, Premiere Partie* (April 1927): 49.

6. Albert Einstein, "Die Grundlage der allgemeinen Relativitätstheorie," *Annalen der Physik* 354 (1916): 769–22, doi:10.1002/andp.19163540702. The English translation is in *The Principle of Relativity* by H. A. Lorentz, A. Einstein, H. Minkowski, and H. Weyl with notes by A. Sommerfeld and translated by W. Perrett and G. B. Jeffrey (London: Methuen and Co., 1923), 109–64.

7. R. Laird Harris, Gleason L. Archer, and Bruce K. Waltke, *Theological Wordbook of the Old Testament*, vol. 1 (Chicago: Moody, 1980), 127.

8. Harris, Archer, and Waltke, vol. 2, 916.

9. Harris, Archer, and Waltke, vol. 2, 935.

10. Jack J. Lissauer, "It's Not Easy to Make the Moon," *Nature* 389 (September 25, 1997): 327–28, doi:10.1038/38596; Shigeru Ida, Robin M. Canup, and Glen R. Stewart, "Lunar Accretion from an Impact-Generated Disk," *Nature* 389 (September 25, 1997): 353–57, doi:10.1038/38669; P. Jonathan Patchett, "Scum of the Earth After All," *Nature* 382 (August 29, 1996): 758–59, doi:10.1038/382758a0; Hugh Ross, *The Genesis Question: Scientific Advances and the Accuracy of Genesis* (Colorado Springs, CO: NavPress, 1998), 31–33.

11. Fred Hoyle, "A New Model for the Expanding Universe," *Monthly Notices of the Royal Astronomical Society* 108 (October 1, 1948): 372, doi:10.1093/mnras/108.5.372.

Chapter 4 – The Discovery of the Twentieth Century

1. Nigel Hawkes, "Hunt on for Dark Secret of Universe," *London Times* 25 (April 1992), 1.

2. Hawkes, "Dark Secret of Universe."

3. Associated Press, "U.S. Scientists Find a 'Holy Grail': Ripples at Edge of the Universe," *International Herald Tribune* (London), (April 24, 1992), 1.

4. Associated Press, 1.

5. Thomas H. Maugh II, "Relics of 'Big Bang' Seen for First Time," *Los Angeles Times*, April 24, 1992.

6. David Briggs, "Science, Religion, Are Discovering Commonality in Big

Bang Theory," *Los Angeles Times*, May 2, 1992.

7. Nightline with Ted Koppel, *ABC Television Network*, April 25, 1992.

8. Nightline with Ted Koppel, *ABC Television Network*.

9. Stephen Strauss, "An Innocent's Guide to the Big Bang Theory: Finger-print in Space Left by the Universe as a Baby Still Has Doubters Hurling Stones," *Globe and Mail* (Toronto), April 25, 1992.

10. Richard C. Tolman, "Thermodynamic Treatment of the Possible Formation of Helium from Hydrogen," *Journal of the American Chemical Society* 44 (September 1922): 1902–8, doi:10.1021/ja01430a008.

11. George Gamow, "Expanding Universe and the Origin of Elements," *Physical Review* 70 (October 1, 1946): 572–73, doi:10.1103/PhysRev.70.572.2.

12. Ralph A. Alpher and Robert Herman, "Evolution of the Universe," *Nature* 162 (November 13, 1948): 774–75, doi:10.1038/162774b0.

13. Arno A. Penzias and Robert W. Wilson, "A Measurement of Excess Antenna Temperature at 4080 Mc/s," *Astrophysical Journal* 142 (July 1965): 419–21, doi:10.1086/148307; Robert H. Dicke et al., "Cosmic Black-Body Radiation," *Astrophysical Journal* 142 (July 1965): 414–19, doi:10.1086/148306.

14. George F. Smoot, "Comments and Summary on the Cosmic Background Radiation," *Proceedings of the International Astronomical Union Symposium, No. 104: Early Evolution of the Universe and Its Present Structure*, ed. G. O. Abell and G. Chincarini (Dordrecht, Holland; Boston, MA: Reidel Publishing, 1983): 153–58.

15. Craig J. Hogan, "Experimental Triumph," *Nature* 344 (March 8, 1990): 107–8, doi:10.1038/344107a0; J. C. Mather et al., "A Preliminary Measurement of the Cosmic Microwave Background Spectrum by the Cosmic Background Explorer (COBE) Satellite," *Astrophysical Journal Letters* 354 (May 10, 1990): L37–L40, doi:10.1086/185717.

16. Hugh Ross, *The Fingerprint of God: Recent Scientific Discoveries Reveal the Unmistakable Identity of the Creator*, commemorative ed. (Covina, CA: RTB Press, 2010), 69–71.

17. Ross, *Fingerprint of God*, 101.

18. George F. Smoot et al., "Structure in the COBE Differential Microwave Radiometer First-Year Maps," *Astrophysical Journal Letters* 396 (September 1, 1992): L1–L5, doi:10.1086/186504; C. L. Bennett et al., "Preliminary Separation of Galactic and Cosmic Microwave Emission for the COBE Differential Microwave Radiometer," *Astrophysical Journal Letters* 396 (September 1, 1992): L7–L12, doi:10.1086/186505.

19. E. L. Wright et al., "Interpretation of the Cosmic Microwave Background Radiation Anisotropy Detected by the COBE Differential Microwave Radiometer," *Astrophysical Journal Letters* 396 (September 1, 1992): L13–L18, doi:10.1086/186506.

20. Geoffrey Burbidge's comments were made on a radio talk show called *Live from LA* with host Phil Reid on KKLA in Los Angeles, CA. The program aired May 11, 1992 and included comments on the big bang ripples discovery from Drs. G. De Amici, Geoffrey Burbidge, Russell Humphreys, and Hugh Ross.

21. Ron Cowen, "Balloon Survey Backs COBE Cosmos Map," *Science News* 142 (December 19, 1992): 420.

22. S. Hancock et al., "Direct Observation of Structure in the Cosmic Background Radiation," *Nature* 367 (January 27, 1994): 333–38, doi:10.1038/367333a0.

23. A. C. Clapp et al., "Measurements of Anistropy in the Cosmic Microwave Background Radiation at Degree Angular Scales Near the Stars Sigma Herculis and IOTA Draconis," *Astrophysical Journal Letters* 433 (October 1, 1994): L57–L60, doi:10.1086/187547.

24. C. L. Bennett et al., "Four-Year COBE* DMR Cosmic Microwave Background Observations: Maps and Basic Results," *Astrophysical Journal Letters* 464 (June 10, 1996): L1–L4, doi:10.1086/310075; C. M. Gutiérrez et al., "New Cosmological Structures on Medium Angular Scales Detected with the Tenerife Experiments," *Astrophysical Journal Letters* 480 (May 10, 1997): L83–L86, doi:10.1086/310634; E. S. Cheng et al., "Detection of Cosmic Microwave Background Anisotropy by the Third Flight of the Medium-Scale Anisotropy Measurement," *Astrophysical Journal Letters* 488 (October 20, 1997): L59–L62, doi:10.1086/310923; B. Femenía et al., "The Instituto de Astrofísica de Canarias-Bartol Cosmic Microwave Background Anisotropy Experiment: Results of the 1994 Campaign," *Astrophysical Journal* 498 (May 1, 1998): 117–36, doi:10.1086/305549; Angelica de Oliveira-Costa et al., "Mapping the Cosmic Microwave Background Anisotropy: Combined Analysis of QMAP Flights," *Astrophysical Journal Letters* 509 (December 20, 1998): L77–L80, doi:10.1086/311767; C. B. Netterfield et al., "A Measurement of the Angular Power Spectrum of the Anisotropy in the Cosmic Microwave Background," *Astrophysical Journal* 474 (January 1, 1997): 47–66, doi:10.1086/303438; S. R. Platt, "Anisotropy in the Microwave Sky at 90 GHz: Results from Python III," *Astrophysical Journal Letters* 475 (January 20, 1997): L1–L4, doi:10.1086/310453;

K. Coble et al., "Anisotropy in the Cosmic Microwave Background at Degree Angular Scales: Python V Results," *Astrophysical Journal Letters* 519 (July 1, 1999): L5–L8, doi:10.1086/312093; Bharat Ratra et al., "Using White Dish CMB Anisotropy Data to Probe Open and Flat-Λ CDM Cosmogonies," *Astrophysical Journal* 505 (September 20, 1998): 8–11, doi:10.1086/306139; Joanne C. Baker et al., "Detection of Cosmic Microwave Background Structure in a Second Field with the Cosmic Anisotropy Telescope," *Monthly Notices of the Royal Astronomical Society* 308 (October 1, 1999): 1173–78, doi:10.1046/j.1365-8711.1999.02829.x; Bharat Ratra et al., "ARGO Cosmic Microwave Background Anisotropy Measurement Constraints on Open and Flat-Λ Cold Dark Matter Cosmogonies," *Astrophysical Journal* 510 (January 1, 1999): 11–19, doi:10.1086/306577; Martin White et al., "Interferometric Observation of Cosmic Microwave Background Anisotropies," *Astrophysical Journal* 514 (March 20, 1999): 12–24, doi:10.1086/306911; Bharat Ratra et al., "Cosmic Microwave Background Anisotropy Constraints on Open and Flat-Λ Cold Dark Matter Cosmogonies from UCSB South Pole, ARGO, MAX, White Dish, and SuZIE Data," *Astrophysical Journal* 517 (June 1, 1999): 549–64, doi:10.1086/307236; E. Torbet et al., "A Measurement of the Angular Power Spectrum of the Microwave Background Made from the High Chilean Andes," *Astrophysical Journal Letters* 521 (July 28, 1999): L79–L82, doi:10.1086/312197; A. D. Miller et al., "A Measurement of the Angular Power Spectrum of the Cosmic Microwave Background from l = 100 to 400," *Astrophysical Journal Letters* 524 (September 13, 1999): L1–L4, doi:10.1086/312293; E. M. Leitch et al., "A Measurement of Anisotropy in the Cosmic Microwave Background on 7'–22' Scales," *Astrophysical Journal* 532 (March 20, 2000): 37–56, doi:10.1086/308529.

25. Ron Cowen, "COBE: A Match Made in Heaven," *Science News* 143 (1993): 43; J. C. Mather et al., "Measurement of the Cosmic Microwave Background Spectrum by the COBE FIRAS Instrument," *Astrophysical Journal* 420 (January 1994): 439–44, doi:10.1086/173574.

26. Katherine C. Roth, David M. Meyer, and Isabel Hawkins, "Interstellar Cyanogen and the Temperature of the Cosmic Microwave Background Radiation," *Astrophysical Journal Letters* 413 (1993): L67–L71, doi:10.1086/186961.

27. Antoinette Songaila et al., "Measurement of the Microwave Background Temperature at a Redshift of 1.776," *Nature* 371 (September 1, 1994): 43–45, doi:10.1038/371043a0.

28. David M. Meyer, "A Distant Space Thermometer," *Nature* 371 (September 1, 1994): 13, doi:10.1038/371013a0.

29. K. C. Roth et al., "C I Fine-Structure Excitation by the CMBR at z = 1.973," *American Astronomical Society 189th Meeting*, id. 122.17, January 1997.

30. R. Srianand, P. Petitjean, and C. Leadoux, "The Cosmic Microwave Background Radiation Temperature at a Redshift of 2.34," *Nature* 408 (December 21, 2000): 931–35, doi:10.1038/35050020.

31. In 1998 Reasons to Believe produced a one-hour television documentary, *Journey toward Creation*, that portrayed through astronomical images, video clips, and computer animations a simulated trip from planet Earth to the most distant entities in the universe, a journey toward the creation event itself. A DVD is available at shop.reasons.org.

32. Hugh Ross and Guillermo Gonzalez, "You Must Be Here," *Facts for Faith*, vol. 1, no. 1 (2000), 36–41.

33. Stephen Hawking, *A Brief History of Time* (New York: Bantam Books, 1988), 163–65.

Chapter 5 – Twenty-First Century Discoveries, Part I

1. James Glanz, "Cosmic Motion Revealed," *Science* 282 (December 18, 1998): 2156–57, doi:10.1126/science.282.5397.2156a; Floyd E. Bloom, "Breakthroughs 1998," *Science* 282 (December 18, 1998): 2193, doi:10.1126/science.282.5397.2193.

2. Lawrence M. Krauss, "The End of the Age Problem and the Case for a Cosmological Constant Revisited," *Astrophysical Journal* 501 (July 10, 1998): 461, doi:10.1086/305846.

3. Hugh Ross, *The Fingerprint of God: Recent Scientific Discoveries Reveal the Unmistakable Identity of the Creator*, 2nd ed. (Orange, CA: NavPress, 1991), 27–29; Immanuel Kant, "Universal Natural History and Theory of the Heavens," in *Theories of the Universe*, ed. Milton K. Munitz (Glencoe, IL: Free Press, 1957), 242–47.

4. Albert Einstein, "Kosmologische Betrachtungen zur allgemeinen Relativitätstheorie," in *Sitzungsberichte der Königlich Preußischen Akademie der Wissenschaften* (1917), Feb. 8, 142–52. The English translation is in *The Principle of Relativity: A Collection of Original Memoirs on the Special and General Theory of Relativity* by H. A. Lorentz, A. Einstein, H. Minkowski, and H. Weyl with notes by A. Sommerfeld and translated by W. Perrett and G. B. Jeffrey (London, UK: Methuen and Co., 1923), 175–88; Albert

Einstein, "Die Grundlage der allgemeinen Relativitätstheorie," *Annalen der Physik* 354 (1916): 769–822. The English translation is in *The Principle of Relativity*, 109–64, doi:10.1002/andp.19163540702.

5. A. Vibert Douglas, "Forty Minutes with Einstein," *Journal of the Royal Astronomical Society of Canada* 50 (June 1956): 100.

6. Adam G. Riess et al., "Observational Evidence from Supernovae for an Accelerating Universe and a Cosmological Constant," *Astronomical Journal* 116 (September 1998): 1009–38, doi:10.1086/300499.

7. Richard C. Tolman and Morgan Ward, "On the Behavior of Non-Static Models of the Universe When the Cosmological Term Is Omitted," *Physical Review* 39 (March 1, 1932): 841–43, doi:10.1103/PhysRev.39.835; John D. Barrow and Joseph Silk, *The Left Hand of Creation: The Origin and Evolution of the Expanding Universe* (New York: Basic Books, 1983), 32.

8. S. Perlmutter et al., "Measurements of Ω and Λ from 42 High-Redshift Supernovae," *Astrophysical Journal* 517 (June 1, 1999): 565–86, doi:10.1086/307221.

9. Jeppe Trøst Nielsen, Alberto Guffanti, and Subir Sarkar, "Marginal Evidence for Cosmic Acceleration from Type Ia Supernovae," *Scientific Reports* 6 (October 21, 2016): id. 35596, doi:10.1038/srep35596.

10. David Rubin and Brian Hayden, "Is the Expansion of the Universe Accelerating? All Signs Point to Yes," *Astrophysical Journal Letters* 833 (December 20, 2016): L30, doi:10.3847/2041-8213/833/2/L30; H. I. Ringermacher and L. R. Mead, "In Defense of an Accelerating Universe: Model Insensitivity of the Hubble Diagram," published electronically November 2, 2016, arxiv.org/ftp/arxiv/papers/1611/1611.00999.pdf.

11. D. O. Jones et al., "Measuring the Properties of Dark Energy with Photometrically Classified Pan-STARRS Supernovae. I. Systematic Uncertainty from Core-collapse Supernova Contamination," *Astrophysical Journal* 843 (June 26, 2017): doi:10.3847/1538-4357/aa767b; Ravi Gupta, "Supernovae from the Dark Energy Survey," (March 2016), APS April Meeting 2016, abstract #J4.00001; Christopher D'Andrea, "Supernovae in the First Two Years of the Dark Energy Survey," (January 2016), American Astronomical Society Meeting #227, id. 349.12; G. Narayan et al., "Light Curves of 213 Type Ia Supernovae from the ESSENCE Survey," *Astrophysical Journal Supplement Series* 224 (May 6, 2016): id. 3, doi:10.3847/0067-0049/224/1/3; E. S. Walker et al., "First Results from the La Silla-QUEST Supernova Survey and the Carnegie Supernova Project," *Astrophysical Journal Supplement Series* 219 (July 27, 2015): id. 13, doi:10.1088/0067-

0049/219/1/13; *The Active Universe*, project.pan-starrs.ifa.hawaii.edu/ public/science-goals/active-universe.html (accessed November 30, 2016).

12. T. de Haan et al., "Cosmological Constraints from Galaxy Clusters in the 2500 Square-Degree SPT-SZ Survey," *Astrophysical Journal* 832 (November 18, 2016): id. 95, doi:10.3847/0004-637X/832/1/95; B. Sartoris et al., "Next Generation Cosmology: Constraints from the Euclid Galaxy Cluster Survey," *Monthly Notices of the Royal Astronomical Society* 459 (June 21, 2016): 1764–80, doi:10.1093/mnras/stw630; Ariel G. Sánchez et al., "The Clustering of Galaxies in the Completed SDSS-III Baryon Oscillation Spectroscopic Survey: Cosmological Implications of the Configuration-Space Clustering Wedges," *Monthly Notices of the Royal Astronomical Society* 464 (January 11, 2017): 1640–58, doi:10.1093/mnras/stw2443; Jan Niklas Grieb et al., "The Clustering of Galaxies in the Completed SDSS-III Baryon Oscillation Spectroscopic Survey: Cosmological Implications of the Fourier Space Wedges of the Final Sample," *Monthly Notices of the Royal Astronomical Society* 467 (May 21, 2017): 2085–112, doi:10.1093/mnras/stw3384; J. Kwan et al., "Cosmology from Large-Scale Galaxy Clustering and Galaxy-Galaxy Lensing with Dark Energy Survey Science Verification Data," *Monthly Notices of the Royal Astronomical Society* 464 (February 1, 2017): 4045–62, doi:10.1093/mnras/stw2464; Vincent R. Bouillot et al., "Probing Dark Energy Models with Extreme Pairwise Velocities of Galaxy Clusters from the DEUS-FUR Simulations," *Monthly Notices of the Royal Astronomical Society* 450 (June 11, 2015): 145–59, doi:10.1093/mnras/stv558; Alejo Stark, Christopher J. Miller, and Daniel Gifford, "On Escaping a Galaxy Cluster in an Accelerating Universe," *Astrophysical Journal* 830 (October 17, 2016): id. 109, doi:10.3847/0004-637X/830/2/109; Christian Marinoni and Adeline Buzzi, "A Geometric Measure of Dark Energy with Pairs of Galaxies," *Nature* 468 (November 25, 2010): 539–41, doi:10.1038/nature09577; T. Abbott et al., "Cosmology from Cosmic Shear with Dark Energy Survey Science Verification Data," *Physical Review D* 94 (July 6, 2016): id. 022001, doi:10.1103/PhysRevD.94.022001; Masato Shirasaki, Takashi Hamana, and Naoki Yoshida, "Probing Cosmology with Weak Lensing Selected Clusters. II. Dark Energy and f(R) Gravity Models," *Publications of the Astronomical Society of Japan* 68 (February 1, 2016): id. 414, doi:10.1093/pasj/psv105; Adam Mantz et al., "Weighing the Giants: Galaxy Cluster Cosmology Anchored by Weak Gravitational Lensing," (American Astronomical Society HEAD Meeting #14, Chicago, IL, August 2014); Fulvio Melia, Jun-Jie Wei, and Xue-Feng

Wu, "A Comparison of Cosmological Models Using Strong Gravitational Lensing Galaxies," *Astronomical Journal* 149 (November 25, 2014): id. 2, doi:10.1088/0004-6256/149/1/2; Xiao-Dong Li et al., "Cosmological Constraints from the Redshift Dependence of the Alcock-Paczynski Effect: Application to the SDSS-III Boss DR12 Galaxies," *Astrophysical Journal* 832 (November 21, 2016): id. 103, doi:10.3847/0004-637X/832/2/103; Xue Li, Jens Hjorth, and Radosław Wojtak, "Cosmological Parameters from Supernovae Associated with Gamma Ray Bursts," *Astrophysical Journal Letters* 796 (October 31, 2014): id. L4, doi:10.1088/2041-8205/796/1/L4; L. Izzo et al., "New Measurements of Ωm from Gamma-Ray Bursts," *Astronomy & Astrophysics* 582 (October 2015): id. A115, doi:10.1051/0004-6361/201526461; Marek Demianski et al., "Cosmology from Gamma-Ray Bursts II. Cosmography Challenges and Cosmological Scenarios for the Accelerated Universe," *Astronomy & Astrophysics* 598 (February 2017): id. A113, doi:10.1051/0004-6361/201628911; Marek Demianski et al., "Cosmology with Gamma-Ray Bursts. I. The Hubble Diagram through the Calibrated Ep,i–Eiso Correlation," *Astronomy & Astrophysics* 598 (February 2017): id. A122, doi:10.1051/0004-6361/201628909.

13. Jones et al.

14. Gary Hinshaw et al., "Nine-Year Wilkinson Microwave Anisotropy Probe (WMAP) Observations: Cosmological Parameter Results," *Astrophysical Journal Supplement Series* 208 (September 2013): id. 19, p. 1, doi:10.1088/0067-0049/208/2/19.

15. P. A. R. Ade et al., Planck Collaboration, "Planck 2015 Results. XIII. Cosmological Parameters," *Astronomy & Astrophysics* 594 (October 2016): id. A13, p. 31, doi:10.1051/0004-6361/201525830.

16. Ariel G. Sánchez et al., "The Clustering of Galaxies in the Completed SDSS-III Baryon Oscillation Spectroscopic Survey: Cosmological Implications of the Configuration-Space Clustering Wedges," *Monthly Notices of the Royal Astronomical Society* 464 (January 11, 2017): 1640–58, doi:10.1093/mnras/stw2443.

17. B. P. Abbott et al., LIGO Scientific Collaboration, Virgo Collaboration, "Upper Limits on the Stochastic Gravitational-Wave Background from Advanced LIGO's First Observing Run," *Physical Review Letters* 118 (March 24, 2017): id. 121101, doi:10.1103/PhysRevLett.118.121101.

18. E. Komatsu et al., "Five-Year Wilkinson Microwave Anisotropy Probe Observations: Cosmological Interpretation," *Astrophysical Journal Supplement Series* 180 (February 11, 2009): 333–35, doi:10.1088/0067-

0049/180/2/330; Hinshaw et al., "Nine-Year Wilkinson Microwave," 9–15.

19. Hinshaw et al., "Nine-Year Wilkinson Microwave," 9–11; Ade et al., Planck Collaboration, "Planck 2015 Results," 1; Salvador Salazar-Albornoz et al., "The Clustering of Galaxies in the Completed SDSS-III Baryon Oscillation Spectroscopic Survey: Angular Clustering Tomography and Its Cosmological Implications," *Monthly Notices of the Royal Astronomical Society* 468 (July 1, 2017): 2938–56, doi:10.1093/mnras/stx633; Éric Aubourg et al., "Cosmological Implications of Baryon Acoustic Oscillation Measurements," *Physical Review D* 92 (December 14, 2015): id. 123576, p. 1, doi:10.1103/PhysRevD.92.123516; G. S. Sharov and E. G. Vorontsova, "Parameters of Cosmological Models and Recent Astronomical Observations," *Journal of Cosmology and Astroparticle Physics* 2014 (October 22, 2014): id. 057, p. 1, doi:10.1088/1475-7516/2014/10/057; T. de Haan et al., "Cosmological Constraints from Galaxy Clusters in the 2500 Square Degree SPT-SZ Survey," *Astrophysical Journal* 832 (November 18, 2016): id. 95, p. 1, doi:10.3847/0004-637X/832/1/95; Chia-Hsun Chuang et al., "The Clustering of Galaxies in the SDSS-III Baryon Oscillation Spectroscopic Survey: Single-Probe Measurements from CMASS Anisotropic Galaxy Clustering," *Monthly Notices of the Royal Astronomical Society* 461 (October 1, 2016): 3781, doi:10.1093/mnras/stw1535; Li et al., "Cosmological Constraints from the Redshift Dependence," p. 1; M. Betoule et al., "Improved Cosmological Constraints from a Joint Analysis of the SDSS-II and SNLS Supernova Samples," *Astronomy & Astrophysics* 568 (August 2014): id. A22, p. 1, doi:10.1051/0004-6361/201423413; Nico Hamaus et al., "Constraints on Cosmology and Gravity from the Dynamics of Voids," *Physical Review Letters* 117 (August 25, 2016): id. 091302, p. 1, doi:10.1103/PhysRevLett.117.091302; Raul E. Angulo and Stefan Hilbert, "Cosmological Constraints from the CFHTLenS Shear Measurements Using a New, Accurate, and Flexible Way of Predicting Non-Linear Mass Clustering," *Monthly Notices of the Royal Astronomical Society* 448 (March 21, 2015): 364, doi:10.1093/mnras/stv050; David N. Spergel, Raphael Flauger, and Renée Hložek, "Planck Data Reconsidered," *Physical Review D* 91 (January 27, 2015): id. 023518, p. 1, doi:10.1103/PhysRevD.91.023518.

20. Philip Ball, "Is Physics Watching Over Us?," *Nature*, August 13, 2002, doi:10.1038/news020812-2.

21. Ball, "Is Physics Watching Over Us?"

22. Lisa Dyson, Matthew Kleban, and Leonard Susskind, "Disturbing

Implications of a Cosmological Constant," *Journal of High Energy Physics* 2002 (November 12, 2002): id. 011, p. 17, doi:10.1088/1126-6708/2002/10/011.

23. Lawrence M. Krauss, "The End of the Age Problem, and the Case for a Cosmological Constant Revisited," *Astrophysical Journal* 501 (July 10, 1998): 46, doi:10.1086/305846.

24. Florian Bauer, Joan Solá, and Hrvoje Štefančić, "Relaxing a Large Cosmological Constant," *Physics Letters B* 678 (August 3, 2009): 427, doi:10.1016/j.physletb.2009.06.065.

25. Hugh Ross, *Why the Universe Is the Way It Is* (Grand Rapids: Baker, 2008): 209–11.

26. Arguably the best example of humanly achieved fine-tuning design is the Advanced LIGO instrument. This amazing machine is able to detect a change in a 4-kilometer length as small as one-thousandth the charge diameter of a proton.

27. Idit Zehavi and Avishai Dekel, "Evidence for a Positive Cosmological Constant from Flows of Galaxies and Distant Supernovae," *Nature* 401 (September 16, 1999): 252, doi:10.1038/45748.

28. Norbet Straumann, "On the Cosmological Constant Problems and the Astronomical Evidence for a Homogeneous Energy Density with Negative Pressure," in *Poincaré* Seminar 2002: Vacuum Energy—Renormalization, ed. Vincent Rivasseau (Berlin: Birkhauser Verlag, 2003), 7.

29. Varun Sahni, "The Cosmological Constant Problem and Quintes-sence," *Classical and Quantum Gravity* 19 (June 12, 2002): 3435, doi:10.1088/0264-9381/19/13/304.

30. S. Perlmutter et al., "Measurements of Ω and Λ," 584.

31. Lawrence M. Krauss and Glenn D. Starkman, "Life, the Universe, and Nothing: Life and Death in an Ever-Expanding Universe," *Astrophysical Journal* 531 (2000): 22–30, doi:10.1086/308434.

32. Psalm 19:1; 50:6; 97:6 (NIV).

33. Hugh Ross, *Why the Universe Is the Way It Is* (Grand Rapids: Baker, 2008), 79–89.

34. Revelation 21–22, *The Holy Bible*; Hugh Ross, *Why the Universe Is the Way It Is*, 193–206; Hugh Ross, *Beyond the Cosmos: The Transdimensionality of God*, 4th ed. (Covina, CA: RTB Press, 2017), 185–94.

Chapter 6 – Twenty-First Century Discoveries, Part II

1. P. A. R. Ade et al., Planck Collaboration, "Planck 2015 Results. XIII.

Cosmological Parameters," *Astronomy & Astrophysics* 594 (October 2016): id. A13, p. 47, doi:10.1051/0004-6361/201525830.

2. A. Peimbert, M. Peimbert, and V. Luridiana, "The Primordial Helium Abundance and the Number of Neutrino Families," *Revista Mexicana de Astronomía y Astrofísica* 52 (October 2016): 419–28.

3. Erik Aver, Keith A. Olive, and Evan D. Skillman, "The Effects of He I l10830 on Helium Abundance Determinations," *Journal of Cosmology and Astroparticle Physics* 2015 (July 7, 2015): id. 11, doi:10.1088/1475-7516/2015/07/011.

4. P. A. R. Ade et al., Planck Collaboration, "Planck 2015 Results," p. 47.

5. Ryan J. Cooke et al., "The Primordial Deuterium Abundance of the Most Metal-Poor Damped Ly-a System," *Astrophysical Journal* 830 (October 18, 2016): id. 148, doi:10.3847/0004-637X/830/2/148.

6. P. A. R. Ade et al., Planck Collaboration, "Planck 2015 Results," p. 47.

7. Brian D. Fields, "The Primordial Lithium Problem," *Annual Review of Nuclear and Particle Science* 61 (November 2011): 48, doi:10.1146/annurev-nucl-102010-130445.

8. P. A. R. Ade et al., Planck Collaboration, "Planck 2015 Results," p. 6; Elizabeth Vangioni and Alain Coc, "Updating Standard Big-Bang Nucleosynthesis after Planck" (paper, XIII Nuclei in the Cosmos Conference, Debrecen, Hungary, July 7–11, 2014).

9. C. Charbonnel and F. Primas, "The Lithium Content of the Galactic Halo Stars," *Astronomy & Astrophysics* 442 (November 2005): 961–92, doi:10.1051/0004-6361:20042491.

10. A. Mucciarelli, M. Salaris, and P. Bonifacio, "Giants Reveal What Dwarfs Conceal: Li Abundance in Lower Red Giant Branch Stars as Diagnostic of the Primordial Li," *Monthly Notices of the Royal Astronomical Society* 419 (January 21, 2012): 2195–205, doi:10.1111/j.1365-2966.2011.19870.x; P. E. Nissen and W. J. Schuster, "Lithium Abundances in High- and Low-Alpha Halo Stars," *Memorie Della Societa Astronomica Italiana Supplement* 22 (2012): 41.

11. T. Nordlander et al., "Lithium in Globular Clusters: Significant Systematics, Atomic Diffusion, the Temperature Scale, and Pollution in NGC 6397," *Memorie Della Societa Astronomica Italiana Supplement* 22 (2012): 110; A. Mucciarelli et al., "The Cosmological Lithium Problem Outside the Galaxy: the Sagittarius Globular Cluster M54," *Monthly Notices of the Royal Astronomical Society* 444 (September 3, 2014): 1812–20, doi:10.1093/mnras/stu1522.

12. Martin Asplund et al., "Lithium Isotopic Abundances in Metal-Poor Halo Stars," *Astrophysical Journal* 644 (June 10, 2006): 229–59, doi:10.1086/503538; S. Inoue et al., "^{6}Li in Very Metal-Poor Halo Stars Observed by Subaru/HDS and Implications," *From Lithium to Uranium: Elemental Tracers of Early Cosmic Evolution* 1 (May 2005): 59–64, doi:10.1017/S1743921305005223.

13. K. Lind et al., "Evidence for a Vanishing ^{6}Li/^{7}Li Isotopic Signature in the Metal-Poor Halo Star HD 84937," *Memorie della Società Astronomica Italiana Supplementi* 22 (2012): 142.

14. Charbonnel and Primas, "Lithium Content," 961.

15. Vangioni and Coc, "Updating Standard Big Bang Nucleosynthesis," p. 2.

16. Fields, "Primordial Lithium Problem," 54.

17. J. Christopher Howk et al., "Observation of Interstellar Lithium in the Low-Metallicity Small Magellanic Cloud," *Nature* 489 (September 6, 2012): 121–23, doi:10.1038/nature11407.

18. Richard H. Cyburt and Maxim Pospelov, "Resonant Enhancement of Nuclear Reactions as a Possible Solution to the Cosmological Lithium Problem," *International Journal of Modern Physics E* 21 (February 6, 2012): id. 1250004-1-125004-13, doi:10.1142/S0218301312500048; Fields, "Primordial Lithium Problem," 57.

19. Ming-ming Kang et al., "Cosmic Rays During BBN As Origin of Lithium Problem," *Journal of Cosmology and Astroparticle Physics* 2012 (May 10, 2012): id. 011, doi:10.1088/1475-7516/2012/05/011; Richard H. Cyburt, Brian D. Fields, and Keith A. Olive, "An Update on the Big Bang Nucleosynthesis Prediction for ^{7}Li: The Problem Worsens," *Journal of Cosmology and Astroparticle Physics* 2008 (November 17, 2008): id. 012, doi:10.1088/1475-7516/2008/11/012.

20. Motohiko Kusakabe et al., "Revised Big Bang Nucleosynthesis with Long-Lived, Negatively-Charged Massive Particles: Updated Recombination Rates, Primordial ^{9}Be Nucleosynthesis, and Impact of New ^{6}Li Limits," *Astrophysical Journal Supplement Series* 214 (August 28, 2014): id. 5, doi:10.1088/0067-0049/214/1/5; Andreas Goudelis, Maxim Pospelov, and Josef Pradler, "Light Particle Solution to the Cosmic Lithium Problem," *Physical Review Letters* 116 (May 25, 2016): id. 211303, doi:10.1103/PhysRevLett.116.211303.

21. Dai G. Yamazaki et al., "Cosmological Solutions to the Lithium Problem: Big Bang Nucleosynthesis with Photon Cooling, X-Particle Decay, and a Primordial Magnetic Field," *Physical Review D* 90 (July 1, 2014): id.

023001, doi:10.1103/PhysRevD.90.023001.

22. Motohiko Kusakabe and Masahiro Kawasaki, "Chemical Separation of Primordial Li+ During Structure Formation Caused by Nanogauss Magnetic Field," *Monthly Notices of the Royal Astronomical Society* 446 (January 11, 2015): 1597–624, doi:10.1093/mnras/stu2115; Yamazaki et al.

23. P. A. R. Ade et al., Planck Collaboration, "Planck 2015 Results. XIX. Constraints on Primordial Magnetic Fields," *Astronomy & Astrophysics* 594 (October 2016): id. A19, doi:10.1051/0004-6361/201525821; Alex Zucca, Yun Li, and Levon Pogosian, "Constraints on Primordial Magnetic Fields from Planck Data Combined with the South Pole Telescope CMB B-Mode Polarization Measurements," *Physical Review D* 95 (March 7, 2017): id. 063506, doi:10.1103/PhysRevD.95.063506; Dylan R. Sutton, Chang Feng, and Christian L. Reichardt, "Current and Future Constraints on Primordial Magnetic Fields," *Astrophysical Journal* 846 (September 13, 2017): id. 164, doi:10.3847/1538-4357/aa85e2.

24. Yamazaki et al., "Cosmological Solutions to the Lithium Problem."

25. The online calculation tool can be accessed at astro.ucla.edu/~wright/CosmoCalc.html.

26. Gary Hinshaw et al., "Nine-Year Wilkinson Microwave Anisotropy Probe (WMAP) Observations: Cosmological Parameter Results," *Astrophysical Journal Supplement Series* 208 (September 2013): id. 19, doi:10.1088/0067-0049/208/2/19.

27. P. A. R. Ade et al., Planck Collaboration, ". . . Cosmological Parameters," id. A13.

28. C. Y. Kuo et al, "The Megamaser Cosmology Project. V. An Angular-Diameter Distance to NGC 6264 at 140 Mpc," *Astrophysical Journal* 767 (April 8, 2013): id. 155, doi:10.1088/0004-637X/767/2/155.

29. F. Gao et al., "The Megamaser Cosmology Project. VIII. A Geometric Distance to NGC 5765b," *Astrophysical Journal* 817 (January 27, 2016): id. 128, doi:10.3847/0004-637X/817/2/128.

30. M. J. Reid et al., "The Megamaser Cosmology Project. IV. A Direct Measurement of the Hubble Constant from UGC 3789," *Astrophysical Journal* 767 (April 8, 2013): id. 154, doi:10.1088/0004-637X/767/2/154.

31. E. M. L. Humphreys, "Toward a New Geometric Distance to the Active Galaxy NGC 4258. III. Final Results and the Hubble Constant," *Astrophysical Journal* 775 (August 29, 2013): id. 13, doi:10.1088/0004-637X/775/1/13.

32. Hinshaw et al., "Nine-Year Wilkinson Microwave," id. 19.

33. P. A. R. Ade et al., Planck Collaboration, " . . . Cosmological Parameters," id. A13.

34. Éric Aubourg et al., BOSS Collaboration, "Cosmological Implications of Baryon Acoustic Oscillation Measurements," *Physical Review D* 92 (December 14, 2015): id. 123516, doi:10.1103/PhysRevD.92.123516.

35. M. Rigault et al., "Confirmation of a Star Formation Bias in Type Ia Supernova Distances and Its Effect on the Measurement of the Hubble Constant," *Astrophysical Journal* 802 (March 17, 2015): id. 20, doi:10.1088/0004-637X/802/1/20.

36. Yun Chen, Suresh Kumar, and Bharat Ratra, "Determining the Hubble Constant from Hubble Parameter Measurements," *Astrophysical Journal* 835 (January 20, 2017): id. 86, doi:10.3847/1538-4357/835/1/86.

37. I. de Martino et al., "Constraining the Redshift Evolution of the Cosmic Microwave Background Blackbody Temperature with Planck Data," *Astrophysical Journal* 808 (July 27, 2015): id. 128, doi:10.1088/0004-637X/808/2/128; S. Muller et al., "A Precise and Accurate Determination of the Cosmic Microwave Background Temperature at z = 0.89," *Astronomy & Astrophysics* 551 (March 2013): id. A109, doi:10.1051/0004-6361/201220613; P. Noterdaeme et al., "The Evolution of the Cosmic Microwave Background Temperature. Measurements of T_{CMB} at High Redshift from Carbon Monoxide Excitation," *Astronomy & Astrophysics* 526 (February 2011): id. L7, doi:10.1051/0004-6361/201016140; G. Luzzi et al., "Redshift Dependence of the Cosmic Microwave Background Temperature from Sunyaev-Zeldovich Measurements," *Astrophysical Journal* 705 (October 19, 2009): 1122–28, doi:10.1088/0004-637X/705/2/1122; P. Molaro et al., "The Cosmic Microwave Background Radiation Temperature at z_{abs} = 3.025 toward QSO 0347-3819," *Astronomy & Astrophysics* 381 (January 2002): L64–L67, doi:10.1051/0004-6361:20011698; R. Quast, R. Baade, and D. Reimers, "Fine-Structure Diagnostics of Neutral Carbon toward HE 0515-4414," *Astronomy & Astrophysics* 386 (May 2002): 796–800, doi:10.1051/0004-6361:20020342; E. S. Battistelli et al., "Cosmic Microwave Background Temperature at Galaxy Clusters," *Astrophysical Journal Letters* 580 (October 31, 2002): L101–L104, doi:10.1086/345589; Jian Ge, Jill Bechtold, and Varsha P. Kulkarni, "H_2, C I, Metallicity, and Dust Depletion in the z = 2.34 Damped Lya Absorption System toward QSO 1232+0815*," *Astrophysical Journal Letters* 547 (January 16, 2001): L1–L5, doi:10.1086/318890; Antoinette Songaila et al., "Measurement of the Microwave Background Temperature at a Redshift of 1.776," *Nature*

371 (September 1, 1994): 43–45, doi:10.1038/371043a0; David M. Meyer, "A Distant Space Thermometer," *Nature* 371 (September 1, 1994): 13, doi:10.1038/371013a0; K. C. Roth et al., "C I Fine-Structure Excitation by the CMBR at z=1.973," *Bulletin of the American Astronomical Society* 29 (January 1997): id. 122.17, p. 736; R. Srianand, P. Petitjean, and C. Ledoux, "The Cosmic Microwave Background Radiation Temperature at a Redshift of 2.34," *Nature* 408 (December 21, 2000): 931–35, doi:10.1038/35050020.

38. Muller et al., "Precise and Accurate Determination."
39. I. de Martino et al., "Measuring the Redshift Dependence of the Cosmic Microwave Background Monopole Temperature with Planck Data," *Astrophysical Journal* 757 (September 12, 2012): id. 144, p. 1, doi:10.1088/0004-637X/757/2/144.
40. I. de Martino et al., "Constraining the Redshift Evolution," id. 128, p. 9.
41. Alan H. Guth, "Inflationary Universe: A Possible Solution to the Horizon and Flatness Problems," *Physical Review D* 23 (January 15, 1981): 347–58, doi:10.1103/PhysRevD.23.347.
42. Hinshaw et al., "Nine-Year Wilkinson Microwave," id. 19.
43. P. A. R. Ade et al., Planck Collaboration, " . . . Cosmological Parameters," id. A13.
44. A. T. Crites et al., "Measurements of E-Mode Polarization and Temperature-E-Mode Correlation in the Cosmic Microwave Background from 100 Square Degrees of SPTPOL Data," *Astrophysical Journal* 805 (May 18, 2015): id. 36, doi:10.1088/0004-637X/805/1/36.
45. Shin'ichiro Ando and Alexander Kusenko, "Evidence for Gamma-Ray Halos around Active Galactic Nuclei and the First Measurement of Intergalactic Magnetic Fields," *Astrophysical Journal Letters* 722 (September 17, 2010): id. L39, doi:10.1088/2041-8205/722/1/L39.
46. Andrii Neronov and Ievgen Vovk, "Evidence for Strong Extragalactic Magnetic Fields from Fermi Observations of TeV Blazars," *Science* 328 (April 2, 2010): 73–75, doi:10.1126/science.1184192.
47. P. A. R. Ade et al. (Planck Collaboration), "Planck 2015 Results. XIX."; *Astronomy & Astrophysics* 594 (October 2016): id. A19, doi:10.1051/0004-6361/201525821.
48. Peter A. R. Ade et al. (POLARBEAR Collaboration), "POLARBEAR Constraints on Cosmic Birefringence and Primordial Magnetic Fields," *Physical Review D* 92 (December 8, 2015): id. 123509, doi:10.1103/PhysRevD.92.123509.

49. Dylan R. Sutton, Chang Feng, and Christian L. Reichardt, "Current and Future Constraints on Primordial Magnetic Fields," *Astrophysical Journal* 846 (September 13, 2017): id. 164, doi:10.3847/1538-4357/aa85e2.
50. Sutton, Feng, and Reichardt, "Current and Future Constraints," p. 13.
51. Sutton, Feng, and Reichardt, "Current and Future Constraints," p. 17.
52. Sutton, Feng, and Reichardt, "Current and Future Constraints," p. 25.
53. S. C. Keller et al., "A Single Low-Energy, Iron-Poor Supernova as the Source of Metals in the Star SMSS J031300.36-670839.3," *Nature* 506 (February 27, 2014): 463–66, doi:10.1038/nature12990.
54. Michael S. Bessell et al., "Nucleosynthesis in a Primordial Supernova: Carbon and Oxygen Abundances in SMSS J031300.36-670839.3," *Astrophysical Journal Letters* 806 (June 8, 2015): id. L16, doi:10.1088/2041-8205/806/1/L16.
55. Yutaka Komiya, Takuma Suda, and Masayuki Y. Fujimoto, "The Most Iron-Deficient Stars as the Polluted Population III Stars," *Astrophysical Journal Letters* 808 (July 30, 2015): id. L47, doi:10.1088/2041-8205/808/2/L47.
56. Komiya, Suda, and Fujimoto, "The Most Iron-Deficient Stars."
57. Keller et al., "Single Low-Energy, Iron Poor Supernova."
58. Anna Frebel and Karl-Ludwig Kratz, "Stellar Age Dating with Thorium, Uranium and Lead," *Proceedings of the International Astronomical Union* 4 (October 2008): 449–56, doi:10.1017/S1743921309032104.
59. Anna Frebel et al., "Discovery of HE 1523-0901, a Strongly r-Process-Enhanced Metal-Poor Star with Detected Uranium," *Astrophysical Journal Letters* 660 (April 11, 2007): L117–L120, doi:10.1086/518122.
60. R. Cayrel et al., "Measurement of Stellar Age from Uranium Decay," *Nature* 409 (February 8, 2001): 691–92, doi:10.1038/35055507.
61. V. Hill et al., "First Stars. I. The Extreme r-Element Rich, Iron-Poor Halo Giant CS 31082-001. Implications for the r-Process Site(s) and Radioactive Cosmochronology," *Astronomy & Astrophysics* 387 (May 2002): 560–79, doi:10.1051/0004-6361:20020434.
62. Brad M. S. Hansen et al., "Hubble Space Telescope Observations of the White Dwarf Cooling Sequence of M4," *Astrophysical Journal Supplement Series* 155 (December 2004): 551–76, doi:10.1086/424832; Luigi R. Bedin et al., "The End of the White Dwarf Cooling Sequence in M4: An Efficient Approach," *Astrophysical Journal* 697 (May 6, 2009): 965–79, doi:10.1088/0004-637X/697/2/965.
63. Santiago Torres et al., "The White Dwarf Population of NGC 6397,"

Astronomy & Astrophysics 581 (September 2015): id. A90, doi:10.1051/0004-6361/201526157.

64. Hugh Ross, *The Fingerprint of God: Recent Scientific Discoveries Reveal the Unmistakable Identity of the Creator*, commemorative ed. (Covina, CA: RTB Press, 2010), 39–112.

65. Arthur S. Eddington, "The End of the World from the Standpoint of Mathematical Physics," *Nature* 127 (March 21, 1931): 450, doi:10.1038/127447a0.

66. Fred Hoyle, "The Universe: Past and Present Reflections," *Annual Review of Astronomy and Astrophysics* 20 (September 1982): 3, doi:10.1146/annurev.aa.20.090182.000245.

Chapter 7 – Einstein's Challenge

1. Immanuel Kant, "Universal Natural History and Theory of the Heavens," in *Theories of the Universe: From Babylonian Myth to Modern Science*, ed. Milton K. Munitz (Glencoe, IL: Free Press, 1957), 240.

2. Rudolf Thiel, *And There Was Light: The Discovery of the Universe* (New York: Alfred A. Knopf, 1957), 218; John Herman Randall Jr., *The Career of Philosophy*, vol. 2 (New York: Columbia University Press, 1965), 113; Kant, "Universal Natural History and Theory of the Heavens," 242–47.

3. Hugh Ross, *The Fingerprint of God: Recent Scientific Discoveries Reveal the Unmistakable Identity of the Creator*, commemorative ed. (Covina, CA: RTB Press, 2010), 22–29.

4. Albert Einstein, "Zur Elektrodynamik bewegter Körper," *Annalen der Physik* 322 (1905): 891–921, doi:10.1002/andp.19053221004; Hendrik A. Lorentz et al., *The Principle of Relativity*, with notes by Arnold Sommerfeld, trans. W. Perrett and G. B. Jeffrey (London: Methuen and Co., 1923), 35–65; Albert Einstein, "Ist die Trägheit eines Körpers von seinem Energieinhalt abhängig?" *Annalen der Physik* 14 (1905): 225–28, doi:10.1002/andp.200590007; Lorentz et al., *The Principle of Relativity*, 67–71.

5. Mario Rabinowitz, "Thoroughly Testing Einstein's Special Relativity Theory, and More," *Journal of Modern Physics* 7 (January 2016): 87–105, doi:10.4236/jmp.2016.71009; Dieter Hils and J. L. Hall, "Improved Kennedy-Thorndike Experiment to Test Special Relativity," *Physical Review Letters* 64 (April 9, 1990): 1697–1700, doi:10.1103/PhysRevLett.64.1697; M. Nagel et al., "Testing Lorentz Invariance by Comparing Light Propagation in Vacuum and Matter" (paper, Fifth Meeting on CPT and Lorentz Symmetry, Bloomington, IN, June 28–July 2, 2010); Achim Peters, "Modern

Optical Tests of Special Relativity" (paper, 39th Annual Meeting of the APS Division of Atomic, Molecular, and Optical Physics, State College, PA, May 27–31, 2008); G. Saathoff et al., "Improved Test of Time Dilation in Special Relativity," *Physical Review Letters* 91 (November 4, 2003): id. 190403, doi:10.1103/PhysRevLett.91.190403; S. K. Lamoreaux et al., "New Limits on Spatial Anisotropy from Optically Pumped ^{201}Hg and ^{199}Hg," *Physical Review Letters* 58 (February 16, 1987): 3125–28, doi:10.1103/PhysRevLett.58.746. This experiment confirms a prediction of special relativity to better than one part in 10^{21}.

6. Albert Einstein, "Die Feldgleichungen der Gravitation," *Sitzungsberichte der Königlich Preußischen Akademie der Wissenschaften* (November 1915): 844–47 (the following reference includes this reference); Albert Einstein, "Die Grundlage der allgemeinen Relativitätstheorie," *Annalen der Physik* 354 (1916): 769–822, doi:10.1002/andp.19163540702; Lorentz et al., *The Principle of Relativity*, 109–164.

7. Albert Einstein, "Kosmologische Betrachtungen zur allgemeinen Relativitätstheorie," *Sitzungsberichte der Königlich Preußischen Akademie der Wissenschaften* (February 8, 1917): 142–52. The English translation is in *The Principle of Relativity* by H. A. Lorentz, A. Einstein, H. Minkowski, and H. Weyl with notes by A. Sommerfield and translated by W. Perrett and G. B. Jeffrey (London, UK: Methuen and Co., 1923), 175–88.

8. Einstein, "Die Grundlage," 769–822; Lorentz et al., 109–64.

9. A. Vibert Douglas, "Forty Minutes with Einstein," *Journal of the Royal Astronomical Society of Canada* 50 (1956): 100.

10. Lincoln Barnett, *The Universe and Dr. Einstein* (New York: William Sloane Associates, 1948), 106.

11. Edwin Hubble, "A Relation Between Distance and Radial Velocity among Extra-Galactic Nebulae," *Proceedings of the National Academy of Sciences USA* 15 (March 1929): 168–73, doi:10.1073/pnas.15.3.168.

12. Albert Einstein, *Out of My Later Years* (New York: Philosophical Library, 1950), 27.

13. Hugh Ross, *Beyond the Cosmos: The Transdimensionality of God*, 3rd ed. (Covina, CA: RTB Press, 2017), 131–49.

Chapter 8 – Closing Loopholes: Round One

1. Arthur S. Eddington, "The End of the World: From the Standpoint of Mathematical Physics," *Nature* 127 (1931): 450, doi:10.1038/127447a0.

2. Arthur S. Eddington, "On the Instability of Einstein's Spherical World,"

Monthly Notices of the Royal Astronomical Society 90 (May 9, 1930): 672, doi:10.1093/mnras/90.7.668.l

3. Fazale Rana and Hugh Ross, *Origins of Life: Biblical and Evolutionary Models Face Off* (Covina, CA: RTB Press, 2014).

4. Herman Bondi and T. Gold, "The Steady-State Theory of the Expanding Universe," *Monthly Notices of the Royal Astronomical Society* 108 (1948): 252–70, doi:10.1093/mnras/108.3.252; Fred Hoyle, "A New Model for the Expanding Universe," *Monthly Notices of the Royal Astronomical Society* 108 (1948): 372–82, doi:10.1093/mnras/108.5.372.

5. Herman Bondi, *Cosmology*, 2nd ed. (Cambridge, UK: Cambridge University Press, 1960), 140; Hoyle, "A New Model for the Expanding Universe," 372.

6. Fred Hoyle, *The Nature of the Universe*, 2nd ed. (Oxford, UK: Basil Blackwell, 1952), 111; Fred Hoyle, "The Universe: Past and Present Reflections," *Annual Review of Astronomy and Astrophysics* 20 (September 1982): 3, doi:10.1146/annurev.aa.20.090182.000245.

7. Hugh Ross, *The Fingerprint of God: Recent Scientific Discoveries Reveal the Unmistakable Identity of the Creator*, commemorative ed. (Covina, CA: RTB Press, 2010), 65–77; J. C. Mather et al., "Measurement of the Cosmic Microwave Background Spectrum by the COBE FIRAS Instrument," *Astrophysical Journal* 420 (1994): 439–44, doi:10.1086/173574; Alan Dressler et al., "New Images of the Distant, Rich Cluster CL 0939+4713 with WFPC2," *Astrophysical Journal Letters* 435 (November 1994): L23–L26, doi:10.1086/187585.

8. Sir James H. Jeans, *Astronomy and Cosmogony*, 2nd ed. (Cambridge, UK: Cambridge University Press, 1929), 421–22.

9. Thomas L. Swihart, *Astrophysics and Stellar Astronomy* (New York: John Wiley & Sons, 1968), 157–58; Gilles Chabrier and Isabelle Baraffe, "Theory of Low-Mass Stars and Substellar Objects," *Annual Review of Astronomy and Astrophysics* 38 (2000): 337–77, doi:10.1146/annurev. astro.38.1.337.

10. Donald Hamilton, "The Spectral Evolution of Galaxies. I. An Observational Approach," *Astrophysical Journal* 297 (October 15, 1985): 371–89, doi:10.1086/163537.

11. For example, a team led by astronomer Alan Dressler found that for a galaxy cluster 4 billion light-years distant (and hence 4 billion years younger than ours) the ratio of younger (spiral shaped) galaxies to older galaxies (elliptical shaped) was about six times higher than for our own galaxy

cluster. See Sean M. Moran et al., "A Wide-Field Hubble Space Telescope Survey of the Cluster CI 0024+16 at z~0.4. III. Spectroscopic Signatures of Environmental Evolution in Early-Type Galaxies," *Astrophysical Journal* 634 (December 1, 2005), 977, doi:10.1086/497024; Alan Dressler et al., "New Images of the Distant, Rich Cluster."

12. Ross, *The Fingerprint of God*, 65–77; J. C. Mather et al., "Measurement of the Cosmic Microwave Background Spectrum," 439–44; Dressler et al., "New Images of the Distant, Rich Cluster," L23–L26.

13. Paul S. Wesson, "Olber's Paradox and the Spectral Intensity of the Extragalactic Background Light," *Astrophysical Journal* 367 (February 1, 1991): 399–406, doi:10.1086/169638.

14. Hugh Ross, *The Fingerprint of God*, 2nd ed., 57–77.

15. Robert Jastrow, *God and the Astronomers*, 2nd ed. (New York: W. W. Norton, 1992), 67–85.

16. Fred Hoyle, Geoffrey Burbidge, and Jayant V. Narlikar, *A Different Approach to Cosmology: From a Static Universe through the Big Bang towards Reality* (Cambridge, UK: Cambridge University Press, 2000), 65–115.

17. Hoyle, Burbidge, and Narlikar, *A Different Approach*, 107–337.

18. Gretchen Vogel, "Hubble Gives a Quasar House Tour," *Science* 274 (November 29, 1996): 1468, doi:10.1126/science.274.5292.1468b.

19. Faye Flam, "The Space Telescope Spies on Ancient Galaxy Menageries," *Science* 266 (December 16, 1994): 1806, doi:10.1126/science.266.5192.1806; Hugh Ross, "Hubble Space Telescope Captures Infancy of Cosmos," *Facts for Faith*, vol. 9, no. 2, 1–2.

20. Stephen J. Warren, Paul C. Hewett, and Patrick S. Osmer, "A Wide-Field Multicolor Survey for High-Redshift Quasars, $z \geq 2.2$. III. The Luminosity," *Astrophysical Journal* 421 (February 1994): 412–33, doi:10.1086/173660; Maarten Schmidt, Donald P. Schneider, and James E. Gunn, "Spectroscopic CCD Surveys for Quasars at Large Redshift. IV. Evolution of the Luminosity Function From Quasars Detected by Their Lyman-Alpha Emission," *Astronomical Journal* 110 (July 1995): 68–77, doi:10.1086/117497; J. D. Kennefict, S. G. Djorgovski, and R. R. de Carvalho, "The Luminosity Function of $z > 4$ Quasars from the Second Palomar Sky Survey," *Astronomical Journal* 110 (December 1995): 2553–65, doi:10.1086/117711; J. P. Ostriker and J. Heisler, "Are Cosmologically Distant Objects Obscured by Dust? A Test Using Quasars," *Astrophysical Journal* 278 (March 1984): 1–10, doi:10.1086/161762; P. A. Shaver et al., "Decrease in the Space Density of Quasars at High Redshift," *Nature*

384 (December 5, 1996): 439–41, doi:10.1038/384439a0; B. J. Boyle and T. di Matteo, "Limits on Dust Obscuration in QSOs," *Monthly Notices of the Royal Astronomical Society* 277 (November 1, 1995): L63–L66, doi:10.1093/mnras/277.1.L63; Patrick S. Osmer, "The Sharp End of Quasars," *Nature* 384 (December 5, 1996): 416, doi:10.1038/384415a0.

21. H. Sameshima, Y. Yoshii, and K. Kawara, "Chemical Evolution of the Universe at $0.7 < z < 1.6$ Derived from Abundance Diagnostics of the Broad-Line Region of Quasars," *Astrophysical Journal* 834 (January 13, 2017): id. 203, doi:10.3847/1538-4357/834/2/203; Jianhui Lian et al., "The Metallicity Evolution of Blue Compact Dwarf Galaxies from the Intermediate Redshift to the Local Universe," *Astrophysical Journal* 819 (February 29, 2016): id. 73, doi:10.3847/0004-637X/819/1/73; R. Maiolino et al., "AMAZE and LSD: Metallicity and Dynamical Evolution of Galaxies in the Early Universe," *The Messenger* 142 (December 2010), 36–39; G. J. Wasserburg and Y.-Z. Qian, "A Model of Metallicity Evolution in the Early Universe," *Astrophysical Journal Letters* 538 (July 21, 2000): L99–L102, doi:10.1086/312812.

22. M. Elvis, G. Risaliti, and G. Zamorani, "Most Supermassive Black Holes Must Be Rapidly Rotating," *Astrophysical Journal Letters* 565 (January 15, 2002): L75–L77, doi:10.1086/339197; Bernd Eduard Aschenbach, "Evidence for General Relativity Rotational Frame-Dragging in the Light from the Sgr A* Supermassive Black Hole," eprint (November 2009), arXiv:0911.2431; G. S. Bisnovatyi-Kogan, "At the Border of Eternity," *Science* 279 (February 27, 1998): 1321, doi:10.1126/science.279.5355.1321.

23. D. C. Homan and J. F. C. Wardle, "Direct Distance Measurements to Superluminal Radio Sources," *Astrophysical Journal* 535 (June 1, 2000): 575–85, doi:10.1086/308884.

24. Gary Hinshaw et al., "Nine-Year Wilkinson Microwave Anisotropy Probe (WMAP) Observations: Cosmological Parameter Results," *Astrophysical Journal Supplement Series* 208 (September 20, 2013): id. 19, doi:10.1088/0067-0049/208/2/19; P. A. R. Ade et al., Planck Collaboration, "Planck 2015 Results. XIII. Cosmological Parameters," *Astronomy & Astrophysics* 594 (October 2016): id. A13, doi:10.1051/0004-6361/201525830; Bo Qin and Xiang-Ping Wu, "Baryon Distribution in Galaxy Clusters as a Result of Sedimentation of Helium Nuclei," *Astrophysical Journal Letters* 529 (January 20, 2000): L1–L4, doi:10.1086/312445.

25. Hinshaw et al., "Nine-Year Wilkinson Microwave"; P. A. R. Ade et al.,

Planck Collaboration, "Planck 2015 Results"; G. S. Sharov and E. G. Vorontsova, "Parameters of Cosmological Models and Recent Astronomical Observations," *Journal of Cosmology and Astroparticle Physics* 2014 (October 22, 2014): id. 057, doi:10.1088/1475-7516/2014/10/057; T. de Haan et al., "Cosmological Constraints from Galaxy Clusters in the 2500 Square-Degree SPT-SZ Survey," *Astrophysical Journal* 832 (November 18, 2016): id. 95, doi:10.3847/0004-637x/832/1/95; Chia-Hsun Chuang et al., "The Clustering of Galaxies in the SDSS-III Baryon Oscillation Spectroscopic Survey: Single Probe Measurements from CMASS Anisotropic Galaxy Clustering," *Monthly Notices of the Royal Astronomical Society* 461 (October 1, 2016): 3781–93, doi:10.1093/mnras/sts1535.

26. Hinshaw et al., "Nine-Year Wilkinson Microwave"; P. A. R. Ade et al., Planck Collaboration, "Planck 2015 Results"; Sudeep Das et al., "The Atacama Cosmology Telescope: A Measurement of the Cosmic Microwave Background Power Spectrum at 148 and 218 GHz from the 2008 Southern Survey," *Astrophysical Journal* 729 (February 9, 2011): id. 62, doi:10.1088/0004-637X/729/1/62; J. C. Mather et al., "Measurement of the Cosmic Microwave Background Spectrum."

27. Jayant V. Narlikar, Geoffrey Burbidge, and R. G. Vishwakarma, "Cosmology and Cosmogony in a Cyclic Universe," *Journal of Astrophysics and Astronomy* 28 (September 2007): 67–99, doi:10.1007/s12036-007-0007-5; J. V. Narlikar, R. G. Vishwakarma, and G. Burbidge, "Inhomogeneities in the Microwave Background Radiation Interpreted within the Framework of the Quasi-Steady State Cosmology," *Astrophysical Journal* 585 (March 1, 2003): 1–11, doi:10.1086/345928; J. V. Narlikar, R. G. Vishwakarma, and G. Burbidge, "Interpretations of the Accelerating Universe," *Publications of the Astronomical Society of the Pacific* 114 (October 2002): 1092–96, doi:10.1086/342374.

28. Narlikar, Burbidge, and Vishwakarma, "Cosmology and Cosmogony," 70.

29. Narlikar, Burbidge, and Vishwakarma, "Cosmology and Cosmogony," 70.

30. N. Aghanim et al., Planck Collaboration, "Planck Intermediate Results. XLVIII. Disentangling Galactic Dust Emission and Cosmic Infrared Background Anisotropies," *Astronomy & Astrophysics* 596 (December 2016): id. A109, doi:10.1051/0004-6361/201629022; P. A. R. Ade et al., Planck Collaboration, "Planck 2013 Results. XXX. Cosmic Infrared Background Measurements and Implications for Star Formation," *Astronomy & Astrophysics* 571 (November 2014): id. A30, doi:10.1051/0004-6361/201322093;

Anatoliy I. Fisenko and Vladimir Lemberg, "On the Radiative and Thermodynamic Properties of the Cosmic Radiations Using COBE RIRAS Instrument Data: II. Extragalactic Far Infrared Background Radiation," *Astrophysics and Space Science* 352 (July 2014): 231–34, doi:10.1007/s10509-014-1880-4; Chian-Chou Chen et al., "Resolving the Cosmic Far-Infrared Background at 450 and 850 μm with SCUBA-2," *Astrophysical Journal* 776 (October 7, 2013): id. 131, doi:10.1088/0004-637X/776/2/131; Cameron Thacker et al., "H-ATLAS: The Cosmic Abundance of Dust from the Far-Infrared Background Power Spectrum," *Astrophysical Journal* 768 (April 15, 2013): id. 58, doi:10.1088/0004-637X/768/1/58; A. Pénin et al., "An Accurate Measurement of the Anisotropies and Mean Level of the Cosmic Infrared Background at 100 μm and 160 μm," *Astronomy & Astrophysics* 543 (July 2012): id. A123, doi:10.1051/0004-6361/201015929; N. Odegard et al., "Determination of the Far-Infrared Cosmic Background Using COBE DIRBE and WHAM Data," *Astrophysical Journal* 667 (September 20, 2007): 11–25, doi:10.1086/520079; E. L. Wright, "COBE Observations of the Cosmic Infrared Background," *New Astronomy Reviews* 48 (April 2004): 465–68, doi:10.1016/j.newar.2003.12.054.

31. Anthony Aguirre and Zoltan Haiman, "Cosmological Constant or Intergalactic Dust? Constraints from the Cosmic Far-Infrared Background," *Astrophysical Journal* 532 (March 2000): 28–36, doi:10.1086/308557. The authors determine Ω_{dust} must = a few x 10^{-5} to explain the type Ia supernova data where the cosmic dark energy density = 0. The QSSC models require much more dust than this value.

32. Cameron Thacker et al, "H-ATLAS: Cosmic Abundance of Dust."

33. John Gribbin, "Oscillating Universe Bounces Back," *Nature* 259 (January 1, 1976): 15–16, doi:10.1038/259015c0.

Chapter 9 – Closing Loopholes: Round Two

1. Robert H. Dicke et al., "Cosmic Black-Body Radiation," *Astrophysical Journal Letters* 142 (July 1965): 415, doi:10.1086/148306.

2. Dicke et al., "Cosmic Black-Body Radiation," 414–415.

3. Gary Hinshaw et al., "Nine-Year Wilkinson Microwave Anisotropy Probe (WMAP) Observations: Cosmological Parameter Results," *Astrophysical Journal Supplement Series* 208 (October 2013): id. 19, p. 9–11, doi:10.1088/0067-0049/208/2/19; P. A. R. Ade et al., Planck Collaboration, "Planck 2013 Results. XXX. Cosmic Infrared Background Measurements and Implications for Star Formation," *Astronomy & Astrophysics* 571

(November 2014): id. A30, doi:10.1051/0004-6361/201322093; Shadab Alam et al., "The Clustering of Galaxies in the Completed SDSS-III Baryon Oscillation Spectroscopic Survey: Cosmological Analysis of the DR12 Galaxy Sample" *Monthly Notices of the Royal Astronomical Society* 470 (September 21, 2017): 2617–652, doi:10.1093/mnras/stx721; Éric Aubourg et al., "Cosmological Implications of Baryon Acoustic Oscillation Measurements," *Physical Review D* 92 (December 14, 2015): id. 123516, p. 1, doi:10.1103/PhysRevD.92.123516; G. S. Sharov and E. G. Vorontsova, "Parameters of Cosmological Models and Recent Astronomical Observations," *Journal of Cosmology and Astroparticle Physics* 2014 (October 22, 2014): id. 057, p. 1, doi:10.1088/1475-7516/2014/10/057; T. de Haan et al., "Cosmological Constraints from Galaxy Clusters in the 2500 Square Degree SPT-SZ Survey," *Astrophysical Journal* 832 (November 18, 2016): id. 95, p. 1, doi:10.3847/0004-637X/832/1/95; Chia-Hsun Chuang et al., "The Clustering of Galaxies in the SDSS-III Baryon Oscillation Spectroscopic Survey: Single-Probe Measurements from CMASS Anisotropic Galaxy Clustering," *Monthly Notices of the Royal Astronomical Society* 461 (October 1, 2016): 3781, doi:10.1093/mnras/stw1535; Xiao-Dong Li et al., "Cosmological Constraints from the Redshift Dependence of the Alcock-Paczynski Effect: Application to the SDSS-III Boss DR12 Galaxies," *Astrophysical Journal* 832 (November 21, 2016): id. 103, doi:10.3847/0004-637X/832/2/103; M. Betoule et al., "Improved Cosmological Constraints from a Joint Analysis of the SDSS-II and SNLS Supernova Samples," *Astronomy & Astrophysics* 568 (August 2014): id. A22, p. 1, doi:10.1051/0004-6361/201423413; Nico Hamaus et al., "Constraints on Cosmology and Gravity from the Dynamics of Voids," *Physical Review Letters* 117 (August 25, 2016): id. 091302, p. 1, doi:10.1103/PhysRevLett.117.091302; Raul E. Angulo and Stefan Hilbert, "Cosmological Constraints from the CFHTLenS Shear Measurements Using a New, Accurate, and Flexible Way of Predicting Non-Linear Mass Clustering," *Monthly Notices of the Royal Astronomical Society* 448 (March 21, 2015): 364, doi:10.1093/mnras/stv050; David N. Spergel, Raphael Flauger, and Renée Hložek, "Planck Data Reconsidered," *Physical Review D* 91 (January 27, 2015): id. 023518, p. 1, doi:10.1103/PhysRevD.91.023518.

4.   Gary Hinshaw et al., "Nine-Year Wilkinson Microwave Anisotropy Probe (WMAP) Observations: Cosmological Parameter Results," *Astrophysical Journal Supplement Series* 208 (October 2013): id. 19, p. 9–11,

doi:10.1088/0067-0049/208/2/19; P. A. R. Ade et al., Planck Collaboration, "Planck 2013 Results. XXX. Cosmic Infrared Background Measurements and Implications for Star Formation," *Astronomy & Astrophysics* 571 (November 2014): id. A30, doi:10.1051/0004-6361/201322093; Shadab Alam et al., "The Clustering of Galaxies in the Completed SDSS-III Baryon Oscillation Spectroscopic Survey: Cosmological Analysis of the DR12 Galaxy Sample" *Monthly Notices of the Royal Astronomical Society* 470 (September 21, 2017): 2617–52, doi:10.1093/mnras/stx721; Éric Aubourg et al., "Cosmological Implications of Baryon Acoustic Oscillation Measurements," *Physical Review D* 92 (December 14, 2015): id. 123516, p. 1, doi:10.1103/PhysRevD.92.123516; G. S. Sharov and E. G. Vorontsova, "Parameters of Cosmological Models and Recent Astronomical Observations," *Journal of Cosmology and Astroparticle Physics* 2014 (October 22, 2014): id. 057, p. 1, doi:10.1088/1475-7516/2014/10/057; T. de Haan et al., "Cosmological Constraints from Galaxy Clusters in the 2500 Square Degree SPT-SZ Survey," *Astrophysical Journal* 832 (November 18, 2016): id. 95, p. 1, doi:10.3847/0004-637X/832/1/95; Chia-Hsun Chuang et al., "The Clustering of Galaxies in the SDSS-III Baryon Oscillation Spectroscopic Survey: Single-Probe Measurements from CMASS Anisotropic Galaxy Clustering," *Monthly Notices of the Royal Astronomical Society* 461 (October 1, 2016): 3781, doi:10.1093/mnras/stw1535; Xiao-Dong Li et al., "Cosmological Constraints from the Redshift Dependence of the Alcock-Paczynski Effect: Application to the SDSS-III Boss DR12 Galaxies," *Astrophysical Journal* 832 (November 21, 2016): id. 103, doi:10.3847/0004-637X/832/2/103; M. Betoule et al., "Improved Cosmological Constraints from a Joint Analysis of the SDSS-II and SNLS Supernova Samples," *Astronomy & Astrophysics* 568 (August 2014): id. A22, p. 1, doi:10.1051/0004-6361/201423413; Nico Hamaus et al., "Constraints on Cosmology and Gravity from the Dynamics of Voids," *Physical Review Letters* 117 (August 25, 2016): id. 091302, p. 1, doi:10.1103/PhysRevLett.117.091302; Raul E. Angulo and Stefan Hilbert, "Cosmological Constraints from the CFHTLenS Shear Measurements Using a New, Accurate, and Flexible Way of Predicting Non-Linear Mass Clustering," *Monthly Notices of the Royal Astronomical Society* 448 (March 21, 2015): 364, doi:10.1093/mnras/stv050; David N. Spergel, Raphael Flauger, and Renée Hložek, "Planck Data Reconsidered," *Physical Review D* 91 (January 27, 2015): id. 023518, p. 1, doi:10.1103/PhysRevD.91.023518.

5.   Alan H. Guth and Marc Sher, "The Impossibility of a Bouncing Universe,"

Nature 302 (April 7, 1983): 505–7, doi:10.1038/302505a0; Sidney A. Bludman, "Thermodynamics and the End of a Closed Universe," *Nature* 308 (March 22, 1984): 319–22, doi:10.1038/308319a0.

6. Igor D. Novikov and Yakov B. Zeldovich, "Physical Processes Near Cosmological Singularities," *Annual Review of Astronomy and Astrophysics* 11 (September 1973): 387–412, doi:10.1146/annurev.aa.11.090173.002131.

7. Arnold E. Sikkema and Werner Israel, "Black-hole Mergers and Mass Inflation in a Bouncing Universe," *Nature* 349 (January 3, 1991): 45–47, doi:10.1038/349045a0.

8. Andrei Linde, "Self-Reproducing Universe" (lecture, Centennial Symposium on Large Scale Structure, California Institute of Technology, Pasadena, CA, September 27, 1991).

9. Linde, "Self-Reproducing Universe."

10. Stephen Hawking and Roger Penrose, *The Nature of Space and Time* (Princeton, NJ: Princeton University Press, 1996), 36.

11. Hawking and Penrose, *Nature of Space and Time.*

12. B. P. Abbott et al., "Gravitational Waves and Gamma-Rays from a Binary Neutron Star Merger: GW170817 and GRB 170817a," *Astrophysical Journal Letters* 848 (October 16, 2017): id. L13, doi:10.3847/2041-8213/aa920c; Hugh Ross, "Neutron Star Merger Produces a Kilonova and Valuable Metals," *Today's New Reason to Believe* (October 23, 2017), reasons.org/explore/blogs/todays-new-reason-to-believe/read/todays-new-reason-to-believe/2017/10/23/neutron-star-merger-produces-a-kilonova-and-valuable-metals.

13. Eric S. Perlman et al., "New Constraints on Quantum Foam Models from X-Ray and Gamma-Ray Observations of Distant Quasars," (paper, Fourteenth Marcel Grossman Meeting, University of Rome "La Sapienza," July 12–18, 2015); Eric S. Perlman et al., "New Constraints on Quantum Gravity from X-Ray and Gamma-Ray Observations," *Astrophysical Journal* 805 (May 13, 2015): id. 10, doi:10.1088/0004-637X/805/1/10.

14. Perlman et al., "New Constraints on Quantum Gravity"; Eric S. Perlman et al., "Using Observations of Distant Quasars to Constrain Quantum Gravity," *Astronomy & Astrophysics* 535 (November 2011): id. L9, doi:10.1051/0004-6361/201118319; Wayne A. Christiansen et al., "Limits on Spacetime Foam," *Physical Review D* 83 (April 4, 2011): id. 084003, doi:10.1103/PhysRevD.83.084003.

15. Perlman et al., "New Constraints on Quantum Gravity."

16. F. Tamburini et al., "No Quantum Gravity Signature from the Farthest

Quasars," *Astronomy & Astrophysics* 533 (September 2011): id. A71, doi:10.1051/0004-6361/201015808.

17. Richard Lieu and Lloyd W. Hillman, "The Phase Coherence of Light from Extragalactic Sources: Direct Evidence against First-Order Planck Scale Fluctuations in Time and Space," *Astrophysical Journal Letters* 585 (February 11, 2003): L77–L80, doi:10.1086/374350.

18. John Estes et al., "Shining Light on Quantum Gravity with Pulsar-Black Hole Binaries," *Astrophysical Journal* 837 (March 7, 2017): id. 87, doi:10.3847/1538-4357/aa610e.

19. Estes et al., "Shining Light on Quantum Gravity."

20. Anna Ijjas and Paul J. Steinhardt, "Fully Stable Cosmological Solutions with a Non-Singular Classical Bounce," *Physical Letters B* 764 (January 10, 2017), 289–94, doi:10.1016/j.physletb.2016.11.047; Anna Ijjas and Paul J. Steinhardt, "Classically Stable Nonsingular Cosmological Bounces," *Physical Review Letters* 117 (September 16, 2016): id. 121304, doi:10.1103/PhysRevLett.117.121304; Michael Koehn, Jean-Luc Lehners, and Burt Ovrut, "Nonsingular Bouncing Cosmology: Consistency of the Effective Description," *Physical Review D* 93 (May 3, 2016): id. 103501, doi:10.1103/PhysRevD.93.103501; Koushik Balasubramanian and Sujan P. Dabholkar, "Time-Dependent Warping and Non-Singular Bouncing Cosmologies," (January 2014): eprint arXiv:1301.7015; Yi-Fu Cai, Damien A. Easson, and Robert Brandenberger, "Towards a Nonsingular Bouncing Cosmology," *Journal of Cosmology and Astroparticle Physics* 2012 (August 20, 2012): id. 020, doi:10.1088/1475-7516/2012/08/020; Yi-Fu Cai and Emmanuel N. Saridakis, "Non-Singular Cyclical Cosmology without Phantom Menace," *Journal of Cosmology* 17 (November 2011), 7238–7254, arXiv:1108.6052; BingKan Xue and Paul J. Steinhardt, "Unstable Growth of Curvature Perturbations in Nonsingular Bouncing Cosmologies," *Physical Review Letters* 105 (December 21, 2010): id. 261301, doi:10.1103/PhysRevLett.105.261301; Hua-Hui Xiong et al., "Oscillating Universe with Quintom Matter," *Physics Letters B* 666 (August 21, 2008): 212–17, doi:10.1016/j.physletb.2008.07.053; Parampreet Singh, Kevin Vandersloot, and G. V. Vereshchagin, "Nonsingular Bouncing Universes in Loop Quantum Cosmology," *Physical Review D* 74 (August 2006): id. 043510, doi:10.1103/PhysRevD.74.043510; C. Armendáriz-Picón and Patrick B. Greene, "Spinors, Inflation, and Non-Singular Cyclic Cosmologies," *General Relativity and Gravitation* 35 (September 2003): 1637–58, doi:10.1023/A:1025783118888.

21. Gia Dvali et al., "Scales of Gravity," *Physical Review D* 65 (December 26, 2001): id. 024031, doi:10.1103/PhysRevD.65.024031; Shinji Mukohyama, "Brane Gravity, Higher Derivative Terms, and Nonlocality," *Physical Review D* 65 (April 8, 2002): id. 084036, doi:10.1103/PhysRevD.65.084036; Takahiro Tanaka, "Weak Gravity in the Dvali-Gabadadze-Porrati Brane-world Model," *Physical Review D* 69 (January 13, 2004): id. 024001, doi:10.1103/PhysRevD.69.024001; Jihn E Kim, Bumseok Kyae, and Qaisar Shafi, "Brane Gravity, Massless Bulk Scalar, and Self-Tuning of the Cosmological Constant," *Physical Review D* 70 (September 30, 2004): id. 064039, doi:10.1103/PhysRevD.70.064039; Roy Maartens and Kazuya Koyama, "Brane-World Gravity," *Living Reviews in Relativity* 13 (December 2010): id. 5, doi:10.12942/lrr-2010-5.

22. F. R. Klinkhamer and G. E. Volovik, "Brane Realization of q-Theory and the Cosmological Constant Problem," *JETP Letters* 103 (May 2016): 627–30, doi:10.1134/S0021364016100088; M. N. Smolyakov, "Hierarchy Problem and the Cosmological Constant in a Five-Dimensional Brans-Dicke Brane World Model," *General Relativity and Gravitation* 42 (December 2010): 2799–811, doi:10.1007/s10714-010-1026-0; Anzhong Wang and N. O. Santos, "The Cosmological Constant in the Brane World of String Theory on S^1/Z_2," *Physics Letters B* 669 (November 6, 2008): 127–32, doi:10.1016/j.physletb.2008.09.044; Y. Aghababaie et al., "Towards a Naturally Small Cosmological Constant from Branes in 6D Supergravity," *Nuclear Physics B* 680 (March 2004): 389–414, doi:10.1016/j.nuclphysb.2003.12.015.

23. Marc Lilley, Larissa Lorenz, and Sébastien Clesse, "Observational Signatures of a Non-Singular Bouncing Cosmology," *Journal of Cosmology and Astroparticle Physics* 2011 (June 6, 2011): id. 004, doi:10.1088/1475-7516/2011/06/004.k

24. Armendáriz-Picón and Greene, "Spinors, Inflation"; Xue and Steinhardt, "Unstable Growth of Curvature Perturbations"; S. F. Hassan, Stefan Hofmann, and Mikael von Strauss, "Brane Induced Gravity, Its Ghost, and the Cosmological Constant Problem," *Journal of Cosmology and Astroparticle Physics* 2011 (January 20, 2011): id. 020, doi:10.1088/1475-7516/2011/01/020; Cai and Saridakis, "Non-Singular Cyclical Cosmology," 7238–254; Koehn, Lehners, and Ovrut, "Nonsingular Bouncing Cosmology"; Ijjas and Steinhardt, "Fully Stable Cosmological Solutions"; Ijjas and Steinhardt, "Classically Stable Nonsingular."

25. Charles W. Misner, Kip S. Thorne, and John Archibald Wheeler,

Gravitation (San Francisco, CA: W. H. Freeman, 1973), 752.

Chapter 10 – Science Discovers Time before Time

1. Eric J. Lerner, *The Big Bang Never Happened* (New York: Random House, 1991), 120, 295–318.
2. Lerner, 7–8.
3. Lerner, 283–291, 300–301.
4. Roger Penrose, "An Analysis of the Structure of Space-time," *Adams Prize Essay*, Cambridge University (1966); Stephen W. Hawking, "Singularities and the Geometry of Space-time," *Adams Prize Essay*, Cambridge University (1966); Stephen W. Hawking and George F. R. Ellis, "The Cosmic Black-Body Radiation and the Existence of Singularities in Our Universe," *Astrophysical Journal* 152 (April 1968): 25–36, doi:10.1086/149520; Stephen Hawking and Roger Penrose, "The Singularities of Gravitational Collapse and Cosmology," *Proceedings of the Royal Society A* 314 (January 27, 1970): 529–48, doi:10.1098/rspa.1970.0021.
5. Hawking and Penrose, 529–48.
6. Stephen Hawking as quoted by John Boslough, "Inside the Mind of a Genius," *Reader's Digest* (February 1984), 120; Stephen W. Hawking, *A Brief History of Time* (New York: Bantam, April 1988), 46.
7. Hawking, *A Brief History of Time*, 46.
8. Arvind Borde and Alexander Vilenkin, "Eternal Inflation and the Initial Singularity," *Physical Review Letters* 72 (May 23, 1994): 3305–8, doi:10.1103/PhysRevLett.72.3305; Arvind Borde, "Open and Closed Universes, Initial Singularities, and Inflation," *Physical Review D* 50 (September 15, 1994): 3692–702, doi:10.1103/PhysRevD.50.3692; Arvind Borde and Alexander Vilenkin, "Singularities in Inflationary Cosmology: A Review," *International Journal of Modern Physics D* 5 (December 15, 1996): 813–24, doi:10.1142/S0218271896000497; Arvind Borde and Alexander Vilenkin, "Violation of the Weak Energy Condition in Inflating Spacetimes," *Physical Review D* 56 (July 15, 1997): 717–23, doi:10.1103/PhysRevD.56.717.
9. Arvind Borde, Alan H. Guth, and Alexander Vilenkin, "Inflationary Spacetimes Are Incomplete in Past Directions," *Physical Review Letters* 90 (April 15, 2003): id. 151031, doi:10.1103/PhysRevLett.90.151301.
10. Borde, Guth, and Vilenkin, "Inflationary Spacetimes."
11. Borde, Guth, and Vilenkin, "Inflationary Spacetimes."
12. Alexander Vilenkin, *Many Worlds in One* (New York: Hill and Wang,

2006), 176.

13. Sean M. Carroll, "What If Time Really Exists?" (November 23, 2008), eprint: arXiv:0811.3722; Sean Carroll, *From Eternity to Here: The Quest for the Ultimate Theory of Time* (New York: Dutton, 2010).

14. Aron C. Wall, "The Generalized Second Law Implies a Quantum Singularity Theorem," *Classical and Quantum Gravity* 30 (July 12, 2013): id. 165003 doi:10.1088/0264-9381/30/16/165003; Aron C. Wall, "The Generalized Second Law Implies a Quantum Singularity Theorem," (December 6, 2016), eprint: arXiv:1010.5513, version 5.

15. Albert Einstein, "Die Feldgleichungen der Gravitation," *Sitzungsberichte der Königlich Preußischen Akademie der Wissenschaften* (November 1915): 844–47; Albert Einstein, "Die Grundlage der allgemeinen Relativitätstheorie," *Annalen der Physik* 49 (1916): 769–822, doi:10.1002/andp.19163540702; Hendrik A. Lorentz et al., *The Principle of Relativity*, with notes by Arnold Sommerfeld, trans. W. Perrett and G. B. Jeffrey (London: Methuen, 1923), 109–64; Albert Einstein, "Erklärung der Perihelbewegung des Merkur aus der allgemeinen Relativitätstheorie," *Sitzungsberichte der Königlich Preußischen Akademie der Wissenschaften* (November 18, 1915): 831–39.

16. F. W. Dyson, Arthur S. Eddington, and C. Davidson, "A Determination of the Deflection of Light by the Sun's Gravitational Field, from Observations Made at the Total Eclipse of May 29, 1919," *Philosophical Transactions of the Royal Society* A 220 (January 1, 1920): 291–333, doi:10.1098/rsta.1920.0009.

17. Steven Weinberg, *Gravitation and Cosmology: Principles and Applications of the General Theory of Relativity* (New York: J. Wiley and Sons, 1972), 198; Irwin I. Shapiro et al., "Mercury's Perihelion Advance: Determination by Radar," *Physical Review Letters* 28 (June 12, 1972): 1594–97, doi:10.1103/PhysRevLett.28.1594; R. V. Pound and J. L. Snider, "Effect of Gravity on Nuclear Resonance," *Physical Review Letters* 13 (November 2, 1964): 539–40, doi:10.1103/PhysRevLett.13.539.

18. C. Brans and Robert H. Dicke, "Mach's Principle and a Relativistic Theory of Gravitation," *Physical Review* 124 (November 1, 1961): 925–35, doi:10.1103/PhysRev.124.925; J. W. Moffat, "Consequences of a New Experimental Determination of the Quadrupole Moment of the Sun for Gravitation Theory," *Physical Review Letters* 50 (March 7, 1983): 709–12, doi:10.1103/PhysRevLett.50.709; George F. R. Ellis, "Alternatives to the Big Bang," *Annual Reviews of Astronomy and Astrophysics* 22 (September

1984): 157–84, doi:10.1146/annurev.aa.22.090184.001105.

19. Irwin I. Shapiro, Charles C. Counselman III, and Robert W. King, "Verification of the Principle of Equivalence for Massive Bodies," *Physical Review Letters* 36 (April 26, 1976): 555–58, doi:10.1103/PhysRevLett.36.1068.

20. R. D. Reasenberg et al., "Viking Relativity Experiment: Verification of Signal Retardation by Solar Gravity," *Astrophysical Journal Letters* 234 (December 15, 1979): 219–21, doi:10.1086/183144.

21. R. F. C. Vessot et al., "Test of Relativistic Gravitation with a Space-Borne Hydrogen Maser," *Physical Review Letters* 45 (December 29, 1980): 2081–84, doi:10.1103/PhysRevLett.45.2081.

22. J. H. Taylor, "Gravitational Radiation and the Binary Pulsar," *Proceedings of the Second Marcel Grossman Meeting on General Relativity*, part A, ed. Remo Ruffini (Amsterdam: North-Holland Publishing, 1982), 15–19.

23. J. H. Taylor et al., "Experimental Constraints on Strong-field Relativistic Gravity," *Nature* 355 (January 9, 1992): 132–36, doi:10.1038/355132a0.

24. Roger Penrose, *Shadows of the Mind: A Search for the Missing Science of Consciousness* (New York: Oxford University Press, 1994), 230.

25. J. M. Weisberg and Y. Huang, "Relativistic Measurements from Timing the Binary Pulsar PSR B1913+16," *Astrophysical Journal* 829 (September 21, 2016): id. 55, doi:10.3847/0004-637X/829/1/55.

26. Weisberg and Huang, "Relativistic Measurements from Timing."

27. M. N. Iacolina et al., "Long-Term Study of the Double Pulsar J0737-3039 with XMM-Newton Pulsar Timing," *Astrophysical Journal* 824 (June 16, 2016): id. 87, doi:10.3847/0004-637X/824/2/87.

28. R. J. Beswick et al., "High-Resolution Imaging of the Radio Continuum and Neutral Gas in the Inner Kiloparsec of the Radio Galaxy 3C 293," *Monthly Notices of the Royal Astronomical Society* 352 (July 21, 2004): 49–60, doi:10.1111/j.1365-2966.2004.07892.x; E. K. Mahony et al., "The Location and Impact of Jet-Driven Outflows of Cold Gas: The Case of 3C 293," *Monthly Notices of the Royal Astronomical Society: Letters* 435 (October 11, 2013): L58–L62, doi:10.1093/mnrasl/slt094.

29. J. Machalski et al., "Dynamical Analysis of the Complex Radio Structure in 3C 293: Clues on a Rapid Jet Realignment in X-Shaped Radio Galaxies," *Astronomy & Astrophysics* 595 (November 2016): id. A46, doi:10.1051/0004-6361/201629249.

30. Adam Ingram et al., "A Quasi-Periodic Modulation of the Iron Line Centroid Energy in the Black Hole Binary H1743-322," *Monthly Notices*

of the Royal Astronomical Society 461 (September 11, 2016): 1967–80, doi:10.1093/mnras/stw1245.

31. H.-H. Zhao et al., "The X-Ray View of Black Hole Candidate Swift J1842.5-1124 During Its 2008 Outburst," *Astronomy & Astrophysics* 593 (September 2016): id. A23, doi:10.1051/0004-6361/201628647.

32. Jakob van den Eijnden, Adam Ingram, and Phil Uttley, "Proving the Origin of Quasi-Periodic Oscillations: The Short-Time-Scale Evolution of Phase Lags in GRS 1915+105," *Monthly Notices of the Royal Astronomical Society* 458 (June 1, 2016): 3655–66, doi:10.1093/mnras/stw610.

33. Alexandra Veledina et al., "Discovery of Correlated Optical/X-Ray Quasi-Periodic Oscillations in Black Hole Binary SWIFT J1753.5-0127," *Monthly Notices of the Royal Astronomical Society* 454 (December 11, 2015): 2855–62, doi:10.1093/mnras/stv2201.

34. Richard Matzner et al., "LARES Satellite Thermal Forces and a Test of General Relativity," *Metrology for Aerospace* 2016 (September 23, 2016): doi.10.1109/MetroAeroSpace.2016.7573269; Ignazio Ciufolini et al., "A Test of General Relativity Using the LARES and LAGEOS Satellites and a GRACE Earth Gravity Model: Measurement of Earth's Dragging of Inertial Frames," *European Physical Journal* C 76 (March 2016): id. 120, doi:10.1140/epjc/s10052-016-3961-8.

35. C. W. F. Everitt et al., "The Gravity Probe B Test of General Relativity," *Classical and Quantum Gravity* 32 (November 17, 2015): id. 224001, doi:10.1088/0264-9381/32/22/224001.

36. Kajal K. Ghosh and D. Narasimha, "A Quasi-Stellar Object Plus Host System Lensed into a 6" Einstein Ring by a Low-Redshift Galaxy," *Astrophysical Journal* 692 (February 10, 2009): 694–701, doi:10.1088/0004-637X/692/1/694; Richard Lieu, "On the Absence of Shear from Complete Einstein Rings and the Stability of Geometry," *Astrophysical Journal Letters* 679 (May 20, 2008): 25–30, doi:10.1086/587128.

37. Andrew Watson, "Einstein's Theory Rings True," *Science* 280 (April 10, 1998): 205, doi:10.1126/science.280.5361.205.

38. Yiping Shu et al., "The Sloan Lens ACS Survey. XII. Extending Strong Lensing to Lower Masses," *Astrophysical Journal* 803 (April 17, 2015): id. 71, doi:10.1088/0004-637X/803/2/71; H. Tu et al., "Probing the Slope of Cluster Mass Profile with Gravitational Einstein Rings: Application to Abell 1689," *Monthly Notices of the Royal Astronomical Society* 386 (May 21, 2008): 1169–78, doi:10.1111/j.1365-2966.2008.12929.x.

39. M. C. Werner, J. An, and N. W. Evans, "On Multiple Einstein Rings,"

Monthly Notices of the Royal Astronomical Society 391 (December 1, 2008), 668–74, doi:10.1111/j.1365-2966.2008.13829.x.

40. "Gravitational Waves Detected 100 Years after Einstein's Prediction," LIGO, February 11, 2016, ligo.caltech.edu/news/ligo20160211.

41. B. P. Abbott et al. (LIGO Scientific Collaboration and VIRGO Collaboration), "Observation of Gravitational Waves from a Binary Black Hole Merger," *Physical Review Letters* 116 (February 11, 2016): id. 061102, doi: 10.1103/PhysRevLett.116.061102.

42. B. P. Abbott et al. (LIGO Scientific Collaboration and VIRGO Collaboration), "GW151226: Observation of Gravitational Waves from a 22-Solar-Mass Binary Black Hole Coalescence," *Physical Review Letters* 116 (June 15, 2016): id. 241103, doi:10.1103/PhysRevLett.116.241103.

43. B. P. Abbott et al. (LIGO Scientific Collaboration and Virgo Collaboration), "GW170817: Observation of Gravitational Waves from a Binary Neutron Star Inspiral," *Physical Review Letters* 119 (October 16, 2017): id. 161101, doi: 10.1103/PhysRevLett.119.161101.

44. For a review of these observations with citations see Hugh Ross, "Neutron Star Merger Produces a Kilonova and Valuable Metals," *Today's New Reason to Believe* (October 23, 2017): reasons.org/explore/blogs/todays-new-reason-to-believe/read/todays-new-reason-to-believe/2017/10/23/neutron-star-merger-produces-a-kilonova-and-valuable-metals.

Chapter 11: A God Outside of Time, But Knowable

1. Hugh Ross, *Beyond the Cosmos: The Transdimensionality of God*, 3rd ed. (Covina, CA: RTB Press, 2017).

2. John Maddox, "Down with the Big Bang," *Nature* 340 (August 10, 1989): 425, doi:10.1038/340425a0.

3. Maddox, "Down with the Big Bang."

4. Donald Lynden-Bell, J. Katz, and J. H. Redmount, "Sheet Universes and the Shapes of Friedmann Universes," *Monthly Notices of the Royal Astronomical Society* 239 (July 1, 1989): 201, doi:10.1093/mnras/239.1.201.

5. Victor J. Stenger, "The Face of Chaos," *Free Inquiry* (Winter 1992/93), 14.

Chapter 12 – A Brief Look at *A Brief History of Time*

1. Robert McCrum, "The 100 Best Nonfiction Books: No. 6—A Brief History of Time by Stephen Hawking (1988)," *The Guardian*, March 7, 2016, theguardian.com/books/2016/mar/07/100-best-nonfiction-books-6-brief-history-of-time-stephen-hawking.

2. Stephen W. Hawking, *A Brief History of Time: From the Big Bang to Black Holes* (New York: Bantam Books, 1988), 171.
3. Bryan Appleyard, "A Master of the Universe: Will Stephen Hawking Live to Find the Secret?," *Sunday Times*, June 19, 1988.
4. J. B. Hartle and S. W. Hawking, "Wave Function of the Universe," *Physical Review D* 28 (December 15, 1983): 2960–75, doi:10.1103/PhysRevD.28.2960.
5. Carl Sagan, "Introduction," *A Brief History of Time: From the Big Bang to Black Holes* (New York: Bantam Books, 1988), x.
6. An unedited, unabridged DVD of the debate, *RTB Live!* vol. 1: *The Great Debate* is available here: shop.reasons.org/product/332/rtb-live-volume-1-the-great-debate.
7. Leonard Susskind, private communication with Don Page, 2002.
8. Don N. Page, "Susskind's Challenge to the Harle-Hawking No-Boundary Proposal and Possible Resolutions," *Journal of Cosmology and Astroparticle Physics* 2007 (January 9, 2007): id. 004, doi:10.1088/1475-7516/2007/01/004.
9. Page, "Susskind's Challenge."
10. Hawking, *A Brief History of Time*, 138–39.
11. Hawking, *A Brief History of Time*, 136.
12. Stephen Hawking and Leonard Mlodinow, *The Grand Design* (New York: Bantam Books, 2010).
13. Hawking and Mlodinow, *Grand Design*, 34.
14. Hawking and Mlodinow, *Grand Design*, 153.
15. Hawking and Mlodinow, *Grand Design*, 165.
16. Exoplanet TEAM, "Catalog," *The Extrasolar Planets Encyclopaedia*, (April 7, 2017), exoplanet.eu/catalog/.
17. Exoplanet TEAM, "Catalog."
18. I describe and document this need to carefully design each planet and each asteroid-comet belt in the solar system in chapters 4–7 (pages 28–93) of my book, *Improbable Planet: How Earth Became Humanity's Home* (Grand Rapids: Baker, 2016).
19. Hugh Ross, "Rare Solar System, Rare Sun," *Today's New Reason to Believe* (December 13, 2009): reasons.org/explore/blogs/todays-new-reason-to-believe/read/tnrtb/2009/12/13/rare-solar-system-rare-sun; Hugh Ross, *Improbable Planet*, 35–42, 143–64.
20. Shintaro Kadoya and Eiichi Tajika, "Evolutionary Tracks of the Climate of Earth-Like Planets around Different Mass Stars," *Astrophysical Journal*

Letters 825 (July 5, 2016): id. L21, doi:10.3847/2041-8205/825/2/L21; M. Mittag et al., "Chromospheric Activity and Evolutionary Age of the Sun and Four Solar Twins," *Astronomy & Astrophysics* 591 (June 2016): id. A89, doi:10.1051/0004-6361/201527542; Marília Carlos, Poul E. Nissen, and Jorge Meléndez, "Correlation between Lithium Abundances and Ages of Solar Twin Stars," *Astronomy & Astrophysics* 587 (March 2016): id. A100, doi:10.1051/0004-6361/201527478; Takuya Shibayama et al., "Superflares on Solar-Type Stars Observed with Kepler. I. Statistical Properties of Superflares," *Astrophysical Journal Supplement Series* 209 (October 17, 2015): id. 5, doi:10.1088/0067-0049/209/1/5; P. E. Nissen, "High-Precision Abundance of Elements in Solar Twin Stars. Trends with Stellar Age and Elemental Condensation Temperature," *Astronomy & Astrophysics* 579 (July 2015): id. A52, doi:10.1051/0004-6361/201526269; Jorge Meléndez et al., "18 Sco: A Solar Twin Rich in Refactory and Neutron-Capture Elements: Implications for Chemical Tagging," *Astrophysical Journal* 791 (July 21, 2014): id. 14, doi:10.1088/0004-637X/791/1/14; Jorge Meléndez et al., "HIP 114328: A New Refactory-Poor and Li-Poor Solar Twin," *Astronomy & Astrophysics* 567 (July 2014): id. L3, doi:10.1051/0004-6361/201424172; J. Meléndez et al., "The Remarkable Solar Twin HIP 56948: A Prime Target in the Quest for Other Earths," *Astronomy & Astrophysics* 543 (July 2012): id. A29, doi:10.1051/0004-6361/201117222; A. Önehag et al., "M67-1194, An Unusually Sun-Like Solar Twin in M67," *Astronomy & Astrophysics* 528 (April 2011): id. A85, doi:10.1051/0004-6361/201015138; J. Meléndez et al., "The Peculiar Solar Composition and Its Possible Relation to Planet Formation," *Astrophysical Journal Letters* 704 (September 25, 2009): L66–L70, doi:10.1088/0004-637X/704/1/L66; G. F. Porto de Mello and L. da Silva, "HR 6060: The Closest Ever Solar Twin?" *Astrophysical Journal Letters* 482 (June 1997): L89–L92, doi:10.1086/310693; Jorge Meléndez, Katie Dodds-Eden, and José A. Robles, "HD 98618: A Star Closely Resembling Our Sun," *Astrophysical Journal Letters* 641 (March 30, 2006): L133–L136, doi:10.1086/503898; Y. Takeda et al., "Behavior of Li Abundances in Solar-Analog Stars. Evidence for Line-Width Dependence," *Astronomy & Astrophysics* 468 (June 2007): 663–77, doi:10.1051/0004-6361:20077220; Jorge Meléndez and Iván Ramírez, "HIP 56948: A Solar Twin with a Low Lithium Abundance," *Astrophysical Journal Letters* 669 (October 8, 2007): L89–L92, doi:10.1086/523942; Hugh Ross, "Search for the Sun's Twin" *Today's New Reason to Believe* (blog), *Reasons to Believe*, March 17, 2008, reasons.org/explore/publications/tnrtb/read/tnrtb/2008/03/17/search-for-the-sun-s-twin.

21. This oft-repeated claim by both NASA and the media is based on the following two research papers: Jianpo Guo et al., "Probability Distribution of Terrestrial Planets in Habitable Zones Around Host Stars," *Astrophysics and Space Science* 323 (October 2009): 367-373, doi: 10.1007/s10509-009-0081-z; Erik A. Petigura, Andrew W. Howard, and Geoffrey W. Marcy, "Prevalence of Earth-Size Planets Orbiting Sun-Like Stars," *Proceedings of the National Academy of Sciences* 110 (November 26, 2013): 19273–78, doi: 10.1073/pnas.1319909110.

22. Hugh Ross, *Improbable Planet*, 78–93; Glyn Collinson et al., "The Electric Wind of Venus: A Global and Persistent 'Polar Wind'-Like Ambipolar Electric Field Sufficient for the Direct Escape of Heavy Ionospheric Ions," *Geophysical Research Letters* 43 (June 28, 2016): 5926–34, doi:10.1002/2016GL068327; Hugh Ross, "'Electric Wind' Becomes 9th Habitable Zone," *Today's New Reason to Believe* (blog), *Reasons to Believe*, July 4, 2016, reasons.org/explore/blogs/todays-new-reason-to-believe/read/todays-new-reason-to-believe/2016/07/04/electric-wind-becomes-9th-habitable-zone; Hugh Ross, "Overlap of Habitable Zones Gets Much Smaller," *Today's New Reason to Believe* (blog), *Reasons to Believe*, December 27, 2016, reasons.org/explore/blogs/todays-new-reason-to-believe/read/todays-new-reason-to-believe/2016/12/27/overlap-of-habitable-zones-gets-much-smaller.

23. Gene D. McDonald and Michael C. Storrie-Lombardi, "Biochemical Constraints in a Protobiotic Earth Devoid of Basic Amino Acids: The 'BAA(-) World,'" *Astrobiology* 10 (December 2010): 989–1000, doi:10.1089/ast.2010.0484; Hugh Ross, "Rare Amino Acid Challenge to the Origin of Life," *Today's New Reason to Believe* (blog), *Reasons to Believe*, April 11, 2011, reasons.org/explore/blogs/todays-new-reason-to-believe/read/tnrtb/2011/04/11/rare-amino-acid-challenge-to-the-origin-of-life.

24. A. Coutens et al., "Detection of Glycolaldehyde toward the Solar-Type Protostar NGC 1333 IRAS2A," *Astronomy & Astrophysics* 576 (April 2015): id. A5, doi:10.1051/0004-6361/201425484; Michel Nuevo, Christopher K. Materese, and Scott A. Sandford, "The Photochemistry of Pyrimidine in Realistic Astrophysical Ices and the Production of Nucleobases," *Astrophysical Journal* 793 (September 15, 2014): id. 125, doi:10.1088/0004-637X/793/2/125; Abraham F. Jalbout et al., "Sugar Synthesis from a Gas-Phase Formose Reaction," *Astrobiology* 7 (July 2007):

433–42, doi:10.1089/ast.2006.0083.

25. Cornelia Meinert et al., "Ribose and Related Sugars from Ultraviolet Irradiation of Interstellar Ice Analogs," *Science* 352 (April 8, 2016): 208–12, doi:10.1126/science.aad8137; McDonald and Storrie-Lombardi, "Biochemical Constraints in a Protobiotic Earth"; Nuevo, Materese, and Sandford, "Photochemistry of Pyrimidine"; Jalbout et al., "Sugar Synthesis from a Gas-Phase."

26. Hugh Ross, "Homochirality: A Big Challenge for the Naturalistic Origin of Life," *Today's New Reason to Believe* (blog), *Reasons to Believe*, October 2, 2017, reasons.org/explore/blogs/todays-new-reason-to-believe/read/todays-new-reason-to-believe/2017/10/02/homochirality-a-big-challenge-for-the-naturalistic-origin-of-life; Hugh Ross, "Homochirality and the Origin of Life," *Today's New Reason to Believe* (blog), *Reasons to Believe*, November 7, 2011, reasons.org/explore/publications/tnrtb/read/tnrtb/2011/11/07/homochirality-and-the-origin-of-life; Cornella Meinert et al., "Anisotropy-Guided Enantiomeric Enhancement in Alanine Using Far-UV Circularly Polarized Light," *Origins of Life and Evolution of Biospheres* 45 (June 2015): 149–61, doi:10.1007/s11084-015-9413-x.

27. Daniel P. Glavin et al., "Unusual Nonterrestrial L-Proteinogenic Amino Acid Excesses in the Tagish Lake Meteorite," *Meteoritics & Planetary Science* 47 (August 2012): 1247–364, doi:10.1111/j.1945-5100.2012.01400.x.

28. Glavin et al., "Unusual Nonterrestrial L-Proteinogenic."

29. Ivan G. Draganić, "Radiolysis of Water: A Look at Its Origin and Occurrence in the Nature," *Radiation Physics and Chemistry* 72 (February 2005): 181–86, doi:10.1016/j.radphyschem.2004.09.012.

30. Ross, *Improbable Planet*, 93–106 and citations therein.

31. Fazale Rana and Hugh Ross, *Origins of Life: Biblical and Evolutionary Models Face Off* (Covina, CA: RTB Press, 2014) plus an archive of subsequent published articles at reasons.org/origins-of-life-updates; Fazale Rana, *The Cell's Design: How Chemistry Reveals the Creator's Artistry* (Grand Rapids: Baker, 2008); Fazale Rana, *Creating Life in the Lab: How New Discoveries in Synthetic Biology Make a Case for the Creator* (Grand Rapids: Baker, 2011); Ross, *Improbable Planet*.

32. John C. Armstrong, Llyd E. Wells, and Guillermo Gonzalez, "Rummaging through Earth's Attic for the Remains of Ancient Life," *Icarus* 160 (November 2, 2002): 183–96, doi:10.1006/icar.2002.6957.

33. Hugh Ross, "How Would the Discovery of Extraterrestrial Life Affect Biblical Creation Models?" *Today's New Reason to Believe* (blog),

Reasons to Believe, September 28, 2016, reasons.org/explore/blogs/todays-new-reason-to-believe/read/todays-new-reason-to-believe/2016/09/28/how-would-the-discovery-of-extraterrestrial-life-affect-biblical-creation-models.

34. Hugh Ross, *Improbable Planet,* 16–219, 231–35; "RTB Design Compendium (2009)," Reasons to Believe, last updated November 17, 2010, reasons.org/finetuning.

35. Hawking, *A Brief History of Time,* 169.

36. Hawking, *A Brief History of* Time, 175.

37. Stanley L. Jaki, *Cosmos and Creator* (Edinburgh, UK: Scottish Academic Press, 1980), 49– 54; Stanley L. Jaki, *God and the Cosmologists* (Washington, DC: Regnery Gateway, 1989), 104–9.

38. Hawking, *A Brief History of Time,* 168.

39. Hawking, *A Brief History of Time,* 126.

40. Hawking, *A Brief History of Time,* 126.

Chapter 13 – A Modern-Day Goliath

1. Allen Emerson, "A Disorienting View of God's Creation," *Christianity Today,* February 1, 1985, 19.

2. Paul Davies, *God and the New Physics* (New York: Simon and Schuster, 1983), 25–43, specifically 38–39.

3. Paul Davies, *Superforce: The Search for a Grand Unified Theory of Nature* (New York: Simon and Schuster, 1984), 243.

4. Paul Davies, *The Cosmic Blueprint: New Discoveries in Nature's Creative Ability to Order the Universe* (New York: Simon and Schuster, 1988), 141.

5. Davies, *Cosmic Blueprint,* 203.

6. Paul Davies, *The Fifth Miracle: The Search for the Origin and Meaning of Life* (New York: Simon & Schuster, 1999), 93, 120.

7. Lawrence M. Krauss, *A Universe from Nothing* (New York: Free Press, 2012).

8. Krauss, *Universe from Nothing,* 173.

9. Krauss, *Universe from Nothing,* 191.

10. Arvind Borde, Alan H. Guth, and Alexander Vilenkin, "Inflationary Spacetimes Are Incomplete in Past Directions," *Physical Review Letters* 90 (April 15, 2003): id. 151301, doi:10.1103/PhysRevLett.90.151301.

11. Krauss, *Universe from Nothing,* 176.

12. Krauss, *Universe from Nothing,* 147, 190–91.

13. Krauss, *Universe from Nothing,* 147.

14. Krauss, *Universe from Nothing*, 147.
15. Fazale Rana, *Creating Life in the Lab: How New Discoveries in Synthetic Biology Make a Case for the Creator* (Grand Rapids: Baker, 2011).
16. See *The Grand Design* by Stephen Hawking and Leonard Mlodinow (New York: Bantam Books, 2010).
17. Krauss, *Universe from Nothing*, 144.
18. Jeremiah 33; Hugh Ross, *Hidden Treasures in the Book of Job: How the Oldest Book in the Bible Answers Today's Scientific Questions* (Grand Rapids: Baker, 2011), 60–63.
19. Hugh Ross, *Navigating Genesis: A Scientist's Journey through Genesis 1–11* (Covina, CA: RTB Press, 2014), chapters 3–10.
20. Ross, *Navigating Genesis*, Appendix A.
21. Krauss, *Universe from Nothing*, 123.
22. Hugh Ross, *Why the Universe Is the Way It Is* (Grand Rapids: Baker, 2008), chapters 4, 8.
23. Hugh Ross, *More than a Theory: Revealing a Testable Model for Creation* (Grand Rapids: Baker, 2009), 212–16; Jeffrey A. Zweerink, *Who's Afraid of the Multiverse?* (Covina, CA: RTB Press, 2012).
24. Paul Davies, *The Cosmic Blueprint* (New York: Simon & Schuster, 1988), 203.
25. Paul Steinhart, "Big Bang Blunder Bursts the Multiverse Bubble," *Nature* 510 (June 5, 2014): 9.
26. Davies, *Cosmic Blueprint*, 141.
27. Freeman J. Dyson, *Disturbing the Universe* (New York: Basic Books, 1979), 250.
28. Heinz R. Pagels, "Uncertainty and Complementarity," *The World Treasury of Physics, Astronomy, and Mathematics*, eds. Timothy Ferris and Clifton Fadiman (Boston, MA: Little, Brown, 1991), 106–8.
29. Nick Herbert, *Quantum Reality: Beyond the New Physics: An Excursion into Metaphysics and the Meaning of Reality* (New York: Anchor, 1987), 16–29; Stanley L. Jaki, *Cosmos and Creator* (Edinburgh, UK: Scottish Academic Press, 1980), 96–98; James Jeans, "A Universe of Pure Thought," in *Quantum Questions: Mystical Writings of the World's Greatest Physicists*, ed. Ken Wilber (Boston, MA: New Science Library, Shambhala, 1985), 140–44; Ken Wilber, *Quantum Questions* (Boston, MA: Shambhala, 1985), 145–46; Paul Teller, "Relativity, Relational Holism, and the Bell Inequalities," in *Philosophical Consequences of Quantum Theory: Reflections on Bell's Theorem*, eds. James T. Cushing and Eman McMullin (Notre Dame,

IN: University of Notre Dame Press, 1989), 216–23.

30. James S. Trefil, *The Moment of Creation* (New York: Charles Scribner's Sons, 1983), 91–101.

31. David Dvorkin, "Why I Am Not a Jew," *Free Inquiry* 10 (1990), 34. David Dvorkin points out that orthodox Jews and fundamentalist Christians share many beliefs in common and also share the tendency to add dogmas to their doctrines.

Chapter 14 – The Divine Watchmaker

1. William Paley, *Natural Theology on Evidence and Attributes of Deity*, 18th ed. rev. (Edinburgh, UK: Lackington, Allen and Co., and James Sawers, 1818), 12–14.

2. David Hume, *Dialogues Concerning Natural Religion* (London: Collins, 1963), 154–56.

3. Jacques Monod, *Chance and Necessity* (London: Collins, 1972), 110 (emphasis in original).

4. Richard Dawkins, *The Blind Watchmaker: Why the Evidence of Evolution Reveals a Universe without Design* (New York: W. W. Norton, 1987), 5 (emphasis in original).

5. Stephen Jay Gould, *The Panda's Thumb: More Reflections in Natural History* (New York: W. W. Norton, 1980).

6. Steven M. Block, "Real Engines of Creation," *Nature* 386 (March 20, 1997): 217–19, doi:10.1038/386217a0; Hiroyuki Noji, Ryohei Yasuda, Masasuke Yoshida, and Kazuhiko Kinosita Jr., "Direct Observation of the Rotation of F1-ATPase," *Nature* 386 (March 20, 1997): 299–302, doi:10.1038/386299a0.

7. Michael Groll et al., "Structure of 26S Proteasome from Yeast at 2.4Å Resolution," *Nature* 386 (April 3, 1997): 463–71, doi:10.1038/386463a0.

8. For a book length treatment of the amazing designs inside the cell see Fazale Rana, *The Cell's Design* (Grand Rapids: Baker, 2008).

9. Hugh Ross, *More than a Theory: Revealing a Testable Model for Creation* (Grand Rapids: Baker, 2009), 156–79.

10. Janet Raloff, "Earth Day 1980: The 29th Day?" *Science News* 117 (1980): 270; Roger Lewin, "No Dinosaurs This Time," *Science* 221 (September 16, 1983): 1169, doi:10.1126/science.221.4616.1168; John H. Lawton and Robert M. May, eds., *Extinction Rates* (New York: Oxford University Press, 1995).

11. Paul R. Ehrlich, Anne H. Ehrlich, and J. P. Holdren, *Ecoscience: Population,*

Resources, Environment (San Francisco, CA: W. H. Freeman, 1977), 142; Paul R. Ehrlich and Anne H. Ehrlich, *Extinction: The Causes and Consequences of the Disappearance of Species* (New York: Ballantine, 1981), 33; Lawton and May, *Extinction Rates.*

12. Ehrlich and Ehrlich, 23, *Extinction: Causes and Consequences.*

13. For more on these subjects see Fazale Rana with Hugh Ross, *Who Was Adam? A Creation Model Approach to the Origin of Humanity*, 2nd ed. (Covina, CA: RTB Press, 2015); Hugh Ross, *Improbable Planet: How Earth Became Humanity's Home* (Grand Rapids: Baker, 2016); Ross, *More than a Theory*; Hugh Ross, *Hidden Treasures in the Book of Job: How the Oldest Book in the Bible Answers Todays Scientific Questions* (Grand Rapids: Baker, 2014).

14. Peter Gordon, "The Panda's Thumb Revisited: An Analysis of Two Arguments against Design," *Origins Research* 7 (1984): 12–14.

15. Hideki Endo et al., "Role of the Giant Panda's 'Pseudo-Thumb,'" *Nature* 397 (1999): 309–10, doi:10.1038/16830.

Chapter 15 – A "Just-Right" Universe

1. John D. Barrow, *The Constants of Nature* (New York: Pantheon Books, 2002), 165–67.

2. Frank Wilczek, "Particle Physics: Hard Core Revelations," *Nature* 445 (January 11, 2007): 156–57, doi:10.1038/445156a.

3. Martin J. Rees and Willian H. McCrea, "Large Numbers and Ratios in Astrophysics and Cosmology (and Discussion)," *Philosophical Transactions of the Royal Society A* 310 (December 20, 1983): 317, doi:10.1098/rsta.1983.0093.

4. Fred Hoyle, *Galaxies, Nuclei, and Quasars* (New York: Harper and Row, 1965), 147–50; Fred Hoyle, "The Universe: Past and Present Reflection," *Annual Review of Astronomy and Astrophysics* 20 (September 1982): 16, doi:10.1146/annurev.aa.20.090182.000245; Hugh Ross, *The Fingerprint of God: Recent Scientific Discoveries Reveal the Unmistakable Identity of the Creator*, commemorative ed. (Covina, CA: RTB Press, 2010): 103.

5. Fred Hoyle, *The Nature of the Universe*, 2nd ed. (Oxford, U.K.: Basil Blackwell, 1952), 109; Fred Hoyle, *Astronomy and Cosmology: A Modern Course* (San Francisco, CA: W. H. Freeman, 1975), 684–85; Hoyle, "Universe: Past and Present Reflection," 3; Hoyle, *Astronomy and Cosmology*, 522.

6. Hoyle, *Nature of the Universe*, 111.

7. Hoyle, "Universe: Past and Present Reflection," 16.
8. H. Oberhummer, A. Csótó, and H. Schlattl, "Stellar Production Rates of Carbon and Its Abundance in the Universe," *Science* 289 (July 7, 2000): 88–90, doi:10.1126/science.289.5476.88.
9. Oberhummer, Csótó, and Schlattl, "Stellar Production Rates," 90.
10. John D. Barrow and Frank J. Tipler, *The Anthropic Cosmological Principle* (New York: Oxford University Press, 1986), 400.
11. James S. Trefil, *The Moment of Creation* (New York: Collier Books, Macmillan, 1983), 127–34.
12. Jeff Zweerink and I explain exactly where the cosmic density fine-tuning resides in my book, *Why the Universe Is the Way It Is* (Grand Rapids: Baker, 2008), 209–11.
13. Lawrence M. Krauss, "The End of the Age Problem, and the Case for a Cosmological Constant Revisited," *Astrophysical Journal* 501 (1998): 461, doi:10.1086/305846.
14. George F. R. Ellis, "The Anthropic Principle: Laws and Environments," in *The Anthropic Principle*, F. Bertola and U. Curi, eds. (New York: Cambridge University Press, 1993), 30; D. Allan Bromley, "Physics," *Science* 209 (July 4, 1980): 116, doi:10.1126/science.209.4452.110.
15. George F. R. Ellis, "The Anthropic Principle," 30; H. R. Marston, Shirley H. Allen, and S. L. Swaby, "Iron Metabolism in Copper-Deficient Rats," *British Journal of Nutrition* 25 (January 1971): 15–30, doi:10.1079/BJN19710062; K. W. J. Wahle and N. T. Davies, "Effect of Dietary Copper Deficiency in the Rat on Fatty Acid Composition of Adipose Tissue and Desaturase Activity of Liver Microsomes," *British Journal of Nutrition* 34 (July 1975): 105–12, doi:10.1017/S000711457500013X; Walter Mertz, "The Newer Essential Trace Elements, Chromium, Tin, Vanadium, Nickel, and Silicon," *Proceedings of the Nutrition Society* 33 (December 1974): 307–13, doi:10.1079/PNS19740054.
16. Christopher C. Page et al., "Natural Engineering Principles of Electron Tunnelling in Biological Oxidation-Reduction," *Nature* 402 (November 4, 1999): 47–52, doi:10.1038/46972.
17. I review the reasons why in my book, *Beyond the Cosmos*, 3rd ed. (Covina, CA: RTB Press, 2017), 32–41.
18. John P. Cox and R. Thomas Giuli, *Principles of Stellar Structure, Volume II: Applications to Stars* (New York: Gordon and Breach, 1968), 944–1028.
19. Hugh Ross, "Part 1. Fine-Tuning for Life in the Universe," *RTB Design Compendium (2009)* (November 17, 2010), reasons.org/finetuning.

20. The previous three editions of this book and the last two editions of my other book, *The Fingerprint of God*, document some of these numbers.

21. Hoyle, "The Universe," 16.

22. Fred Hoyle in Mervyn Stockwood (editor), *Religion and the Scientists: Addresses Delivered in the University Church, Cambridge* (London: SCM Press, 1959), 64.

23. Paul Davies, *God and the New Physics* (New York: Simon & Schuster, 1983), viii, 3–42, 142–43.

24. Paul Davies, *Superforce: The Search for a Grand Unified Theory of Nature* (New York: Simon & Schuster, 1984), 243.

25. Paul Davies, *The Cosmic Blueprint: New Discoveries in Nature's Ability to Order the Universe* (New York: Simon & Schuster, 1988), 203.

26. Paul Davies, "The Anthropic Principle," *Science Digest* 191, October 1983, 24.

27. George Greenstein, *The Symbiotic Universe* (New York: William Morrow, 1988), 27.

28. Tony Rothman, "A 'What You See Is What You Beget' Theory," *Discover*, May 1987, 99.

29. Bernard J. Carr and Martin J. Rees, "The Anthropic Principle and the Structure of the Physical World," *Nature* 278 (April 12, 1979): 612, doi:10.1038/278605a0.

30. Bernard J. Carr, "On the Origin, Evolution, and Purpose of the Physical Universe," in *Physical Cosmology and Philosophy* ed. John Leslie (New York: Macmillan, 1990), 153 (emphasis in the original).

31. Freeman Dyson, *Infinite in All Directions* (New York: Harper and Row, 1988), 298.

32. Freeman Dyson, *Disturbing the Universe* (New York: Harper and Row, 1979), 250.

33. Henry Margenau and Roy Abraham Varghese, eds., *Cosmos, Bios, and Theos: Scientists Reflect on Science, God, and the Origins of the Universe, Life, and Homo Sapiens* (La Salle, IL: Open Court, 1992), 52.

34. Margenau and Varghese, *Cosmos, Bios, and Theos*, 83.

35. Stuart Gannes, "People at the Frontiers of Science," *Fortune*, October 13, 1986, 57.

36. Fang Li Zhi and Li Shu Xian, *Creation of the Universe*, trans. T. Kiang (Singapore: World Scientific, 1989), 173.

37. Roger Penrose, in the movie *A Brief History of Time* (Burbank, CA: Paramount Pictures Incorporated, 1992).

38. George F. R. Ellis, "The Anthropic Principle," 30.

39. Stephen Hawking, *A Brief History of Time* (New York: Bantam Books, April 1988), 127.

40. Edward Harrison, *Masks of the Universe* (New York: Macmillan, 1985), 252, 263.

41. John Noble Wilford, "Sizing Up the Cosmos: An Astronomer's Quest," *New York Times*, March 12, 1991.

42. Tim Stafford, "Cease-Fire in the Laboratory," *Christianity Today*, April 3, 1987, 18.

43. Robert Jastrow, "The Secret of the Stars," *New York Times Magazine*, June 25, 1978, 7.

44. Robert Jastrow, *God and the Astronomers* (New York: W. W. Norton, 1978), 116.

45. Richard Swinburne, "Argument from the Fine-Tuning of the Universe," in *Physical Cosmology and Philosophy*, ed. John Leslie (New York: Macmillan, 1990), 165.

46. William Lane Craig, "Barrow and Tipler on the Anthropic Principle vs. Divine Design," *British Journal for the Philosophy of Science* 38 (September 1, 1988): 392, doi:10.1093/bjps/39.3.389.

47. Joseph Silk, *Cosmic Enigmas* (Woodbury, NY: American Institute of Physics Press, 1994): 8–9.

48. Fazale Rana and Hugh Ross, *Origins of Life: Biblical and Evolutionary Models Face Off* (Covina, CA: RTB Press, 2014).

49. NCSE staff, *Education and Creationism Don't Mix* (Berkeley, CA: National Center for Science Education, 1985), 3; Eugenie C. Scott, "Of Pandas and People," *National Center for Science Education Reports* (January–February 1990), 18; Paul Bartelt, "Patterson and Gish at Morningside College," *The Committees of Correspondence*, Iowa Committee of Correspondence Newsletter, vol. 4, no. 4 (October 1989), 1.

50. *Education and Creationism Don't Mix*, 3; Eugenie C. Scott and Henry P. Cole, "The Elusive Scientific Basis of Creation 'Science'," *The Quarterly Review of Biology* 60 (March 1985): 297, doi:10.1086/414171.

51. Ilya Prigogine and Isabelle Stengers, *Order Out of Chaos: Man's New Dialogue with Nature* (New York: Bantam Books, 1984).

52. John D. Barrow and Frank J. Tipler, *The Anthropic Cosmological Principle* (New York: Oxford University Press, 1986).

53. Barrow and Tipler, *Anthropic Cosmological Principle*, 676–67.

54. Barrow and Tipler, *Anthropic Cosmological Principle*, 676–67, 682;

Martin Gardner, "Notes of a Fringe-Watcher: Tipler's Omega Point Theory," *Skeptical Inquirer* 15 (1991): 128–32.

55. Frank J. Tipler, *The Physics of Immortality: Modern Cosmology, God, and the Resurrection of the Dead* (New York: Doubleday, 1994).

56. Martin Gardner, "WAP, SAP, PAP, and FAP," *The New York Review of Books* 23 (May 8, 1986): 22–25.

57. Roger Penrose, *The Emperor's New Mind* (New York: Oxford University Press, 1989), 3–145, 374–451; Roger Penrose, *Shadows of the Mind* (New York: Oxford University Press, 1994), 7–208.

58. Frank J. Tipler, *Physics of Immortality*, 253–55.

59. Frank J. Tipler, *Physics of Immortality*, 256–57.

60. Gardner, "Notes of a Fringe-Watcher," 132.

61. Frank J. Tipler, *The Physics of Christianity* (New York: Doubleday, 2007).

Chapter 16 – Responding to Nonempirical, Nontheistic Cosmic Models

1. 1 Peter 3:15–16.

2. Ahmed Farag Ali and Saurya Das, "Cosmology from Quantum Potential," *Physics Letters B* 741 (February 4, 2015): 276–79, doi:10.1016/j.physletb.2014.12.057.

3. Farag Ali and Das, "Cosmology from Quantum Potential," 276.

4. Farag Ali and Das, "Cosmology from Quantum Potential," 276.

5. Stanley L. Miller, "A Production of Amino Acids under Possible Primitive Earth Conditions," *Science* 117 (May 15, 1953): 528–29, doi:10.1126/science.117.3046.528.

6. Iris Fry, *The Emergence of Life on Earth: A Historical and Scientific Overview* (New Brunswick, NJ: Rutgers University Press, 2000), 83–88. This book offers the best scholarly review of the early history of origin of life research.

7. S. Fox and K. Dose, *Molecular Evolution and the Origin of Life* (San Francisco: Freeman, 1972), 44–45.

8. J. R. Cronin and S. Pizzarello, "Amino Acids in Meteorites," *Advances in Space Research* 3 (February 1983): 5–18, doi:10.1016/0273-1177(83)90036-4.

9. Jamie E. Elsila, Daniel P. Glavin, and Jason P. Dworkin, "Cometary Glycine Detected in Samples Returned by Stardust," *Meteoritics & Planetary Science* 44 (September 2009): 1323–30, doi:10.1111/j.1945-5100.2009.tb01224.x.

10. Gene D. McDonald and Michael C. Storrie-Lombardi, "Biochemical Con-

straints in a Protobiotic Earth Devoid of Basic Amino Acids: The 'BAA(-) World,'" *Astrobiology* 10 (December 2010): 989–1000, doi:10.1089/ ast.2010.0484; Hugh Ross, "Rare Amino Acid Challenge to the Origin of Life," *Today's New Reason To Believe* (blog), *Reasons to Believe*, April 11, 2010, reasons.org/explore/publications/tnrtb/read/tnrtb/2011/04/11/rare-amino-acid-challenge-to-the-origin-of-life.

11. L. E. Snyder et al., "A Rigorous Attempt to Verify Interstellar Glycine," *Astrophysical Journal* 619 (February 1, 2005): 914–30, doi:10.1086/426677; Yi Jehng Kuan et al., "A Search for Interstellar Pyrimidine," *Monthly Notices of the Royal Astronomical Society* 345 (October 21, 2003): 650–56, doi:10.1046/j.1365-8711.2003.06975.x.

12. Hugh Ross, "Homochirality: A Big Problem for the Naturalistic Origin of Life," Today's New Reason to Believe (October 2, 2017): reasons.org/ explore/blogs/todays-new-reason-to-believe/read/todays-new-reason-to-believe/2017/10/02/homochirality-a-big-challenge-for-the-naturalistic-origin-of-life; Fazale Rana and Hugh Ross, *Origins of Life: Biblical and Evolutionary Models Face Off* (Covina, CA: RTB Press, 2014), 125–36.

13. Hugh Ross, *Improbable Planet: How Earth Became Humanity's Home* (Grand Rapids: Baker, 2016), 97–106.

14. Ross, *Improbable Planet*, 97–230.

15. Rana and Ross, *Origins of Life*.

16. Fazale Rana, *Creating Life in the Lab: How New Discoveries in Synthetic Biology Make a Case for the Creator* (Grand Rapids: Baker, 2011).

Chapter 17 – Earth: The Place for Life

1. Iosif S. Shklovsky and Carl Sagan, *Intelligent Life in the Universe* (San Francisco, CA: Holden-Day, 1966), 343–50.

2. Shklovsky and Sagan, *Intelligent Life*, 413.

3. Dava Sobel, "Is Anybody Out There?" *Life*, September 1992, 62.

4. Pieter G. van Dokkum et al., "A High Merger Fraction in the Rich Cluster MS 1054-03 at z = 0.83: Direct Evidence for Hierarchical Formation of Massive Galaxies," *Astrophysical Journal Letters* 520 (June 25, 1999): L95–L98, doi:10.1086/312154.

5. Lulu Liu et al., "How Common Are the Magellanic Clouds?" *Astrophysical Journal* 733 (May 5, 2011): id. 62, doi:10.1088/0004-637X/733/1/62; Hugh Ross, "Milky Way Galaxy's Midlife Crisis," *Today's New Reason to Believe* (blog), *Reasons to Believe*, October 3, 2011, reasons.org/explore/publica-tions/tnrtb/read/tnrtb/2011/10/03/milky-way-galaxy-s-midlife-crisis.

6. Juntai Shen et al., "Our Milky Way as a Pure-Disk Galaxy—a Challenge for Galaxy Formation," *Astrophysical Journal Letters* 720 (August 12, 2010): L72–L76, doi:10.1088/2041-8205/720/1/L72; F. Hammer et al., "The Milky Way, an Exceptionally Quiet Galaxy: Implications for the Formation of Spiral Galaxies," *Astrophysical Journal* 662 (June 10, 2007): 322–34, doi:10.1086/516727; Ross, "Milky Way Galaxy's Midlife Crisis."

7. Robert Irion, "A Crushing End for our Galaxy," *Science* 287 (January 7, 2000): 62–64, doi:10.1126/science.287.5450.62.

8. Ron Cowen, "Were Spiral Galaxies Once More Common?," *Science News* 142 (1992): 390; Alan Dressler et al., "New Images of the Distant, Rich Cluster CL 0939+4713 with WFPC2," *Astrophysical Journal Letters* 435 (November 1994): L23–L26, doi:10.1086/187585.

9. Chris Flynn et al., "On the Mass-to-Light Ratio of the Local Galactic Disc and the Optical Luminosity of the Galaxy," *Monthly Notices of the Royal Astronomical Society* 372 (November 1, 2006): 1149–60, doi:10.1111/j.1365-2966.2006.10911.x; Hammer et al., "The Milky Way, an Exceptionally Quiet Galaxy."

10. Simonetta Puccetti et al., "The Variable Hard X-Ray Emission of NGC 4945 as Observed by NUSTAR," *Astrophysical Journal* 793 (September 2, 2014): id. 26, doi:10.1088/0004-637X/793/1/26.

11. Hugh Ross, *Improbable Planet: How Earth Became Humanity's Home* (Grand Rapids: Baker, 2016), 28–42.

12. S. Scarano Jr. and J. R. D. Lépine, "Radial Metallicity Distribution Breaks at Corotation Radius in Spiral Galaxies," *Monthly Notices of the Royal Astronomical Society* 428 (January 1, 2013): 625–40, doi:10.1093/mnras/sts048; D. A. Barros, J. R. D. Lépine, and T. C. Junqueira, "A Galactic Ring of Minimum Stellar Density near the Solar Orbit Radius," *Monthly Notices of the Royal Astronomical Society* 435 (November 1, 2013): 2299–321, doi:10.1093/mnras/stt1454.

13. Barros, Lépine, and Junqueira, "A Galactic Ring," 2299–321.

14. J. D. Gilmour and C. A. Middleton, "Anthropic Selection of a Solar System with a High ^{26}Al/^{27}Al Ratio: Implications and a Possible Mechanism," *Icarus* 201 (June 2009): 821–23, doi:10.1016/j.icarus.2009.03.013.

15. T. Hayakawa et al., "Supernova Neutrino Nucleosynthesis of the Radioactive ^{92}Nb Observed in Primitive Meteorites," *Astrophysical Journal Letters* 779 (November 22, 2013): id. 9, doi:10.1088/2041-8205/779/1/L9; A. Takigawa et al., "Injection of Short-Lived Radionuclides into the Early Solar System from a Faint Supernova with Mixing Fallback," *Astrophysical*

Journal 688 (December 1, 2008): 1382–87, doi:10.1086/592184; Richard J. Parker and James E. Dale, "Did the Solar System Form in a Sequential Triggered Star Formation Event?" *Monthly Notices of the Royal Astronomical Society* 456 (February 11, 2016): 1066–72, doi:10.1093/mnras/stv2765; Liubin Pan et al., "Mixing of Clumpy Ejecta into Molecular Clouds," *Astrophysical Journal* 756 (August 20, 2012): id. 102, doi:10.1088/0004-637X/756/1/102.

16. Guillermo Gonzalez, "Solar System Bounces in the Right Range for Life," *Facts for Faith* 11 (first quarter, 1997), 4–5.

17. Raymond E. White III and William C. Keel, "Direct Measurement of the Optical Depth in a Spiral Galaxy," *Nature* 359 (September 10, 1992): 129–30, doi:10.1038/359129a0; W. C. Keel and R. E. White III, "HST and ISO Mapping of Dust in Silhouetted Spiral Galaxies," *Bulletin of the American Astronomical Society* 29 (December 1997): 1327; Raymond E. White III, William C. Keel, and Christopher J. Conselice, "Seeing Galaxies through Thick and Thin. I. Optical Opacity Measures in Overlapping Galaxies," *Astrophysical Journal* 542 (2000): 761–67, doi:10.1086/317011.

18. Psalm 8:1–3, 19:1–4, 50:6, 89:5, 97:6; Romans 1:20, *The Holy Bible*.

19. Ross, *Improbable Planet*, 35–42.

20. Ross, *Improbable Planet*, 78–93; Hugh Ross, "'Electric Wind' Becomes 9th Habitable Zone," *Today's New Reason to Believe* (blog), *Reasons to Believe*, July 4, 2016, reasons.org/explore/blogs/todays-new-reason-to-believe/read/todays-new-reason-to-believe/2016/07/04/electric-wind-becomes-9th-habitable-zone.

21. Kristen Menou, "Water-Trapped Worlds," *Astrophysical Journal* 774 (August 16, 2013): id. 51, doi:10.1088/0004-637X/774/1/51.

22. Ross, *Improbable Planet*, 143–59.

23. Robert H. Dicke, "Dirac's Cosmology and Mach's Principle," *Nature* 192 (November 4, 1961): 440, doi:10.1038/192440a0.

24. Michael H. Hart, "Habitable Zones about Main Sequence Stars," *Icarus* 37 (January 1979): 351–57, doi:10.1016/0019-1035(79)90141-6.

25. George Ogden Abell, *Exploration of the Universe* (New York: Holt, Rinehart, and Winston, 1964), 244–47; John C. Brandt and Paul W. Hodge, *Solar System Astrophysics* (New York: McGraw-Hill, 1964), 395–416.

26. Charles B. Thaxton, Walter L. Bradley, and Roger L. Olsen, *The Mystery of Life's Origin: Reassessing Current Theories* (New York: Philosophical Library, 1984), 43–46, 73–94.

27. Jianpo Guo et al., "Habitable Zones and UV Habitable Zones around

Host Stars," *Astrophysics and Space Science* 325 (January 2010): 25–30, doi:10.1007/s10509-009-0173-9; Charles H. Lineweaver, Yeshe Fenner, and Brad K. Gibson, "The Galactic Habitable Zone and the Age Distribution of Complex Life in the Milky Way," *Science* 303 (January 2, 2004): 59–62, doi:10.1126/science.1092322; Frederick S. Colwell and Steven D'Hondt, "Nature and Extent of the Deep Biosphere," *Reviews in Mineralogy and Geochemistry* 75 (January 2013): 547–74, doi:10.2138/rmg.2013.75.17; Steven D'Hondt, Scott Rutherford, and Arthur J. Spivack, "Metabolic Activity of Subsurface Life in Deep-Sea Sediments," *Science* 295 (March 15, 2002): 2067–70, doi:10.1126/science.1064878; Ingrid Cnossen et al., "Habitat of Early Life: Solar X-Ray and UV Radiation at Earth's Surface 4–3.5 Billion Years Ago," *Journal of Geophysical Research* 112 (February 16, 2007): id. E02008, doi:10.1029/2006JE002784; Ross, *Improbable Planet*, 84–85.

28. "Catalog," Exoplanet TEAM, The Extrasolar Planet Encyclopaedia, accessed May 17, 2017, exoplanet.eu/catalog/.

29. Ross, *Improbable Planet*, 78–93; Ross, "'Electric Wind' Becomes 9th Habitable Zone."

30. George W. Wetherill, "Possible Consequences of Absence of 'Jupiters' in Planetary Systems," *Astrophysics and Space Science* 212 (February 1994): 23–32, doi:10.1007/BF00984505; J. Horner, B. W. Jones, and J. Chambers, "Jupiter—Friend or Foe? III: The Oort Cloud Comets," *International Journal of Astrobiology* 9 (January 2010): 1–10, doi:10.1017/S1473550409990346.

31. Mordecai-Mark Lac Low and Kevin Zahnle, "Explosion of Comet Shoemaker-Levy 9 on Entry into the Jovian Atmosphere," *Astrophysical Journal Letters* 434 (1994): L33–L36.

32. Editors, "Our Friend Jove," *Discover*, July 1993, 15.

33. Jacques Laskar, "Large-Scale Chaos in the Solar System," *Astronomy & Astrophysics* 287 (June 1994): 112.

34. T. A. Michtchenko and S. Ferraz-Mello, "Resonant Structure of the Outer Solar System in the Neighborhood of the Planets," *Astronomical Journal* 122 (July 2001): 474–81, doi:10.1086/321129.

35. Kimmo Innanen, Seppo Mikkola, and Paul Wiegert, "The Earth-Moon System and the Dynamical Stability of the Inner Solar System," *Astronomical Journal* 116 (October 1998): 2055–57, doi:10.1086/300552.

36. Robin M. Canup, "Dynamics of Lunar Formation," *Annual Review of Astronomy and Astrophysics* 42 (September 22, 2004): 441–75, doi:10.1146/

annurev.astro.41.082201.113457; Robin M. Canup, "Lunar-Forming Collisions with Pre-Impact Rotation," *Icarus* 196 (August 2008): 518–38, doi:10.1016/j.icarus.2008.03.011.

37. Hidenori Genda and Yutaka Abe, "Enhanced Atmospheric Loss on Proto-planets at the Giant Impact Phase in the Presence of Oceans," *Nature* 433 (February 24, 2005): 842–44, doi:10.1038/nature03360.

38. Robin Canup, "Planetary Science: Lunar Conspiracies," *Nature* 504 (December 4, 2013): 27, doi:10.1038/504027a.

39. Robin M. Canup, "Forming a Moon with an Earth-Like Composition Via a Giant Impact," *Science* 338 (October 17, 2012): 1052–55, doi:10.1126/science.1226073.

40. Matija Ćuk and Sarah T. Stewart, "Making the Moon from a Fast-Spinning Earth: A Giant Impact Followed by Resonant Despinning," *Science* 338 (November 23, 2012): 1047–52, doi:10.1126/science.1225542.

41. Sarah T. Stewart, "Weak Links Mar Lunar Model," *Nature* 504 (December 5, 2013): 91.

42. Stewart, "Weak Links."

43. Tim Elliott, "A Chip Off the Old Block," *Nature* 504 (December 5, 2013): 90.

44. John Emsley, *The Elements,* 3rd ed. (Oxford, UK: Clarendon Press, 1998), 26, 40, 56, 58, 60, 62, 78, 102, 106, 120, 122, 130, 138, 152, 160, 188, 194, 198, 214, 222, 230; A. Scott McCall et al., "Bromine Is an Essential Trace Element for Assembly of Collagen IV Scaffolds in Tissue Development and Architecture," *Cell* 157 (June 5, 2014): 1380–92, doi:10.1016/j.cell.2014.05.009.

45. Michel Mayor and Didier Queloz, "A Jupiter-Mass Companion to a Solar-Type Star," *Nature* 378 (November 23, 1995): 355–59, doi:10.1038/378355a0.

46. "Catalog," Exoplanet TEAM, exoplanet.eu/catalog/.

47. Linda T. Elkins-Tanton and Sara Seager, "Ranges of Atmospheric Mass and Composition of Super-Earth Exoplanets," *Astrophysical Journal* 685 (October 1, 2008): 1237–46, doi:10.1086/591433; Hugh Ross, "Planet Formation: Problems with Water, Carbon, and Air," *Today's New Reason to Believe* (blog), *Reasons to Believe,* January 12, 2009, reasons.org/explore/publications/tnrtb/read/tnrtb/2009/01/11/planet-formation-problems-with-water-carbon-and-air.

48. M. S. Sisodia, "Evidences Support an Extraordinary Event, Possibly an Impact During the Proterozoic for Phosphorus Abundance on the

Earth," *Astrobiology* 8 (April 2008): 360; Hugh Ross, "Where Did Earth Get Its Phosphorus?" *Today's New Reason to Believe* (blog), *Reasons to Believe*, October 13, 2008, reasons.org/explore/publications/tnrtb/read/tnrtb/2008/10/12/where-did-earth-get-its-phosphorus.

49. Fabrice Gaillard and Bruno Scaillet, "The Sulfur Content of Volcanic Gases on Mars," *Earth and Planetary Science Letters* 279 (March 15, 2009): 34–43, doi:10.1016/j.epsl.2008.12.028; Hugh Ross, "Sulfur-Poor Earth Conducive to Life," *Today's New Reason to Believe* (blog), *Reasons to Believe*, May 4, 2009, reasons.org/explore/publications/tnrtb/read/tnrtb/2009/05/03/sulfur-poor-earth-conducive-to-life; Benton Clark, "Death by Sulfur: Consequences of Ubiquitous S before and after the Biotic Transition for Mars and Other S-Rich Planets," *Astrobiology* 8 (April 2008): 4331; M. J. Benton, *When Life Nearly Died: The Greatest Mass Extinction of All Time* (London: Thames & Hudson, 2005); Zhong-Qiang Chen and Michael J. Benton, "The Timing and Pattern of Biotic Recovery following the End-Permian Mass Extinction," *Nature Geoscience* 5 (June 2012): 375–83, doi:10.1038/ngeo1475; Bernadette C. Proemse et al., "Ocean Anoxia Did Not Cause the Latest Permian Extinction," (paper, EGU General Assembly 2014, Vienna, Austria, April 27–May 2, 2014).

50. Rogerio Deienno et al., "Is the Grand Tack Model Compatible with the Orbital Distribution of Main Belt Asteroids?" *Icarus* 272 (July 1, 2016): 114–24, doi:10.1016/j.icarus.2016.02.043; R. Brasser et al., "Analysis of Terrestrial Planet Formation by the Grand Tack Model: System Architecture and Tack Location," *Astrophysical Journal* 821 (April 12, 2016): id. 75, doi:10.3847/0004-637X/821/2/75; Arnaud Pierens et al., "Outward Migration of Jupiter and Saturn in 3:2 or 2:1 Resonance in Radiative Disks: Implications for the Grand Tack and Nice Models," *Astrophysical Journal Letters* 795 (November 1, 2014): id. L11, doi:10.1088/2041-8205/795/1/L11; A. Pierens and S. N. Raymond, "Two Phase, Inward-Then-Outward Migration of Jupiter and Saturn in the Gaseous Solar Nebula," *Astronomy & Astrophysics* 533 (September 2011): id. A131, doi:10.1051/0004-6361/201117451; David Nesvorný, "Young Solar System's Fifth Giant Planet?," *Astrophysical Journal Letters* 742 (November 7, 2011): id. L22, doi:10.1088/2041-8205/742/2/L22; David Nesvorný and Alessandro Morbidelli, "Statistical Study of the Early Solar System's Instability with Four, Five, and Six Giant Planets," *Astronomical Journal* 144 (September 13, 2012): id. 117, doi:10.1088/0004-6256/144/4/117; R. Brasser, K. J. Walsh, and D. Nesvorný, "Constraining the Primordial Orbits of the Terrestrial

Planets," *Monthly Notices of the Royal Astronomical Society* 433 (August 21, 2013): 3417–27, doi:10.1093/mnras/stt986; Konstantin Batygin, Michael E. Brown, and Hayden Betts, "Instability-Driven Dynamical Evolution Model of a Primordially Five-Planet Outer Solar System," *Astrophysical Journal Letters* 744 (December 8, 2011): id. L3, doi:10.1088/2041-8205/744/1/L3; R. Brasser et al., "Constructing the Secular Architecture of the Solar System II: The Terrestrial Planets," *Astronomy & Astrophysics* 507 (November 2009): 1053–65, doi:10.1051/0004-6361/200912878; Harold F. Levison and Alessandro Morbidelli, "The Formation of the Kuiper Belt by the Outward Transport of Bodies during Neptune's Migration," *Nature* 426 (November 27, 2003): 419–21, doi:10.1038/nature02120; David Nesvorný, David Vokrouhlicky, and Alessandro Morbidelli, "Capture of Trojans by Jumping Jupiter," *Astrophysical Journal* 768 (April 12, 2013): id. 45, doi:10.1088/0004-637X/768/1/45; Kevin J. Walsh et al., "Populating the Asteroid Belt from Two Parent Source Regions Due to the Migration of Giant Planets—'The Grand Tack,'" *Meteoritics & Planetary Science* 47 (December 2012): 1941–47, doi:10.1111/j.1945-5100.2012.01418.x; Kevin J. Walsh et al., "A Low Mass for Mars from Jupiter's Early Gas-Driven Migration," *Nature* 475 (July 14, 2011): 206–69, doi:10.1038/nature10201.

51. Laura Vican and Adam Schneider, "The Evolution of Dusty Debris Disks around Solar Type Stars," *Astrophysical Journal* 780 (December 20, 2013): id. 154, doi:10.1088/0004-637X/780/2/154.

52. Kate Y. L. Su et al., "Asteroid Belts in Debris Disk Twins: Vega and Fomalhaut," *Astrophysical Journal* 763 (January 16, 2013): id. 118, doi:10.1088/0004-637X/763/2/118; B. Acke et al., "Herschel Images of Fomalhaut. An Extrasolar Kuiper Belt at the Height of Its Dynamical Activity," *Astronomy & Astrophysics* 540 (April 2012): id. A125, doi:10.1051/0004-6361/201118581.

53. Ross, *Improbable Planet*, 63–70, 72–75.

54. There exists, for example, a probability of a little less than one chance in 10^{80} that the hot air molecules arising from the flames on a gas stove instead of dissipating throughout the room could bunch together inside a small volume element, move toward you, and burn a hole through your chest and into your heart. This probability, however, is so tiny that we can safely conclude that such an event can never happen at any time in the history of the universe or at any location throughout the universe.

55. Fazale Rana and Hugh Ross, *Origins of Life: Biblical and Evolutionary Models Face Off* (Covina, CA: RTB Press, 2014), 180–85.

56. Rana and Ross, *Origins of Life*; Fazale Rana, *The Cell's Design: How Chemistry Reveals the Creator's Artistry* (Grand Rapids: Baker, 2008); Fazale Rana, *Creating Life in the Lab: How New Discoveries in Synthetic Biology Make a Case for the Creator* (Grand Rapids, Baker, 2011); Hugh Ross, *Why the Universe Is the Way It Is* (Grand Rapids: Baker, 2008); Hugh Ross, *More Than a Theory: Revealing a Testable Model for Creation* (Grand Rapids: Baker, 2009); Hugh Ross, *Improbable Planet*.

Chapter 18 – Extradimensional Power

1.   Hugh Ross, *Beyond the Cosmos: The Transdimensionality of God*, 3rd edition (Covina, CA: RTB Press, 2017).
2.   Genesis 16:13, 28:16; Deuteronomy 30:14; Psalm 34:18, 119:151, 145:18; Jeremiah 23:24; Acts 17:28; and Romans 10:8 are a few of many examples.
3.   Genesis 28:16; Exodus 33:20; Job 9:11, 37:23; and John 6:46 are a few of many examples.
4.   1 Timothy 6:16.
5.   Edwin Abbott, *Flatland: A Romance of Many Dimensions*, with notes by David W. Davies (Pasadena, CA: Grant Dahlstrom, 1978).
6.   John 16:5–10.
7.   John 16:6.
8.   John 16:7.
9.   Philippians 2:5–9.
10. John 14:12–14.
11. Matthew 28:20.

Chapter 19 – The Point

1.   Hebrews 11:6.
2.   Psalm 34:18, 145:18.
3.   Ephesians 2:13.
4.   J. N. D. Anderson, *The Evidence for the Resurrection* (Downers Grove, IL: InterVarsity Press, 1966).
5.   James 4:8.
6.   Revelation 3:8.

Appendix A – Evidence for the Fine-Tuning of the Universe

1.   Hugh Ross, "Part 1. Fine-Tuning for Life in the Universe," *RTB Design Compendium (2009)* (November 17, 2010), reasons.org/finetuning.

Index

About the Author

 **Hugh Ross** is founder and president of Reasons to Believe, an organization that researches and communicates how God's revelation in the words of the Bible harmonizes with the facts of nature.

With a degree in physics from the University of British Columbia and a grant from the National Research Council of Canada, Dr. Ross earned a PhD in astronomy from the University of Toronto. For several years he continued his research on quasars and galaxies as a postdoctoral fellow at the California Institute of Technology. His writings include journal and magazine articles and numerous books—*Improbable Planet, Navigating Genesis, Why the Universe Is the Way It Is*, and more. He has spoken on hundreds of university campuses as well as at conferences and churches around the world.

He lives in Southern California with his wife, Kathy.

About Reasons to Believe

Uniquely positioned within the science-faith discussion since 1986, Reasons to Believe (RTB) communicates that science and faith are, and always will be, allies, not enemies. Distinguished for integrating science and faith respectfully and with integrity, RTB welcomes dialogue with both skeptics and believers. Addressing topics such as the origin of the universe, the origin of life, and the history and destiny of humanity, RTB's website offers a vast array of helpful resources. Through their books, blogs, podcasts, and speaking events, RTB scholars present powerful reasons from science to trust in the reliability of the Bible and the message it conveys about creation and redemption.

For more information, contact us via:
reasons.org
818 S. Oak Park Rd.
Covina, CA 91724
(855) REASONS | (855) 732-7667
ministrycare@reasons.org

Explore our Creator's intent in designing a home with you in mind.

Dr. Hugh Ross helps nonscientists understand the countless miracles that undergird the exquisitely fine-tuned planet we call home—as if Someone had us in mind all along.

www.reasons.org

RTB_OFFICIAL

If God made the universe...

Why would he
make it
so vast?

Why would he
wait to create
humans?

Why believe
life has
meaning?

Why allow
death and
decay?

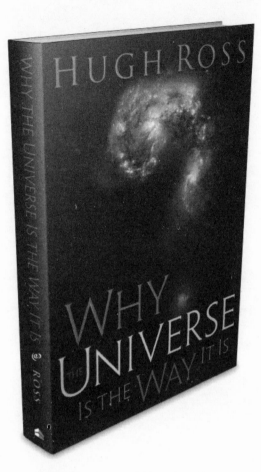

Why should I believe?

Within these pages you will find compelling answers
that give you reasons to believe that our finely tuned universe
"shouts loudly that life is more than a cosmic accident."

www.reasons.org

RTB_OFFICIAL

A small group study has never tackled a bigger subject!

Drawing from his popular book *Why the Universe Is the Way It Is*, Dr. Hugh Ross shares Scripture, stunning satellite photos, and the most recent scientific findings to explain the great love story that is our universe.

www.reasons.org

RTB_OFFICIAL [f] [y] [o] [▶]